Table of Contents

Chapter 1

PERSONAL ACCOUNTING

— Assessment Questions —

AS-1 (❶)

Define accounting and state the purpose of accounting.

_____

_____

_____

AS-2 (❶)

What is net worth?

_____

_____

AS-3 (❷)

In simple terms, what are assets and liabilities?

_____

_____

AS-4 (❷)

What are revenues and expenses?

_____

_____

_____

_____

AS-5 (❷)

Explain the role of the balance sheet.

_____

_____

_____

_____

AS-6 (❷)

Explain the role of the income statement.

_____

_____

_____

AS-7 (❷)

What are some advantages of using monthly accounting periods in your personal balance sheet?

_____

_____

_____

AS-8 (❸)

What is the accounting equation?

_____

_____

AS-9 (❶)

What is the equation for calculating closing net worth for a period?

_____

_____

AS-10 (❷)

Define surplus (and deficit).

_____

_____

_____

AS-11 (❹)

What is a T-Account?

_____

_____

_____

AS-12 (❺)

Define the principle of accrual accounting.

_____

_____

_____

AS-13 (❺)

Briefly describe the cash-based method of accounting.

_____

_____

AS-14 (❻)

Explain the matching principle.

_____

_____

AS-15 (❶)

True or False: When you borrow money, you have more cash but your net worth decreases.

_____

AS-16 (❶)

True or False: When you pay off a loan, your cash decreases and your net worth increases.

_____

_____

AS-17 (❶)

True or False: Buying an asset has no impact on net worth.

_____

AS-18 (❼)

Describe the concept of depreciation.

_____

_____

_____

_____

AS-19 (❺)

What is a prepaid expense?

_____

_____

AS-20 (❺)

When an expense is initially prepaid, which accounts increase or decrease?

_____

_____

AS-21 (⑥)

What are the three ways to pay an expense?

_____

_____

_____

AS-22 (⑥)

Describe the concept of materiality in the context of assets and expenses.

_____

_____

_____

AS-23 (⑧)

What is capital?

_____

_____

AS-24 (⑩)

Define market value.

_____

_____

AS-25 (⑩)

Define book value.

_____

_____

Application Questions

AP-1 (❶)

Darryl purchased a new laptop on January 1, 2013 worth $2,000. He paid the entire amount using cash. He also purchased a new cell phone worth $300 and an MP3 player worth $100, on account. How will these transactions affect Darryl's net worth?

_____

_____

AP-2 (❷)

April Rose had the following financial data for the year ended December 31, 2013:

Cash	$6,000
Jewelry	10,000
Automobile	18,000
House	56,000
Bank Loan	45,000
Credit Card (Unpaid Accounts)	5,000
Mortgage Payable	40,000

Required:

a)   Calculate April Rose's total assets.

_____

_____

_____

_____

b)   Calculate April Rose's total liabilities.

_____

_____

_____

_____

AP-3 (❶, ❷)

Consider the following information of Julius Troy:

Cash	$12,000
Jewelry	18,000
Automobile	22,000
House	61,000
Credit Card (Unpaid Accounts)	5,000
Bank Loan	10,000
Mortgage Payable	25,000

Required:

a) Calculate Julius Troy's total assets.

_____

_____

_____

_____

b) Calculate Julius Troy's total liabilities.

_____

_____

_____

_____

c) Calculate Julius Troy's net worth.

_____

_____

_____

_____

AP-4 (❶, ❸)

Consider the following information:

Cash	$6,000
Automobile	50,000
Prepaid Insurance	3,000
Mortgage Payable	10,000
Unpaid Credit Card Bills	2,000
Net Worth	?

How much is the net worth?

_____

_____

_____

_____

AP-5 (❷, ❸)

A worker has the following information with regards to his own balance sheet, but the liability section is missing.

Cash	$35,000
Automobile	58,000
House	100,000
Net Worth	55,000

Required: Determine the amount of liability.

_____

_____

_____

_____

AP-6 (❶, ❷, ❹)

The following information was taken from the personal records of Juliet Lahm:

Opening Balances:
Cash	$3,000
Jewelry	2,000
House	90,000
Mortgage Payable	80,000
Net Worth	15,000

The following are the transactions for the month of May 2013:

1. Received monthly salary — $5,000
2. Paid cash for utilities — 1,200
3. Purchased an automobile on account — 10,000
4. Paid cash for food expenses — 600
5. Received interest earned on bank deposits — 50
6. Paid cash for gas — 400

a) What is the ending balance of cash?

INCREASE (DR)		DECREASE (CR)
+	**CASH**	-
Opening Bal.		

b) What is the surplus or deficit for the period?

Personal Income Statement For the Month Ended May 31, 2013	

c) What is Juliet Lahm's net worth on May 31?

_____

_____

_____

AP-7 (❶, ❸)

As of December 31, 2012, Maria Green had total assets of $40,000, and total liabilities of $15,000. As of December 31, 2013, Maria's total assets and liabilities increased to $50,000 and $30,000, respectively. How has Maria's net worth changed since the end of 2012?

_____

_____

_____

_____

AP-8 (❶, ❷, ❸, ❹)

The following information pertains to Ken White's personal financial transactions:

Opening Balances at January 1, 2013

Cash	$9,000
House	56,000
Automobile	29,000
Contents of Home	6,000
Unpaid Accounts	5,500
Bank Loan	60,000
Net Worth	34,500

The following are the transactions for the month of January 2013:

1.	Paid maintenance expense for the month of January with cash	$120
2.	Sold furniture for cash (assume the furniture is sold at the balance sheet value)	2,000
3.	Purchased new furniture as a replacement for the old one, using cash	2,500
4.	Paid credit card liability in full	5,500
5.	Paid telephone, electricity and water bill for January with cash	1,200

6.	Purchased groceries and goods for personal consumption with cash	2,000
7.	Deposited salary earned during the month	4,000
8.	Earned interest on savings account	40

Required:

a) Using the information provided, record the opening balances in the T-accounts.

b) Record the transactions for the month of January in the T-accounts.

c) Complete the personal balance sheet and income statement.

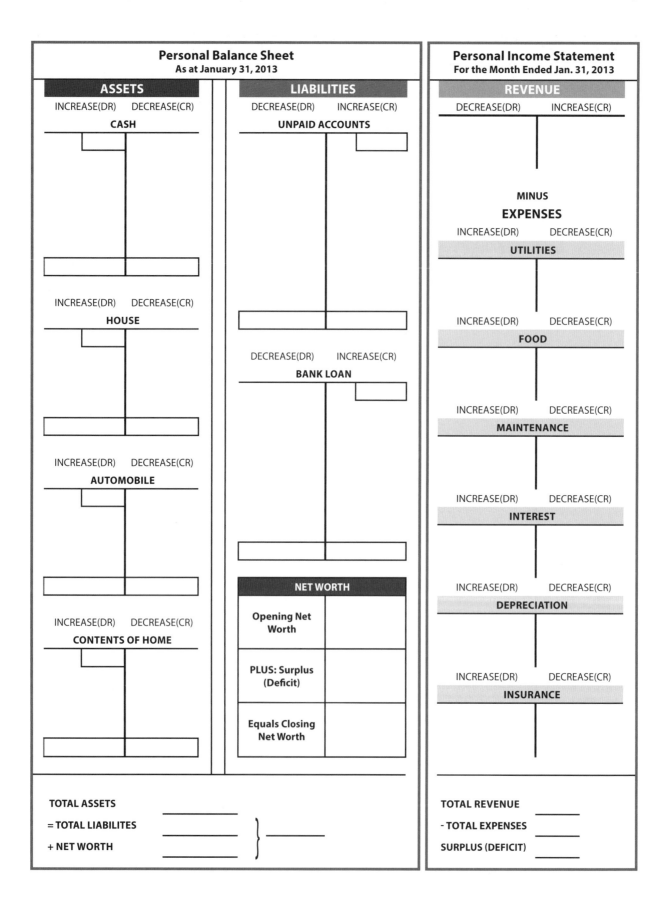

Personal Balance Sheet
As at January 31, 2013

ASSETS

INCREASE(DR)   DECREASE(CR)

CASH

INCREASE(DR)   DECREASE(CR)

HOUSE

INCREASE(DR)   DECREASE(CR)

AUTOMOBILE

INCREASE(DR)   DECREASE(CR)

CONTENTS OF HOME

LIABILITIES

DECREASE(DR)   INCREASE(CR)

UNPAID ACCOUNTS

DECREASE(DR)   INCREASE(CR)

BANK LOAN

NET WORTH

Opening Net Worth	
PLUS: Surplus (Deficit)	
Equals Closing Net Worth	

TOTAL ASSETS   _____

= TOTAL LIABILITES   _____

+ NET WORTH   _____   } _____

Personal Income Statement
For the Month Ended Jan. 31, 2013

REVENUE

DECREASE(DR)   INCREASE(CR)

MINUS

EXPENSES

INCREASE(DR)   DECREASE(CR)

UTILITIES

INCREASE(DR)   DECREASE(CR)

FOOD

INCREASE(DR)   DECREASE(CR)

MAINTENANCE

INCREASE(DR)   DECREASE(CR)

INTEREST

INCREASE(DR)   DECREASE(CR)

DEPRECIATION

INCREASE(DR)   DECREASE(CR)

INSURANCE

TOTAL REVENUE   _____

- TOTAL EXPENSES   _____

SURPLUS (DEFICIT)   _____

Ken White Personal Balance Sheet As at January 31, 2013	

Ken White Personal Income Statement For the Month Ended January 31, 2013	

AP-9 (❶, ❷, ❸, ❹)

Alan Marshall is preparing his balance sheet and income statement for the month ended April 30, 2013. Use the following information to help him prepare his financial statements.

Opening Balances - April 1, 2013	
Cash	$5,000
Contents of Home	1,000
Automobile	4,000
House	80,000
Unpaid Accounts	10,000
Auto Loan	30,000
Net Worth	50,000

The following are the transactions for the month of April:

1.	Purchased new furniture for home using the credit card	$2,000
2.	Paid credit card bill with cash	3,000
3.	Paid utility bills for the month of April using the credit card	800
4.	Purchased groceries and food using cash	2,500
5.	Made the annual principal payment for the auto loan	1,250
6.	Paid the April's rent with cash	1,500
7.	Deposited salaries earned during the month	4,000
8.	Earned interest on savings account	50

Required:

a) Using the information provided, record the opening balances in the T-accounts.

b) Record the transactions for the month of April in the T-accounts.

c) Complete the personal balance sheet and income statement.

Personal Balance Sheet
As at April 30, 2013

ASSETS (what we OWN)

INCREASE(DR)   DECREASE(CR)
CASH

INCREASE(DR)   DECREASE(CR)
CONTENTS OF HOME

INCREASE(DR)   DECREASE(CR)
AUTOMOBILE

INCREASE(DR)   DECREASE(CR)
HOUSE

TOTAL ASSETS

= TOTAL LIABILITES

+ NET WORTH

LIABILITIES (what we OWE)

DECREASE(DR)   INCREASE(CR)
UNPAID ACCOUNTS

DECREASE(DR)   INCREASE(CR)
AUTO LOAN

NET WORTH

Opening Net Worth	
PLUS: Surplus (Deficit)	
Equals Closing Net Worth	

Personal Income Statement
For the Month Ended April 30, 2013

REVENUE
DECREASE(DR)   INCREASE(CR)

MINUS
EXPENSES

INCREASE(DR)   DECREASE(CR)
UTILITIES

INCREASE(DR)   DECREASE(CR)
FOOD

INCREASE(DR)   DECREASE(CR)
RENT

INCREASE(DR)   DECREASE(CR)
DEPRECIATION

INCREASE(DR)   DECREASE(CR)
MAINTENANCE

INCREASE(DR)   DECREASE(CR)
ENTERTAINMENT

TOTAL REVENUE

TOTAL EXPENSES

SURPLUS (DEFICIT)

Alan Marshall Personal Balance Sheet As at April 30, 2013	

Alan Marshall Personal Income Statement For the Month Ended April 30, 2013	

AP-10 (❶, ❷)

John Black is a senior administrator at a market research firm, and has recently experienced a salary increase from $3,500 per month to $4,000 per month. He feels richer and would like to know the increase in his net worth. However, he has never prepared a personal balance sheet or an income statement that would help him understand his net worth. The following information has been gathered by John in an attempt to better understand his financial position.

	September 30, 2013	October 31, 2013	November 30, 2013
Cash	$1,000	$2,150	$4,050
House	120,000	120,000	120,000
Bank Loan	400	350	300
Salary	3,500	3,500	4,000
Entertainment Expense	200	500	400
Food Expense	1,500	1,200	1,100
Insurance Expense	150	150	150
Utilities Expense	200	400	300
Miscellaneous Expense	175	50	100

Required: Prepare John Black's income statement and balance sheet for the three months.

John Black Personal Income Statement For the Month				
	September	**October**	**November**	**Total**

John Black Balance Sheet As at Month End			
	September	**October**	**November**

AP-11 (❶, ❷)

Ethan is a famous songwriter and composer. His income is based solely on royalties that he receives regularly. Ethan opted to use three months as his accounting period.

The following information pertains to income earned and expenses incurred from January 1, 2013 to March 31, 2013

	January	February	March
Royalty Income	$12,000	$13,000	$10,000
Interest Expense	60	60	60
Food Expense	2,000	2,100	1,900
Maintenance Expense	350	500	180
Clothing Expense	900	1,500	0
Utilities Expense	300	500	0
Rent Expense	1,500	1,500	1,500
Miscellaneous Expense	15	50	5

Required:

a) Prepare a personal income statement for each of the three months.

Ethan Personal Income Statement For the Period Ended March 31, 2013				
	January	February	March	Total

b) What amount should be added to Ethan's net worth for the three months ending on March 31, 2013.

_____

_____

_____

_____

AP-12 (❸)

Calculate the missing amounts in the following table.

	Scenario 1	Scenario 2
Total Assets	$123,000	
Total Liabilities		$34,000
Net Worth	$94,000	$114,000

AP-13 (❷)

Using the opening balances provided in the balance sheets below, enter the updated amounts for each transaction in the blank balance sheets marked "Answers".

1. **Borrowed $4,000 from the bank.**

Opening Balances

Assets		Liabilities	
Cash	5,000	Bank Loan	0
House	80,000	Unpaid Accounts	3,000
Automobile	20,000	Mortgage Payable	50,000
Contents of Home	6,000	Automobile Loan	5,000
Investment	8,000	Student Loan	6,000
		Total Liabilities	64,000
		Net Worth	55,000
Total Assets	**119,000**	**Liabilities + Net Worth**	**119,000**

Answers:

Assets		Liabilities	
Cash		Bank Loan	
House		Unpaid Accounts	
Automobile		Mortgage Payable	
Contents of Home		Automobile Loan	
Investment		Student Loan	
		Total Liabilities	
		Net Worth	
Total Assets		**Liabilities + Net Worth**	

2. **Sold investments for $8,000 cash.**

Opening Balances

Assets		Liabilities	
Cash	1,000	Bank Loan	0
House	80,000	Unpaid Accounts	3,000
Automobile	20,000	Mortgage Payable	50,000
Contents of Home	6,000	Automobile Loan	5,000
Investment	8,000	Student Loan	6,000
		Total Liabilities	64,000
		Net Worth	51,000
Total Assets	**115,000**	**Liabilities + Net Worth**	**115,000**

Answers:	Assets		Liabilities	
	Cash		Bank Loan	
	House		Unpaid Accounts	
	Automobile		Mortgage Payable	
	Contents of Home		Automobile Loan	
	Investment		Student Loan	
			Total Liabilities	
			Net Worth	
	Total Assets		**Liabilities + Net Worth**	

3. Paid $1,000 to reduce an outstanding automobile loan (principal portion).

Opening Balances

Assets		Liabilities	
Cash	3,000	Bank Loan	0
House	80,000	Unpaid Accounts	3,000
Automobile	20,000	Mortgage Payable	50,000
Contents of Home	6,000	Automobile Loan	5,000
		Student Loan	6,000
		Total Liabilities	**64,000**
		Net Worth	45,000
Total Assets	**109,000**	**Liabilities + Net Worth**	**109,000**

Answers:	Assets		Liabilities	
	Cash		Bank Loan	
	House		Unpaid Accounts	
	Automobile		Mortgage Payable	
	Contents of Home		Automobile Loan	
			Student Loan	
			Total Liabilities	
			Net Worth	
	Total Assets		**Liabilities + Net Worth**	

4. Bought a motorcycle for $6,000 - paid a $1,000 deposit with cash and borrowed $5,000 from the bank.

Opening Balances

Assets		Liabilities	
Cash	2,000	Bank Loan	1,000
House	80,000	Unpaid Accounts	3,000
Automobile	20,000	Mortgage Payable	50,000
Contents of Home	4,000	Automobile Loan	5,000
Motorcycle	-	Student Loan	6,000
		Total Liabilities	**65,000**
		Net Worth	41,000
Total Assets	**106,000**	**Liabilities + Net Worth**	**106,000**

Answers: Assets		Liabilities	
Cash		Bank Loan	
House		Unpaid Accounts	
Automobile		Mortgage Payable	
Contents of Home		Automobile Loan	
Motorcycle		Student Loan	
		Total Liabilities	
		Net Worth	
Total Assets		**Liabilities + Net Worth**	

AP-14 (❷)

Using the following chart, indicate whether there would be an increase, decrease or no change to the bank balance and net worth for the transactions provided. *The first transaction has been completed for you.*

	Transaction	Bank Balance			Net Worth		
		Increase	Decrease	No Change	Increase	Decrease	No Change
1	Deposit salary	X			X		
2	Pay cash for food						
3	Purchase a new car						
4	Sell a stereo for cash equal to its book value						
5	Reduce student loan principal						
6	Buy a new computer for cash						
7	Obtain a bank loan						
8	Pay entertainment expenses						
9	Record interest received on savings						

AP-15 (❶, ❸)

State how the following transactions would impact net worth (increase, decrease, no change):

Item	Effect on Net Worth
Borrow cash	
Pay entertainment expense with cash	
Pay food expense with cash	
Buy assets with cash	
Charge home repairs expense on credit card	
Pay insurance expense with cash	
Pay loan principal with cash	
Purchase assets on account	
Receive salary	
Pay rent expense with cash	

AP-16 (❶, ❷, ❸, ❻)

On December 1, 2013, Shervin decided to track his finances. On this date, his assets and liabilities were as follows:

Cash	$14,000
Prepaid Rent	3,000
Prepaid Insurance	300
House	60,000
Contents of Home	19,000
Automobile	30,000
Student Loan	10,000
Unpaid Accounts	17,000
Bank Loan	25,000
Mortgage Payable	25,000

a) What is the value of his total assets?

b) What is the value of his total liabilities?

c) What is Shervin's net worth on December 1, 2013?

d) During the month of December, Shervin recognized $150 of prepaid expenses as an actual expense on the income statement.

Calculate the change in his cash account and personal net worth.

Transaction	Cash	Net Worth
Effect		

AP-17 (❸, ❺, ❻)

Arthur's financial records show that his assets and net worth as of May 1, 2013 are as follows:

Cash	$6,000
Computer	4,000
Automobile	20,000
House	37,500
Contents of Home	17,500
Student Loan	?
Net Worth	13,000

a) Arthur wants to find out how much he owes. Determine his total liabilities.

_____

_____

_____

_____

_____

_____

_____

b) During the month of May, Arthur paid $2,000 for two months of rent in advance ($1,000 per month). Calculate the change in Arthur's cash account and personal net worth.

Transaction	Cash	Net Worth
Effect		

AP-18 (❻)

Peter's total net worth is $235,000. Use the materiality principle to help classify each of the following as an asset or an expense.

Item	Amount	Expense/Asset
CD	$15	
House	100,000	
Laptop	2,000	
Food	80	
Gas for Automobile	30	
Concert Tickets	250	
Furniture	3,000	

AP-19 (❼)

On January 1, 2013, Tristan purchased a brand new car and a cell phone worth $45,000 and $1,200 respectively. It is estimated that the useful life of the car is 9 years while the cell phone has a useful life of 4 years. The depreciation is to be equally distributed each year. Calculate the depreciation expense for the first year.

_____

_____

_____

_____

_____

_____

_____

AP-20 (❼)

The market value of some of Jessica's personal assets on January 1, 2013 are listed below:

    Automobile $11,000
    Computer $1,200

The automobile and computer were newly purchased on January 1, 2013. The automobile has a useful life of 10 years and the computer has a useful life of 3 years. Calculate the annual depreciation.

_____

_____

_____

_____

_____

_____

_____

_____

AP-21 (⑧)

John Hollister collected the following amounts in cash for the month of February 2013:

Salary paid by employer	$2,400
Winnings at the casino	$270
Gifts	$220
Performance bonus paid by employer	$450

Required: Calculate John's total revenue and total capital items for February 2013.

_____

_____

_____

AP-22 (⑧)

Joana Harwin collected the following amounts in cash for the month of March 2013:

Interest earned on savings account	$75
Full-time employment income	$1,200
Income from part-time babysitting job	$220
Rental income	$525

Required: Calculate Joana's total revenue and total capital items for March 2013.

_____

_____

_____

AP-23 (9)

Yelena Rollins incurred the following transactions related to cash for the month of May 2013:

- Invested in property
- Borrowed a bank loan
- Paid back a portion of a student loan
- Paid telephone bill
- Earned a salary from a part-time job

Classify each of the above transactions according to the three sources and uses of cash.

_____

_____

_____

_____

AP-24 (10)

Mr. Allen chooses to depreciate the value of his car over 3 years. Assume that the book value of his car is $15,000, but the market value is $20,000. At what value should he record the car in his personal financial statements?

_____

_____

_____

_____

_____

Case Study

CS – 1 (❶, ❷, ❸, ❹)

After taking the first part of this financial accounting course, you excitedly tell a friend of yours what you have learned. You tell him about assets, liabilities and net worth and how they increase and decrease in value with every financial transaction. Your friend decides to start getting organized and apply accounting principles to his personal finance. He compiles everything that he thinks is important and calculates his net worth. He then asks you to look over what he had done to make sure it is correct. His list of important financial items is listed below, along with his version of the T-Account records.

1   He had $950 in his bank account at the beginning of the month.
2   He had a $1,200 balance on his credit card at the beginning of the month.
3   He estimates that he had about $3,000 worth of "stuff" in his apartment at the beginning of the month (TV, sound system, computer and furniture).
4   Deposited his salary of $1,500.
5   At the beginning of the month, paid for three months of rent with $1,350 cash.
6   Paid $600 to pay off a portion of the credit card bill.
7   Purchased a new video game system for $350 with his credit card.
8   Bought $120 worth of food with cash.
9   Got hired at a second job. He will start next month and will earn $800 per month.
10 Spent $250 cash on movies, stage plays and Dave and Buster's.
11 Lived in his apartment for one of the three months he already paid for (see #5)

+	Cash		-			-	Unpaid Accounts		+	
1	$950	5	$1,350			6	$600	2	$1,200	
4	$1,500	6	$600					7	$350	
		8	$120							
		10	$250							
Total	**$130**							**Total**	**$950**	

-	Net Worth		+	
5	$1,350	3	$3,000	
8	$120	4	$1,500	
10	$250	7	$350	
		9	$800	
Total		**$3,930**		

Required:

1. What are some immediate problems that you see with what your friend has prepared?

_____

_____

_____

_____

_____

2. With all the problems you see, your friend asks you to show him what the correct records should look like. Use the provided templates located at the end of this problem to record the transactions.

_____

After showing your friend the corrected version, he starts asking you a number of questions.

3. Why did you use all of these accounts when I only used three (Cash, Unpaid Accounts and Net Worth)?

_____

_____

_____

_____

_____

4. Why is the $3,000 worth of "stuff" not considered net worth?

_____

_____

_____

_____

_____

5. I was having trouble figuring out how to record my second job which I start next month. They are going to be paying me $800 a month! I figured it will increase my net worth, but I didn't know where else to put it. I knew it couldn't be cash, because they haven't paid me yet. What did you do with it and why?

_____

_____

_____

_____

6. What did you do with my rent? Shouldn't the entire $1,350 decrease my net worth? And what would happen if I did it my way?

_____

_____

_____

_____

_____

_____

_____

_____

_____

_____

_____

7. Suppose that the $600 credit card payment included $30 of interest. Since the total payment amount is the same, this won't change anything, right?

_____

_____

_____

8. You may have noticed that I am running low on cash. Any suggestions on how I can
    raise more cash?

    _____

    _____

    _____

    _____

    _____

    _____

    _____

    _____

    _____

9. This is very useful and I would like to do this more often. I think I can do it this
    weekend, then two weeks from now once I finish with my exams, then probably not
    for another month after that. I'm going on a well-deserved vacation after my exams, so
    I won't be around to look after it. Do you think this will work out well?

    _____

    _____

    _____

    _____

    _____

    _____

Personal Balance Sheet

Assets   ## Liabilities

INCREASE (DR)   DECREASE (CR)   DECREASE (DR)   INCREASE (CR)

Opening: Opening:

Ending   Ending

INCREASE (DR)   DECREASE (CR)   DECREASE (DR)   INCREASE (CR)

Opening: Opening:

Ending   Ending

INCREASE (DR)   DECREASE (CR)

Opening:

NET WORTH	
Opening Net Worth	
Add: Capital	
Add: Surplus (Deficit)	
Equals Closing Net Worth	

Ending

Total Assets

= Total Liabilities

+ Net Worth

Personal Income Statement

DECREASE (DR)	**REVENUE**	INCREASE (CR)

Minus
EXPENSES

INCREASE (DR)	DECREASE (CR)

INCREASE (DR)	DECREASE (CR)

INCREASE (DR)	DECREASE (CR)

INCREASE (DR)	DECREASE (CR)

INCREASE (DR)	DECREASE (CR)

INCREASE (DR)	DECREASE (CR)

Total Revenue	
Total Expenses	
Surplus (Deficit)	

Chapter 2

LINKING PERSONAL ACCOUNTING TO BUSINESS ACCOUNTING

—————— **Assessment Questions** ——————

AS-1 (❶)

Net worth in personal accounting is similar to which item in accounting for businesses?

_____

_____

AS-2 (❷)

In what order are the assets of a business listed? Explain.

_____

_____

_____

AS-3 (❷)

In what order are the liabilities of a business listed? Explain.

_____

_____

_____

AS-4 (❸)

What is owner's equity?

_____

_____

_____

AS-5 (❸)

What is the formula for calculating the ending owner's equity balance (or ending capital account balance)?

_____

_____

AS-6 (❸)

Describe owner's contributions and owner's drawings and explain how they affect the balance sheet.

_____

_____

_____

AS-7 (❹)

What is a sole proprietorship?

_____

_____

AS-8 (❹)

Explain unlimited liability.

_____

_____

_____

AS-9 (❹)

What is a partnership?

_____

_____

AS-10 (❹)

What are the three types of partnerships that can be created?

_____

_____

_____

AS-11 (❹)

What is the difference between a general partnership and a limited partnership?

_____

_____

_____

_____

AS-12 (❹)

What is a cooperative?

_____

_____

_____

AS-13 (❹)

Describe a corporation.

_____

_____

_____

_____

AS-14 (❹)

What is a not-for-profit organization?

_____

_____

_____

AS-15 (❹)

Provide three examples of not-for-profit organizations.

_____

_____

AS-16 (❺)

Define internal and external stakeholders.

_____

_____

_____

AS-17 (❻)

List the three main types of businesses.

_____

_____

AS-18 (❻)

Explain what a service business does. Provide two examples of service businesses.

_____

_____

_____

AS-19 (❻)

Explain what a merchandising business does. Provide an example of a merchandising business.

_____

_____

_____

AS-20 (❻)

Explain what a manufacturing business does. Provide two examples of a manufacturing business.

_____

_____

_____

AS-21 (❼)

Give three examples of expenses that businesses commonly prepay.

_____

_____

_____

AS-22 (❼)

Explain cash flow.

_____

_____

——————————— **Application Questions** ———————————

AP-1 (❸, ❼)

Jessica recently started her own shoe repair business. The following are the transactions during the first month of operations (June 2013):

1.	Jessica invested money in the business.	$10,000
2.	Paid two months of rent in advance.	1,000
3.	Purchased store appliances for cash.	3,000
4.	Incurred business registration expenses, paid with cash.	600
5.	Paid travel expenses with cash.	1,100
6.	Made cash sales during the month.	2,300
7.	Paid salary to an assistant.	600
8.	Borrowed money from the bank.	3,000
9.	Received bills for electricity, water and telephone, to be paid next month.	800
10.	Jessica withdrew cash for personal purposes.	500

Required: Post the above transactions to the T-Account worksheet.

BALANCE SHEET
As at June 30, 2013

ASSETS

INCREASE(DR)   DECREASE(CR)

CASH

INCREASE(DR)   DECREASE(CR)

PREPAID RENT

INCREASE(DR)   DECREASE(CR)

PPE - EQUIPMENT

LIABILITIES

DECREASE(DR)   INCREASE(CR)

ACCOUNTS PAYABLE

DECREASE(DR)   INCREASE(CR)

BANK LOAN

OWNER'S EQUITY

DECREASE(DR)   INCREASE(CR)

CAPITAL ACCOUNT

INCREASE(DR)   DECREASE(CR)

OWNER'S DRAWINGS

TOTAL ASSETS _____

= TOTAL LIABILITES _____

+ OWNER'S EQUITY _____

} _____

INCOME STATEMENT
For the Month Ended June 30, 2013

REVENUE

DECREASE(DR)   INCREASE(CR)

MINUS

EXPENSES

INCREASE(DR)   DECREASE(CR)

RENT

INCREASE(DR)   DECREASE(CR)

REGISTRATION AND LICENSES

INCREASE(DR)   DECREASE(CR)

TRAVEL

INCREASE(DR)   DECREASE(CR)

SALARIES

INCREASE(DR)   DECREASE(CR)

TELEPHONE & UTILITIES

TOTAL REVENUE _____

- EXPENSES _____

NET INCOME (LOSS) _____

AP-2 (❸, ❼)

Edward decided to start his own rent-a-car business after graduation, instead of looking for a job. The following are the transactions during the first month of operations (January 2014):

1.	Edward invested money in the business.	$20,000
2.	Borrowed money from the bank.	20,000
3.	Purchased brand new car for business use with cash.	35,000
4.	Paid the principal of bank loan with cash.	2,000
5.	Paid for maintenance expense with cash.	800
6.	Paid monthly salaries for personnel with cash.	1,000
7.	Paid miscellaneous expenses with cash.	300
8.	Received service revenue in cash for the month.	8,000
9.	Received utilities bill for the month, payable next month.	600
10.	Paid monthly interest on the bank loan with cash.	200
11.	Paid insurance for the next five months in advance.	1,500
12.	Edward withdrew cash for personal use.	1,000

Required: Prepare the T-Account worksheet, income statement and balance sheet.

BALANCE SHEET
As at January 31, 2014

ASSETS

INCREASE(DR)	DECREASE(CR)

CASH

INCREASE(DR)	DECREASE(CR)

PREPAID INSURANCE

INCREASE(DR)	DECREASE(CR)

PPE - AUTOMOBILE

LIABILITIES

DECREASE(DR)	INCREASE(CR)

ACCOUNTS PAYABLE

DECREASE(DR)	INCREASE(CR)

BANK LOAN

OWNER'S EQUITY

DECREASE(DR)	INCREASE(CR)

CAPITAL ACCOUNT

INCREASE(DR)	DECREASE(CR)

OWNER'S DRAWINGS

TOTAL ASSETS _____

= TOTAL LIABILITES _____

+ OWNER'S EQUITY _____   } _____

INCOME STATEMENT
For the Month Ended January 31, 2014

REVENUE

DECREASE(DR)	INCREASE(CR)

MINUS

EXPENSES

INCREASE(DR)	DECREASE(CR)

RENT

INCREASE(DR)	DECREASE(CR)

MAINTENANCE

INCREASE(DR)	DECREASE(CR)

SALARIES

INCREASE(DR)	DECREASE(CR)

MISCELLANEOUS

INCREASE(DR)	DECREASE(CR)

TELEPHONE & UTILITIES

INCREASE(DR)	DECREASE(CR)

INTEREST

TOTAL REVENUE _____

- EXPENSES _____

NET INCOME (LOSS) _____

Edward's Rent-A-Car
Income Statement
For the Month Ended January 31, 2014

Edward's Rent-A-Car
Balance Sheet
As at January 31, 2014

AP-3 (❸, ❼)

Health-Plus Clinic is a medical clinic that started operations in January 2013. Consider the following opening balances as of January 1, 2014.

Cash	$15,000
Prepaid Rent	6,000
Prepaid Insurance (separate from prepaid rent)	5,000
PPE - Equipment	30,000
Accounts Payable	3,000
Bank Loan	10,000
Owner's Equity (Capital Account)	43,000

The following are the transactions during the whole month of January:

1. Purchased plane tickets for travelling with cash. $1,500
2. Paid cash to reduce the balance of accounts payable.   3,000
3. The owner invested additional cash in the company.   5,000
4. Purchased equipment with a bank loan.   4,000
5. Paid cash for maintenance expenses.   1,000
6. Earned revenue from patients on a cash basis.   15,000
7. Received a bill for utilities used during the month.
   A check was issued to pay the bill immediately.   900
8. Recognized prepaid rent as an expense.   2,000
9. Paid interest for the month of January with cash.   100
10. Paid monthly salaries to all medical practitioners and
    clinic personnel.   4,000
11. The owner withdrew cash from the business to
    pay for personal expenses.   2,000

Required: Prepare the T-Account worksheet, income statement and balance sheet.

BALANCE SHEET
As at January 31, 2014

ASSETS

INCREASE(DR)   DECREASE(CR)

INCREASE(DR)   DECREASE(CR)

INCREASE(DR)   DECREASE(CR)

INCREASE(DR)   DECREASE(CR)

LIABILITIES

DECREASE(DR)   INCREASE(CR)

DECREASE(DR)   INCREASE(CR)

OWNER'S EQUITY

DECREASE(DR)   INCREASE(CR)

INCREASE(DR)   DECREASE(CR)

TOTAL ASSETS _____

= TOTAL LIABILITES _____

+ OWNER'S EQUITY _____ } _____

INCOME STATEMENT
For the Month Ended January 31, 2014

REVENUE

DECREASE(DR)   INCREASE(CR)

MINUS
EXPENSES

INCREASE(DR)   DECREASE(CR)

INCREASE(DR)   DECREASE(CR)

INCREASE(DR)   DECREASE(CR)

INCREASE(DR)   DECREASE(CR)

INCREASE(DR)   DECREASE(CR)

INCREASE(DR)   DECREASE(CR)

TOTAL REVENUE _____

- EXPENSES _____

NET INCOME (LOSS) _____

Health-Plus Clinic Income Statement For the Month Ended January 31, 2014	

Health-Plus Clinic Balance Sheet As at January 31, 2014			

AP-4 (❸, ❼)

For each transaction, indicate whether the total assets (A), liabilities (L) or owner's equity (OE) increased (+), decreased (-) or did not change (o) by placing the sign in the appropriate column.

	A	L	OE
1. Paid salaries for current month.			
2. Purchased equipment on credit.			
3. Purchased furniture using cash.			
4. Additional investment into the business.			
5. Received payment for services provided.			
6. Made partial payment for equipment purchased on credit.			
7. Billed customers for services performed.			
8. Withdrew cash for personal use.			
9. Received payment from customers already billed.			
10. Received bills for utilities to be paid next month.			

AP-5 (❸, ❼)

Sheila opened a dormitory locator business called Dormitory Locators near a college campus. During the first month of operations, June 2013, Sheila had the following transactions:

1. Invested $10,000 of personal funds to start the business.
2. Incurred travel expenses for $650, which will be paid next month.
3. Paid $700 cash for maintenance expense.
4. Received $5,000 cash for services provided to clients.
5. Made the $650 payment for travel expenses purchased on account in transaction 2.
6. Paid three months of office rent costing $1,500 in advance.
7. Incurred $300 of utilities expense, which will be paid next month.
8. Recognized one month of office rent that was previously prepaid.
9. Sheila withdrew $1,000 cash for personal use.
10. Purchased second-hand car worth $10,000 for business use with cash.

Required: Prepare a T-Account worksheet.

BALANCE SHEET
As at June 30, 2013

ASSETS

INCREASE(DR)   DECREASE(CR)

INCREASE(DR)   DECREASE(CR)

INCREASE(DR)   DECREASE(CR)

INCREASE(DR)   DECREASE(CR)

LIABILITIES

DECREASE(DR)   INCREASE(CR)

DECREASE(DR)   INCREASE(CR)

OWNER'S EQUITY

DECREASE(DR)   INCREASE(CR)

INCREASE(DR)   DECREASE(CR)

TOTAL ASSETS _____

= TOTAL LIABILITES _____

+ OWNER'S EQUITY _____   } _____

INCOME STATEMENT
For the Month Ended June 30, 2013

REVENUE

DECREASE(DR)   INCREASE(CR)

MINUS
EXPENSES

INCREASE(DR)   DECREASE(CR)

INCREASE(DR)   DECREASE(CR)

INCREASE(DR)   DECREASE(CR)

INCREASE(DR)   DECREASE(CR)

INCREASE(DR)   DECREASE(CR)

TOTAL REVENUE _____

- EXPENSES _____

NET INCOME (LOSS) _____

AP-6 (❸)

For each of the given transactions, determine the effect on owner's equity by placing a checkmark in the space provided.

	Increase	Decrease	No Effect
1. Invested money in the business.			
2. Purchased equipment on account.			
3. Paid one-third of the amount owing for the purchase of equipment.			
4. Received cash for the services rendered.			
5. Paid salaries for the month.			
6. Withdrew cash for personal use.			
7. Paid monthly rent.			
8. Additional investment by the owner.			
9. Purchased supplies using cash.			
10. Acquired land using cash.			

Effect on Owner's Equity

AP-7 (❸, ❼)

The given transactions were completed by Juliet's Delivery Services during May 2014. Indicate the effects of each transaction by placing the appropriate letter in the space provided.

a. Increase in asset, decrease in another asset
b. Increase in asset, increase in liability
c. Increase in asset, increase in owner's equity
d. Decrease in asset, decrease in liability
e. Decrease in asset, decrease in owner's equity

_____ 1. Received cash for providing delivery services.
_____ 2. Paid amount owing that was outstanding to a creditor.
_____ 3. Invested additional cash in the business.
_____ 4. Paid advertising expense with cash.
_____ 5. Billed customers for delivery services on account.
_____ 6. Purchased office furniture on account.
_____ 7. Paid rent for the month.
_____ 8. Received cash from customers on account.
_____ 9. Obtained bank loan.
_____ 10. Owner withdrew cash for personal use.

AP-8 (❸, ❼)

For the following transactions, fill in the table on the right with the two accounts related to each transaction.

TRANSACTIONS

ACCOUNT TITLE	
1.	**2.**

1. Invested cash in the business.
2. Purchased service vehicle for business use.
3. Collected cash for services provided this week.
4. Provided services this week on credit.
5. Paid operating expenses in cash.
6. Received a bill for operating services incurred this week.
7. Borrowed a car loan.
8. Collected cash on accounts receivable for services provided previously.
9. Paid monthly salaries to employees with cash.
10. Incurred operating expenses this week, to be paid next month.
11. Paid cash on accounts payable for expenses incurred previously.
12. Paid cash for an insurance policy expiring after two years.

AP-9 (❸, ❼)

Jeff Roberts Communications is a public relations firm. On April 30, 2014, the firm had the following financial data:

Account balances

Cash	$20,000
Prepaid Rent	10,000
PPE - Office Equipment	25,000
Accounts Payable	8,000
Owner's Equity (Capital Account)	47,000

During the month of May, the company completed the following transactions:

1.	Purchased office equipment on account.	$800
2.	Paid amount owing that was outstanding to a supplier.	6,000
3.	Received cash from customers for services rendered.	5,000
4.	Paid utilities bill for May with cash.	700
5.	Purchased a computer (office equipment) on account.	1,500
6.	Received a bill to be paid in July for advertisements placed in a national newspaper during the month of May to promote Jeff Roberts Communications.	1,000
7.	Paid May's salaries with cash.	1,900
8.	Withdrew cash for personal use.	3,000
9.	Recognized rent for May (which was previously prepaid).	2,000

Required: Prepare the T-Account worksheet.

Note: the ending balance for the month of April is the opening balance for the month of May.

BALANCE SHEET
As at May 31, 2014

ASSETS		LIABILITIES	
INCREASE(DR)	DECREASE(CR)	DECREASE(DR)	INCREASE(CR)

INCREASE(DR)	DECREASE(CR)

INCREASE(DR)	DECREASE(CR)

INCREASE(DR)	DECREASE(CR)

DECREASE(DR)	INCREASE(CR)

OWNER'S EQUITY

DECREASE(DR)	INCREASE(CR)

INCREASE(DR)	DECREASE(CR)

TOTAL ASSETS _____

= TOTAL LIABILITES _____

+ OWNER'S EQUITY _____

} _____

INCOME STATEMENT
For the Month Ended May 31, 2014

REVENUE	
DECREASE(DR)	INCREASE(CR)

MINUS

EXPENSES

INCREASE(DR)	DECREASE(CR)

INCREASE(DR)	DECREASE(CR)

INCREASE(DR)	DECREASE(CR)

INCREASE(DR)	DECREASE(CR)

INCREASE(DR)	DECREASE(CR)

TOTAL REVENUE _____

- EXPENSES _____

NET INCOME (LOSS) _____

AP-10 (❸, ❼)

On December 1, 2013, Mary Ann established City Laundry. During the first month, the following transactions occurred:

1. Mary Ann deposited $15,000 into City Laundry's bank account.
2. Bought one washing machine worth $1,000 with cash.
3. Received and paid utilities bill for $1,200 in cash.
4. Purchased washers and dryers for a total of $4,000; where $2,000 is the down payment and the remainder is due in 30 days.
5. Purchased two additional dryers worth $1,100 from Marky Distributors, on account.
6. Made cash sales of $4,000 in the first half of the month.
7. Paid $900 cash for a one-year insurance policy.
8. Paid $1,000 cash for current month's rent.
9. Paid the amount owing to Marky Distributors.
10. Made cash sales of $3,500 in the second half of the month.
11. Paid employee salaries of $1,400.
12. Withdrew $2,000 cash for personal use.
13. Recorded first month's insurance expense of $75.

Required: Prepare the T-Account worksheet.

BALANCE SHEET
As at December 31, 2013

ASSETS	
INCREASE(DR)	DECREASE(CR)

INCREASE(DR)	DECREASE(CR)

INCREASE(DR)	DECREASE(CR)

INCREASE(DR)	DECREASE(CR)

LIABILITIES	
DECREASE(DR)	INCREASE(CR)

DECREASE(DR)	INCREASE(CR)

OWNER'S EQUITY

DECREASE(DR)	INCREASE(CR)

INCREASE(DR)	DECREASE(CR)

TOTAL ASSETS _____

= TOTAL LIABILITES _____

+ OWNER'S EQUITY _____ } _____

INCOME STATEMENT
For the Month Ended December 31, 2013

REVENUE	
DECREASE(DR)	INCREASE(CR)

MINUS
EXPENSES

INCREASE(DR)	DECREASE(CR)

INCREASE(DR)	DECREASE(CR)

INCREASE(DR)	DECREASE(CR)

INCREASE(DR)	DECREASE(CR)

INCREASE(DR)	DECREASE(CR)

INCREASE(DR)	DECREASE(CR)

TOTAL REVENUE _____

- EXPENSES _____

NET INCOME (LOSS) _____

AP-11 (③, ⑦)

The balance sheet of Jessica's Computer Services on February 28, 2014 is shown below.

Jessica's Computer Services			
Balance Sheet			
As at February 28, 2014			
Assets		**Liabilities**	
Cash	$4,000	Accounts Payable	$3,000
Prepaid Insurance	3,000	Bank Loan	0
PPE - Equipment	25,000		
		Total Liabilities	**$3,000**
		Owner's Equity (Capital Account)	**$29,000**
Total Assets	**$32,000**	**Total Liabilities and Owner's Equity**	**$32,000**

During March, the business engaged in the following transactions:

1. Borrowed a $20,000 bank loan.
2. Purchased computer equipment for $5,000 cash.
3. Performed services for a customer and received $4,000 cash.
4. Purchased printers for $1,000 on credit.
5. Paid $1,500 to a supplier for the amount owed.
6. Paid the following expenses in cash: salaries, $1,000; rent, $1,500; and interest, $200.
7. Received a $900 utilities bill, due next month.
8. Withdrew $3,500 cash for personal use.

Required: Prepare the T-Account worksheet, income statement and balance sheet.

Note: the ending balance for the month of February is the opening balance for the month of March.

BALANCE SHEET	INCOME STATEMENT
As at March 31, 2014	For the Month Ended March 31, 2014

BALANCE SHEET — As at March 31, 2014

ASSETS

INCREASE(DR)	DECREASE(CR)
Cash	
4,000	② 5,000
① 20,000	2,700
③ 4,000	1,500 ⑤
	3,500
15,300	

INCREASE(DR)	DECREASE(CR)
Property Plant	
25,000	
② 5,000	
⑦ 1,000	
31,000	

INCREASE(DR)	DECREASE(CR)
Prepaid Insurance	
3,000	
3,000	

LIABILITIES

DECREASE(DR)	INCREASE(CR)
	Acc. pay
⑤ 1,500	1,000 ④
	900
	3,000
3,400	

DECREASE(DR)	INCREASE(CR)
	Bank loan
	20,000 ①
	200 ②
	20,000

OWNER'S EQUITY

DECREASE(DR)	INCREASE(CR)
	Withdraw
3,500	3,500
3,500	

INCREASE(DR)	DECREASE(CR)
	Capital equity
	29,000
29,000	29,000

TOTAL ASSETS	49,300	
= TOTAL LIABILITES	23,400	} 49,300
+ OWNER'S EQUITY	25,900	

INCOME STATEMENT — For the Month Ended March 31, 2014

REVENUE

DECREASE(DR)	INCREASE(CR)
	4,000 ⑧

MINUS

EXPENSES

INCREASE(DR)	DECREASE(CR)
Salaries	
1,000	1,000 ⑥

INCREASE(DR)	DECREASE(CR)
Utilites	
900 ⑦	

INCREASE(DR)	DECREASE(CR)
Rent	
1,500	1,500 ⑥

INCREASE(DR)	DECREASE(CR)
Interest	
200	200 ⑥

INCREASE(DR)	DECREASE(CR)

INCREASE(DR)	DECREASE(CR)

TOTAL REVENUE	4,000
- EXPENSES	3,600
NET INCOME (LOSS)	400

Jessica's Computer Services
Income Statement
For the Month Ended March 31, 2014

Revenues	
Sale Revenues	4,000
Total Revenues	4,000
expenses:	
Salaries	1,000
Rent	1,500
Interest	200
Utilities	900
Total expense	3,600
net Income	400

Jessica's Computer Services
Balance Sheet
As at March 31, 2014

Asset		Liabilites	
Cash	15,300	acc. pay	3,400
Prepaid Insurance	3,000	Bank loans	20,000
PPE Equip	31,000		
		Total Liab.	23,400
		Owner equity	25,900
Total Assets	49,300	Total Liab + owner	49,300

AP-12 (❷, ❸)

The following is a list of Double Duplicator's accounts and balances as at March 31, 2014.

Cash	$2,700
Owner's Equity (Capital Account)	2,000
Accounts Payable	5,000
Prepaid Insurance	2,300
Bank Loan	10,000
Automobile Loan	18,000
Prepaid Rent	5,000
PPE - Automobile	25,000

Required: Prepare a balance sheet using the above information.

Double Duplicators Balance Sheet As at March 31, 2014			

AP-13 (❸, ❼)

Christine Jacob is a financial planning consultant. During the month of February, she completed the following transactions:

1. Christine invested $8,000 cash in the business.
2. Paid $1,400 cash for February office rent.
3. Received $6,500 from a client for services rendered.
4. Paid $500 cash to Shell Super Service for gas purchases.
5. Paid $700 cash to Helpful Manpower Services for consulting services.
6. Purchased office equipment worth $900 on account.
7. Owner withdrew $2,500 cash for personal use.
8. Donated $800 cash to the National Red Cross.
9. Received $2,000 cash from another client for services rendered.
10. Made partial payment of $500 on the equipment that was purchased on account.

Required: Prepare the T-Account worksheet.

BALANCE SHEET
As at February 28, 2014

ASSETS	
INCREASE(DR)	DECREASE(CR)

INCREASE(DR)　DECREASE(CR)

INCREASE(DR)　DECREASE(CR)

INCREASE(DR)　DECREASE(CR)

LIABILITIES	
DECREASE(DR)	INCREASE(CR)

DECREASE(DR)　INCREASE(CR)

OWNER'S EQUITY	
DECREASE(DR)	INCREASE(CR)

INCREASE(DR)　DECREASE(CR)

TOTAL ASSETS _____

= TOTAL LIABILITES _____

+ OWNER'S EQUITY _____

INCOME STATEMENT
For the Month Ended February 28, 2014

REVENUE	
DECREASE(DR)	INCREASE(CR)

MINUS

EXPENSES

INCREASE(DR)　DECREASE(CR)

INCREASE(DR)　DECREASE(CR)

INCREASE(DR)　DECREASE(CR)

INCREASE(DR)　DECREASE(CR)

INCREASE(DR)　DECREASE(CR)

TOTAL REVENUE _____

- EXPENSES _____

NET INCOME (LOSS)

AP-14 (❸, ❼)

On April 1, 2014, Aaron established a business to manage rental properties. He had the following transactions during its first month of operations:

1. Made a deposit into the business bank account. — $20,000
2. Purchased office equipment on account. — 1,000
3. Received cash for managing rental properties for a client. — 5,000
4. Purchased additional office equipment on account. — 350
5. Paid utilities bill for the month in cash. — 400
6. Borrowed a bank loan and used that money to purchase office equipment. — 5,000
7. Paid cash to reduce the amount of bank loan principal. — 500
8. Paid rent for the month with cash. — 1,800
9. Paid office staff salaries. — 1,500
10. Withdrew cash for personal use. — 1,000

Required: Prepare the T-Account worksheet.

BALANCE SHEET
As at April 30, 2014

ASSETS			LIABILITIES	
INCREASE(DR)	DECREASE(CR)		DECREASE(DR)	INCREASE(CR)

			DECREASE(DR)	INCREASE(CR)
INCREASE(DR)	DECREASE(CR)			

			OWNER'S EQUITY	
INCREASE(DR)	DECREASE(CR)		DECREASE(DR)	INCREASE(CR)

INCREASE(DR)	DECREASE(CR)		INCREASE(DR)	DECREASE(CR)

TOTAL ASSETS _____

= TOTAL LIABILITES _____ } _____

+ OWNER'S EQUITY _____

INCOME STATEMENT
For the Month Ended April 30, 2014

REVENUE	
DECREASE(DR)	INCREASE(CR)

MINUS

EXPENSES

INCREASE(DR)	DECREASE(CR)

INCREASE(DR)	DECREASE(CR)

INCREASE(DR)	DECREASE(CR)

INCREASE(DR)	DECREASE(CR)

INCREASE(DR)	DECREASE(CR)

TOTAL REVENUE _____

- EXPENSES _____

NET INCOME (LOSS) _____

AP-15 (❸, ❼)

Troy, an architect, opened his own business on March 1, 2014. During the month, he completed the following transactions related to his professional practice:

1. Transferred cash from personal bank account to the business account. — $30,000
2. Provided services for cash. — 3,000
3. Purchased office and computer equipment on account, which will be paid next month. — 8,000
4. Paid cash for meals and entertainment. — 1,100
5. Paid insurance expense with cash. — 800
6. Received cash from clients for delivering finished plans. — 4,000
7. Paid cash for miscellaneous expenses. — 600
8. Received utilities bill, to be paid next month. — 1,000
9. Paid cash for office rent for the month of March. — 1,200
10. Paid salary to assistant. — 1,000

Required: Prepare the T-Account worksheet.

BALANCE SHEET
As at March 31, 2014

ASSETS	
INCREASE(DR)	DECREASE(CR)

INCREASE(DR)   DECREASE(CR)

INCREASE(DR)   DECREASE(CR)

INCREASE(DR)   DECREASE(CR)

LIABILITIES	
DECREASE(DR)	INCREASE(CR)

DECREASE(DR)   INCREASE(CR)

OWNER'S EQUITY
DECREASE(DR)   INCREASE(CR)

INCREASE(DR)   DECREASE(CR)

TOTAL ASSETS

= TOTAL LIABILITES

+ OWNER'S EQUITY

INCOME STATEMENT
For the Month Ended March 31, 2014

REVENUE	
DECREASE(DR)	INCREASE(CR)

MINUS
EXPENSES
INCREASE(DR)   DECREASE(CR)

INCREASE(DR)   DECREASE(CR)

INCREASE(DR)   DECREASE(CR)

INCREASE(DR)   DECREASE(CR)

INCREASE(DR)   DECREASE(CR)

INCREASE(DR)   DECREASE(CR)

TOTAL REVENUE

- EXPENSES

NET INCOME (LOSS)

AP-16 (❷)

Organize the following asset and liability accounts in the order they are likely to appear in a balance sheet.

Assets	Liabilities
Accounts Receivable	Bank Loan
Cash	Accounts Payable
Property, Plant & Equipment	
Prepaid Expenses	

_____

_____

_____

_____

_____

AP-17 (❹)

Match each form of an organization with the appropriate description.

A	Sole proprietorship
B	Partnership
C	Cooperative
D	Corporation
E	Not-for-Profit Organization

_____ A business that operates for the benefits of its members (the people who use its products and services).

_____ This type of organization usually does not have an identifiable owner.

_____ There are two types of this type of business: one of that limits the liability of the owners and one that does not.

_____ A business operated by a single owner.

_____ This type of business often elects a board of directors.

AP-18 (❺, ❻)

Match each term with the appropriate description.

A	Merchandising
B	Service
C	Manufacturing
D	Internal Stakeholder
E	External Stakeholder

_____ A law firm is an example of this type of business.

_____ The owner of a business is an example of a(n) _____.

_____ This type of business buys goods to resell to customers.

_____ An automaker is an example of this type of business.

_____ A company's supplier is an example of a(n) _____.

AP-19 (❺)

Fill in the blank by indicating whether the stakeholder is internal or external.

Internal or External	
	Tax authorities are considered _____ stakeholders.
	The players of a football game are _____ stakeholders.
	Customers and trade unions are _____ stakeholders.
	_____ stakeholders rely on financial statements to enable them to manage the business efficiently.
	_____ stakeholders need financial statements to ensure that their investment in the business is protected.

Chapter 3

ACCOUNTING PRINCIPLES AND PRACTICES IN A BUSINESS

——————————— **Assessment Questions** ———————————

AS-1 (❶)

Briefly explain financial accounting.

_____

_____

_____

AS-2 (❶)

Briefly explain managerial accounting.

_____

_____

_____

AS-3 (❷)

Define GAAP. Which entity is responsible for the development and communication of Canadian GAAP?

_____

_____

_____

_____

AS-4 (❷)

According to GAAP, what are the characteristics of effective and useful information?

_____

_____

AS-5 (❷)

Describe the characteristic of relevance.

_____

_____

_____

_____

AS-6 (❷)

Describe timeliness. Which characteristic is timeliness a component of?

_____

_____

_____

AS-7 (❷)

Describe the characteristic of reliability.

_____

_____

_____

_____

AS-8 (❷)

What is verifiability? Which characteristic is verifiability a component of?

_____

_____

_____

AS-9 (❷)

Describe the characteristic of understandability.

_____

_____

_____

AS-10 (❷)

Describe the characteristics of comparability and consistency.

_____

_____

_____

_____

AS-11 (❷)

What is a trade-off?

_____

_____

AS-12 (❷)

Provide an example of a commonly known trade-off.

_____

_____

AS-13 (❸)

What does the economic entity principle state?

_____

_____

_____

AS-14 (❸)

What is the going concern principle?

_____

_____

AS-15 (❸)

Describe the monetary unit principle.

_____

_____

_____

AS-16 (❸)

Describe the objectivity principle.

_____

_____

_____

AS-17 (❸)

What is the cost principle?

_____

_____

AS-18 (❸)

What does the conservatism principle state?

_____

_____

_____

_____

AS-19 (❸)

Explain the time period principle.

_____

_____

AS-20 (❸)

Explain the revenue recognition principle.

_____

_____

_____

AS-21 (❸)

Describe the matching principle.

_____

_____

_____

AS-22 (❸)

What does that materiality principle state?

_____

_____

_____

AS-23 (❸)

Explain the full disclosure principle.

_____

_____

_____

AS-24 (❹)

What is IFRS? What is its purpose?

_____

_____

_____

_____

AS-25 (❹)

Explain the two general similarities between GAAP and IFRS.

_____

_____

_____

_____

AS-26 (❺)

Define controls.

_____

_____

_____

AS-27 (❺)

What is the purpose of internal controls?

_____

_____

_____

AS-28 (❻)

List two ethical standards for accountants.

_____

_____

_____

_____

——————— **Application Questions** ———————

AP-1 (❷)

Match each of the following characteristics of information to the appropriate description in the table below.

- Relevance
- Reliability
- Understandability
- Comparability and Consistency
- Timeliness
- Verifiability

Term (fill in)	Description
	Information is free from material error and bias
	A component of relevance
	The financial statements of a company should be prepared in a similar way year after year
	A component of reliability
	Financial information can be reasonably understood by its users
	All information for decision making is present in the financial statements

AP-2 (❷)

Hawkton Publishing Corporation is a publisher of math textbooks. The company is a large, well-known publicly traded corporation with thousands of shareholders. It produces financial statements on an annual basis. The most recent financial statements (for the year ended December 31, 2013) showed comparative balances for 2013 and 2012. The 2013 balances were derived using accrual-based accounting whereas the 2012 balances were derived using cash-based accounting. Which characteristic(s) of information did Hawkton fail to represent? Explain.

_____

_____

_____

_____

_____

_____

_____

AP-3 (❷)

Reflex Sports Inc. is a manufacturer of sports equipment for children. They rely on GAAP to prepare their financial statements. The nature of their accounting transactions can be quite complex at times. However, the financial statements have no additional notes to support them. The company also does not keep all invoices on record to back up expense amounts reported on the financial statements. Which characteristic(s) of information did Reflex Sports fail to represent? Explain.

_____

_____

_____

_____

AP-4 (❸)

Match each of the following basic GAAP concepts and principles to the appropriate description in the table below.

- Business entity principle
- Going concern principle
- Monetary unit principle
- Objectivity principle
- Cost principle
- Conservatism principle

Term (fill in)	Description
	The accountant should exercise the option that results in a lower balance of assets, lower net income or a higher balance of debt.
	Accounting transactions should be recorded on the basis of verifiable evidence.
	Assumes that a business will continue to operate into the foreseeable future.
	Financial reports should be expressed in a single currency.
	Accounting for a business must be kept separate from the personal affairs of its owner or any other business.
	Accounting for purchases must be recorded at their values on the date of purchase.

AP-5 (③)

Match each of the following basic GAAP concepts and principles to the appropriate description in the table below.

- Time period principle
- Revenue recognition principle
- Matching principle
- Materiality principle
- Full disclosure principle

Term (fill in)	Description
	Accounting takes place over specific fiscal periods.
	Sales must be recorded (recognized) at the time the duties are performed.
	Any and all information that affects the full understanding of a company's financial statements must be included with the financial statements.
	An expense must be recorded in the same accounting period in which it was used to produce revenue.
	Accountants should use GAAP except when doing so would be more expensive or complicated relative to the value of the transaction.

AP-6 (③)

Alton Floral Inc. is a recently incorporated company that operates in the gardening industry. The owner of the company has decided not to hire an accountant but instead maintain the accounting records on his own. He has included his employees as assets on the balance sheet in the account "Human Resources". He has valued them at the present value of their future salaries on the balance sheet. Also, the financial statements are not supported by notes explaining some of the figures. Which of the basic concepts and principles of GAAP has Alton Floral violated? Explain.

_____

_____

_____

_____

_____

AP-7 (❸)

Mackenzie Attire Corporation is currently preparing their annual financial statements for the past fiscal year. The company uses cash-based accounting. The company's policy includes receiving payment for its services well before the service is performed. The owner recently purchased a fish tank for his home and the transaction included a decrease to Mackenzie Attire's equity (an expense was recorded in the income statement). The value of inventory is adjusted annually to be stated at fair value. Which of the basic concepts and principles of GAAP has Mackenzie Attire violated? Explain.

_____

_____

_____

_____

_____

_____

_____

_____

_____

AP-8 (❷, ❸)

For each basic concept/principle of GAAP, indicate which one of the characteristics of information it is most related to.

Characteristic (fill in)	Basic Concept or Principle
	Monetary Unit Principle
	Objectivity Principle
	Cost Principle
	Materiality Principle
	Full Disclosure Principle

AP-9 (❸)

Suppose that a company has changed its policy for depreciation from one year to the next. An employee in the accounting department addressed this change with the owner. The employee asked the owner why the accounting policy was changed and why the reasoning for the change was not disclosed in the financial statements. The owner replied, "GAAP gives you the option to use a different depreciation method from one year to the next. We also are not required to explain our choices." Is the owner correct in his reasoning? Explain.

_____

_____

_____

_____

_____

_____

AP-10 (❸)

The accountant for GYC Consultants is facing an important accounting decision. The company recently incurred a material transaction that can be accounted for in three different ways (options A, B, and C). The effect on the company's net income and total assets for each option is shown below. In the spirit of GAAP, which option should GYC's accountant choose to account for the transaction and why?

Effect on:	Option A	Option B	Option C
Net Income	+$5,200	+$4,100	+$4,600
Total Assets	+$1,100	+$900	+$1,000

_____

_____

_____

_____

_____

AP-11 (❺)

Effective internal controls are designed to address which of the following objectives?

(Check off):	Objective
	Safeguard assets
	Encourage good management
	Provide an accurate valuation of the company
	Cover up accounting errors
	Prevent and detect fraud error

AP-12 (❺)

For each error or mishap below, identify a possible internal control that may have helped prevent it.

a) A check was issued to a supplier by a manufacturer as part of a major transaction. When the supplier tried to cash the check, there were insufficient funds in the manufacturer's bank account. Provide an internal control solution from the manufacturer's perspective.

_____

_____

_____

_____

b) A small business incurs only a few transactions every month. Its accounting clerk incorrectly entered the same transaction twice in the company's computerized accounting system. The error flowed through to the monthly financial statements.

_____

_____

_____

_____

c)   A company incurs a few, significant cash transactions each day. The cash is deposited into the business's bank account on a bi-weekly basis. It is suspected that a disgruntled former employee stole a large sum of cash from the company's premises on the day he was fired.

_____

_____

_____

_____

AP-13 (❻)

Marcus is the senior accountant for a small accounting firm. He is currently performing the year end audit of a particular client: Le Jardin Oak Inc. (LJO), a manufacturer of high quality furniture. After Marcus had met with Le Jardin's CEO in a restaurant, the CEO noticed that Le Jardin's financial records, which were provided to Marcus, were scattered on the ground. At this point, the CEO was extremely disappointed since the records were meant for internal use only. Which ethical standard did Marcus violate? Explain.

_____

_____

_____

_____

_____

AP-14 (❶)

Specify for each of the following statements whether it relates to financial or managerial accounting/accountant.

Statement	Financial or Managerial
It is concerned with the recordkeeping of the business.	
They could assume the role of accounting clerks on one area of the business.	
It serves the internal users of the business by preparing specialized reports.	
They do not have to be employees of the business.	
They analyze budgets and assist with decision making.	

AP-15 (⑥)

Mr. Alley works as an accounting manager for a big accounting firm named Worldwide Audit. He is currently involved with auditing one of the biggest clients of the firm. The client is a public company named, Tech4U Inc.; however, it does not seem to be in a good financial position based on the results of the audit. Mr. Alley's younger brother, Jack, is really interested in the financial health of Tech4U as he happens to be involved in trading Tech4U's stock. Recently, Jack borrowed $2,000 from Mr. Alley to buy some additional shares of the company. In last night's family party, Jack insisted on knowing the financial position of Tech4U before the information becomes available to the public. Mr. Alley knows that if his brother finds out about the audit results, he could sell his shares earlier at a higher price and also pay Mr. Alley back for his debt. Should Mr. Alley reveal any information to his brother? What ethical standards would be violated?

_____

_____

_____

_____

_____

_____

_____

_____

_____

_____

Case Study

CS-1 (❷, ❸)

Gordon is the majority owner of Gordon House Restaurant (GHR), a publicly traded chain of family restaurants. The company is owned by hundreds of shareholders who expect timely, reliable and accurate financial statements. GHR produces financial statements periodically. It is now June 15, 2013. The accountant has prepared the financial statements for the eight-month period ended May 31, 2013. The previous financial statements covered a one year period.

The company was recently sued by another company, the details of which are not disclosed in the financial statements. The court proceedings have not yet ended. However, as of May 31, 2013, it was believed that GHR is very likely to lose the case and eventually pay a significant amount in damages to the plaintiff.

Also consider the following additional information:

- Cash disbursements are not supported by additional source documents
- GHR has recognized revenue at a different time than the costs associated with producing that revenue
- GHR has included the following statement in the supplementary information section of the financial statements: "In preparing the financial statements, Gordon House Restaurant has adhered to the conservatism principle. When judgment needs to be exercised, the option that results in the higher balance of assets, higher net income or lower balance of debt has been chosen."

Required:

a) Which of the required characteristics of information has GHR failed to apply? Explain.

_____

_____

_____

_____

_____

_____

_____

_____

_____

_____

_____

_____

_____

_____

b) Which of the basic concepts and principles of accounting has GHR violated? Explain.

_____

_____

_____

_____

_____

_____

_____

_____

_____

_____

_____

_____

Chapter 4

REVENUE AND EXPENSE RECOGNITION

—————— **Assessment Questions** ——————

AS-1 (❶)

Define revenue.

_____

_____

_____

AS-2 (❶)

What does it mean to *recognize* revenue?

_____

_____

_____

AS-3 (❶)

What are the three possible ways cash related to revenue can be received?

_____

_____

_____

AS-4 (❶)

What is the entry to record revenue if a customer pays *when* the service is delivered?

_____

_____

AS-5 (❶)

What is the entry to record revenue if a customer pays *after* the service is delivered?

_____

_____

AS-6 (❶)

What is the entry if a customer pays *before* the service is delivered? What is the entry to record revenue when the service is finally delivered?

_____

_____

_____

_____

AS-7 (❶)

What type of account is unearned revenue?

_____

_____

AS-8 (❷)

What are the three possible ways to pay for an expense?

_____

_____

_____

AS-9 (❷)

What does it mean to *incur* an expense?

_____

_____

_____

AS-10 (❷)

What is the entry to record an expense if a company pays *when* the expense is incurred?

_____

_____

AS-11 (❷)

What is the entry to record an expense if a company pays *after* the expense is incurred?

_____

_____

AS-12 (❷)

What is the entry if a company pays *before* the expense is incurred? What is the entry to record an expense when the expense is finally incurred?

_____

_____

_____

_____

AS-13 (❷)

How does a company decide whether to include office supplies as a prepaid expense on the balance sheet (an asset) or an expense on the income statement?

_____

_____

_____

_____

AS-14 (❸)

What is an accounting period?

_____

_____

AS-15 (❸)

State the purpose of adjustments.

_____

_____

_____

AS-16 (❸)

What does accrual accounting state regarding revenue and expenses?

_____

_____

_____

AS-17 (❹)

Provide four examples of adjustments.

_____

_____

_____

AS-18 (❹)

Define accrued expenses.

_____

_____

_____

AS-19 (❹)

What is the entry to recognize accrued interest expense?

_____

_____

_____

Application Questions

AP-1 (❶, ❷)

Match each of the following balance sheet accounts to the appropriate description in the table below.

- Prepaid Expense
- Unearned Revenue
- Accounts Receivable
- Office Supplies
- Cash

Term (fill in)	**Account Description**
	Fill in the blank: When a customer pays *immediately* for services provided, the service provider's revenue increases and _____ increases.
	Cash, and this account, are impacted when a company pays for expenses in advance.
	An example of prepaid expenses
	Cash, and this account, are impacted when a service company's customer pays *before* the service is delivered.
	Cash, and this account, are impacted when a service company's customer pays *after* the service is delivered.

AP-2 (❶, ❷)

Melbourne Consulting Company had the following transactions during the month of April 2013:

Date	Description
April 1	Earned $2,000 in cash for services provided
April 2	Paid $2,400 in advance for insurance coverage up to March 31, 2014
April 3	Charged $3,000 on account to customers for services performed
April 15	Customer paid $800 for a service delivered last month.
April 28	Incurred maintenance expense of $350, to be paid next month

Complete the following chart to account for the above transactions. Under the 'Account Type' column, fill the cells with one of the following: Asset, Liability, Revenue or Expense. The first transaction has been completed for you as an example.

Date	Account Name	Account Type	Increase or Decrease	Amount
April 1	Cash	Asset	Increase	$2,000
	Service Revenue	Revenue	Increase	$2,000
April 2				
April 3				
April 15				
April 28				

AP-3 (❶, ❷)

GGY Service Company has a monthly accounting period. GGY had the following transactions during the month of May 2013:

Date	Description
May 1	Paid $2,000 in cash for travel expenses incurred on this day
May 2	Paid $1,000 in advance for maintenance services to be provided next month
May 18	Received a prepayment of $1,500 from a customer for services to be provided in two months.
May 25	Paid $750 for a service that was provided to GGY three months ago
May 30	Incurred repairs expense of $1,000, which was paid for two months ago

Complete the following chart to account for the above transactions. Under the 'Account Type' column, fill the cells with one of the following: Asset, Liability, Revenue or Expense.

Date	Account Name	Account Type	Increase or Decrease	Amount
May 1				
May 2				
May 18				
May 25				
May 30				

AP-4 (❶)

Gwen Lawn Company (GLC) is a lawn maintenance company. On January 1, 2013, one of its customers paid $12,000 in cash to GLC for lawn care services to be provided over the course of the year (until December 31, 2013). The amount of work GLC will do for the customer will be spread evenly throughout the year. The company has a monthly accounting period.

On January 1, 2013, GLC recorded the following incorrect entry to account for the $12,000 payment:

- Increase cash (asset) by $12,000
- Increase revenue (income statement) by $12,000

By how much has GLC overstated or understated revenue as at January 31, 2013?

_____

_____

_____

_____

_____

_____

AP-5 (❶)

Halton & Mauler LLP is a successful corporate law firm. On January 1, 2013, one of its clients paid $16,800 in cash to Halton & Mauler for legal services to be provided over the course of the year (until December 31, 2013). The amount of work the company will do for the client will be spread evenly throughout the year. The law firm provides consulting on a monthly basis.

On January 1, 2013, Halton & Mauler recorded the following incorrect entry to account for the $16,800 payment:

- Increase cash (asset) by $16,800
- Increase revenue (income statement) by $16,800

By how much has Halton & Mauler overstated or understated revenue for each month in 2013?

_____

_____

_____

_____

_____

_____

_____

_____

_____

AP-6 (❶, ❷)

MYK Service Company has a monthly accounting period. MYK had the following transactions during the month of June 2013:

Date	Description
June 3	Paid $1,200 in cash for maintenance expenses incurred on this day
June 4	Paid $950 in advance for services to be provided next month
June 7	Received a prepayment of $1,100 from a customer for services to be provided in one month
June 10	Paid $400 for a service that was provided to MYK two months ago
June 15	Incurred rent expense of $4,000, which was paid for two months ago
June 17	Earned $1,900 in cash for services provided

June 18	Paid $2,400 in advance for one year insurance coverage
June 23	Charged $500 on account to customers for services performed
June 26	Customer paid $400 for a service provided last month
June 30	Incurred supplies expense of $650, to be paid next month

Complete the following chart to account for the above transactions.

Date	Account Name	Increase or Decrease	Amount
June 3			
June 4			
June 7			
June 10			
June 15			
June 17			
June 18			
June 23			
June 26			
June 30			

AP-7 (❶, ❷)

Place a checkmark beside each transaction that affects owner's equity.

Transaction	Affects Owner's Equity? (Place Checkmark)
Made a prepayment for services to be provided in six months	
Made an adjustment to recognize a prepaid expense in the income statement	
Made an adjustment to recognize unearned revenue in the income statement	
Received a payment from a customer for services to be provided in three months	
Performed a service and received cash as payment	
Performed a service, to be paid for by the customer in two months	

AP-8 (❸, ❹)

Which one of the following scenarios will require an adjustment? Place a checkmark beside each one that applies.

Scenario	Requires future adjustment?
Customer makes a prepayment to company for services to be provided in the future	
Company makes prepayment to a supplier for goods to be delivered in the future	
Company provides a service and receives cash for it immediately	*NO*
Company purchases property, plant & equipment	*yes*
Company borrows a three-year interest bearing bond. The entire principal and interest amount is payable at maturity.	*yes*
Company makes cash payment for current month's rent	*NO*

AP-9 (❶, ❷, ❹)

ABC Service Company has a monthly accounting period. ABC had the following transactions during its first month of operations, May 2013:

Transaction #	Date	Description
1	May 2	The owner deposited $50,000 cash into the business
2	May 4	Paid $10,000 in cash for equipment
3	May 5	Paid $1,500 in cash for travel expenses incurred on this day
4	May 8	Paid $1,000 in advance for maintenance services to be provided next month
5	May 15	Received $9,000 cash for services provided
6	May 18	Received a prepayment of $1,300 from a customer for services to be provided in three months.
7	May 30	Paid $1,000 for May's rent expense

Required:

Complete the T-Account worksheet for May 2013.

BALANCE SHEET
As at May 31, 2013

ASSETS

INCREASE(DR)   DECREASE(CR)

Opening Balance

INCREASE(DR)   DECREASE(CR)

Opening Balance

INCREASE(DR)   DECREASE(CR)

Opening Balance

INCREASE(DR)   DECREASE(CR)

Opening Balance

LIABILITIES

DECREASE(DR)   INCREASE(CR)

Opening Balance

DECREASE(DR)   INCREASE(CR)

Opening Balance

DECREASE(DR)   INCREASE(CR)

Opening Balance

OWNER'S EQUITY

DECREASE(DR)   INCREASE(CR)

Opening Balance

INCREASE(DR)   DECREASE(CR)

INCOME STATEMENT
For the Month Ended May 31, 2013

SALES REVENUE

DECREASE(DR)   INCREASE(CR)

MINUS
EXPENSES

INCREASE(DR)   DECREASE(CR)

INCREASE(DR)   DECREASE(CR)

INCREASE(DR)   DECREASE(CR)

INCREASE(DR)   DECREASE(CR)

INCREASE(DR)   DECREASE(CR)

INCREASE(DR)   DECREASE(CR)

TOTAL ASSETS _____

= TOTAL LIABILITES _____

+ OWNER'S EQUITY _____

TOTAL REVENUE _____

- TOTAL EXPENSES _____

= NET INCOME (LOSS) _____

AP-10 (❶, ❷, ❹)

DEFG Consulting Company has a monthly accounting period. DEFG had the following transactions during its first month of operations, June 2013:

Transaction #	Date	Description
1	June 5	The owner deposited $100,000 cash into the business
2	June 10	Paid $30,000 in cash for equipment
3	June 14	Sold $12,000 worth of services to a customer (paid on account)
4	June 20	Paid $2,000 cash for June's rent
5	June 26	Received $3,000 in cash for consulting services to be provided in two months
6	June 30	Paid $6,000 in salaries for June
7	June 30	Accrued interest expense of $1,400

Required:

Complete the T-Account worksheet for June 2013.

BALANCE SHEET
As at June 30, 2013

ASSETS	
INCREASE(DR)	DECREASE(CR)

Opening Balance

INCREASE(DR)   DECREASE(CR)

Opening Balance

INCREASE(DR)   DECREASE(CR)

Opening Balance

LIABILITIES	
DECREASE(DR)	INCREASE(CR)

Opening Balance

DECREASE(DR)   INCREASE(CR)

Opening Balance

DECREASE(DR)   INCREASE(CR)

Opening Balance

OWNER'S EQUITY	
DECREASE(DR)	INCREASE(CR)

Opening Balance

INCREASE(DR)   DECREASE(CR)

TOTAL ASSETS _____

= TOTAL LIABILITES _____

+ OWNER'S EQUITY _____ } _____

INCOME STATEMENT
For the Month Ended June 30, 2013

SALES REVENUE	
DECREASE(DR)	INCREASE(CR)

MINUS
EXPENSES

INCREASE(DR)	DECREASE(CR)

INCREASE(DR)	DECREASE(CR)

INCREASE(DR)	DECREASE(CR)

INCREASE(DR)	DECREASE(CR)

INCREASE(DR)	DECREASE(CR)

INCREASE(DR)	DECREASE(CR)

TOTAL REVENUE _____

- TOTAL EXPENSES _____

= NET INCOME (LOSS) _____

AP -11 (❶, ❷, ❹)

Alton Safety Company has a monthly accounting period. The following are the company's account balances as at June 1, 2013:

Assets	Liabilities
Cash: $40,000	Accounts Payable: $30,000
Accounts Receivable: $21,000	Unearned Revenue: $3,600
Prepaid Rent: $4,800	Loans Payable: $60,000
PPE - Equipment: $50,000	**Owner's Equity**
	Capital Account: $22,200

Consider the following financial information as well:

- On May 31st, the company paid $4,800 as three months of rent in advance to Stratford Grant Properties (for June, July and August)
- On May 31st, Customer A made a deposit of $3,600 for services to be offered evenly over the course of the next three months

Alton Safety Company had the following transactions during June 2013:

Transaction #	Date	Description
1	June 1	The owner deposited an additional $40,000 cash into the business
2	June 10	Paid $30,000 in cash to purchase equipment
3	June 15	Paid $1,200 cash for travel expense
4	June 20	Sold $15,000 worth of services on account
5	June 21	Collected $10,000 cash from a customer who owed money
6	June 30	Recognized rent expense for June (prepaid to Stratford Grant Properties in previous month)
7	June 30	Recognized June's revenue related to payment by Customer A on May 31st
8	June 30	Paid $6,000 for June's salaries

Required:

Complete the T-Account worksheet for June 2013.

BALANCE SHEET
As at June 30, 2013

ASSETS

INCREASE(DR)	DECREASE(CR)
Cash	
Opening Balance 40,000	② 30,000
① 40,000	③ 1,200
⑤ 10,000	⑥ 6,000
52	52,800

INCREASE(DR)	DECREASE(CR)
Accounts Rec	
Opening Balance 21,000	10,000
④ 5,000	
26,000	

INCREASE(DR)	DECREASE(CR)
Prepaid Rent	
Opening Balance 4,800	⑥ 1,600
	3,200

INCREASE(DR)	DECREASE(CR)
PPE equip	
Opening Balance 50,000	
② 30,000	
80,000	80,000

LIABILITIES

DECREASE(DR)	INCREASE(CR)
Acc. pay	
	Opening Balance 30,000
	30,000

DECREASE(DR)	INCREASE(CR)
Unearned Rev	
⑦ 1,200	Opening Balance 3,600
	2,400

DECREASE(DR)	INCREASE(CR)
loan payable	
	Opening Balance 60,000
	60,000

OWNER'S EQUITY

DECREASE(DR)	INCREASE(CR)
Capital Acc	
	Opening Balance 23,200
	4,000 ①
	62,200

DECREASE(DR)	INCREASE(CR)

INCOME STATEMENT
For the Month Ended June 30, 2013

SALES REVENUE

DECREASE(DR)	INCREASE(CR)
	④ 15,000
	⑦ 1,200

MINUS
EXPENSES

INCREASE(DR)	DECREASE(CR)
Rent expense	
⑥ 1,600	

INCREASE(DR)	DECREASE(CR)
Travel EXP	
③ 1,200	

INCREASE(DR)	DECREASE(CR)
Salaries	
6,000	

INCREASE(DR)	DECREASE(CR)

INCREASE(DR)	DECREASE(CR)

INCREASE(DR)	DECREASE(CR)

TOTAL ASSETS	162,000
= TOTAL LIABILITES	92,400 }
+ OWNER'S EQUITY	69,600 }

TOTAL REVENUE	16,200
- TOTAL EXPENSES	8,800
= NET INCOME (LOSS)	7,400

$$62,200 + 40,000 + 7,400 - 0 = 69,600$$
$$22,200$$

Notes

Chapter 5

BUSINESS ACCOUNTING CYCLE PART I

—————————— **Assessment Questions** ——————————

AS-1 (❶)

What does the term debit refer to?

_____

_____

AS-2 (❶)

True or False: A credit will always be an increase to any account.

_____

_____

AS-3 (❶)

Which three types of accounts use the debit side of the T-Account to increase their value?

_____

_____

AS-4 (❶)

Which three types of accounts use the credit side of the T-Account to increase their value?

_____

_____

AS-5 (❶)

What is the normal balance of an asset?

_____

_____

AS-6 (❶)

What is the normal balance of a liability?

_____

_____

AS-7 (❷)

Explain the purpose of a chart of accounts.

_____

_____

_____

AS-8 (❷)

What are the six steps of the accounting cycle?

_____

_____

_____

AS-9 (❷)

In the accounting cycle, what is the purpose of creating journals?

_____

_____

_____

AS-10 (❸)

In the accounting cycle, what is the purpose of the general ledger?

_____

_____

_____

AS-11 (❹)

In the accounting cycle, what is the purpose of the trial balance?

_____

_____

_____

AS-12 (❷)

In the journal, what information will be entered in the PR (posting reference) column?

_____

_____

_____

AS-13 (❸)

What is the relationship between the closing balance and the opening balance for an asset?

_____

_____

_____

AS-14 (❹)

If the trial balance balances, were all transactions correctly recorded? Explain.

_____

_____

_____

Application Questions

AP-1 (❶)

For the following list of accounts, indicate which side of the T-Account causes an increase or decrease. The first account has been done for you.

Account	Debit	Credit
Cash	Increase	Decrease
Advertising Expense	Increase	Decrease
Service Revenue		
Unearned Revenue		
Accounts Receivable		
Accounts Payable		
Capital Account		
Owner's Drawings	Increase	Decrease
Prepaid Rent		
Rent Expense		

AP-2 (❶)

For the accounts listed below, determine if the normal balance is a debit or a credit.
Also, indicate if a debit or a credit will be needed to increase and decrease the account balance.

	Account Title	Normal Balance	Increase	Decrease
1	Cash			
2	Accounts Receivable			
3	Accounts Payable			
4	Loan Payable			
5	Capital Account			
6	Service Revenue			
7	Insurance Expense			
8	Prepaid Insurance			
9	Interest Receivable			
10	PPE - Equipment			
11	Unearned Revenue			
12	Rent Revenue			
13	Owner's Drawings			
14	Salaries Expense			
15	Office Supplies			

AP-3 (❶)

The following are the accounts of Micro Company and their corresponding normal balances on May 31, 2013:

Account Titles	Balance
Capital Account	$23,500
Insurance Expense	900
Accounts Payable	15,500
Service Revenue	8,900
PPE - Equipment	34,500
Supplies Expense	3,000
Cash	6,400
Salaries Expense	4,000
Rent Expense	3,000
Owner's Drawings	3,000
Utilities Expense	1,300
Bank Loan	10,200
Prepaid Insurance	2,000

Required:

Prepare Micro Company's trial balance for the month ended May 31, 2013.

Micro Company Trial Balance May 31, 2013		
ACCOUNT TITLES	DEBIT	CREDIT
Total		

AP-4 (❶)

Esteem Fitness provides fitness services for its customers. During the current month, Esteem Fitness had the following transactions:

1) Sold one-month fitness passes to customers for $4,500 on account.
2) Received a telephone bill for $250 which will be paid next month.
3) Paid an employee's salary of $1,200.
4) Received $3,000 cash from customers paying for an upcoming one-year membership.
5) Paid $6,000 cash for six months of rent (the six months are upcoming).
6) Received a $10,000 loan from the bank.
7) Purchased new equipment with $8,000 cash.

Record each transaction in the table shown below.

	Account Name	Increase or Decrease	Debit	Credit
1				
2				
3				
4				
5				
6				
7				

AP-5 (❶)

Have-a-Bash provides party planning services. During the current month, Have-a-Bash had the following transactions.

1) The owner invested $5,000 cash into the business.
2) Planned a party for a customer and received $900 cash.
3) Received a $500 utilities bill which will be paid later.
4) Paid $50 interest on a bank loan.
5) Paid $400 towards the bank loan principal.
6) Received cash from a customer who owed $1,100.
7) Paid the utilities bill received earlier.

Record each transaction in the table.

	Account Name	Increase or Decrease	Debit	Credit
1				
2				
3				
4				
5				
6				
7				

AP-6 (❷)

Kick-off Sports Training helps train children in various sporting activities. During May 2013, the following transactions took place.

May 3	Received maintenance bill - to be paid next month	$500
May 3	Received cash for services provided	$2,750
May 4	Borrowed cash from the bank	$4,000
May 4	Received interest on company savings account	$220
May 10	Prepaid insurance for one year	$1,200
May 10	Paid telephone expenses for the month with cash	$150
May 11	Paid cash to reduce the balance of accounts payable	$700
May 15	Paid interest on bank loan	$25

Prepare the journal entries for the above transactions.

Date	Account Title and Explanation	Debit	Credit

AP-7 (❷)

Rejuvenation Spa provides a relaxing retreat for people wishing to relax and unwind. During the month of July 2013, the following transactions took place:

July 3	Provided services to a customer on account	$3,600
July 4	Borrowed cash from the bank	$2,000
July 6	Provided services to a customer and received cash	$2,400
July 10	Received the telephone bill, which will be paid later	$250
July 11	Paid cash to reduce the balance of accounts payable	$600
July 15	Collected cash from customers owing on account	$1,800
July 20	Paid the telephone bill from July 10	$250
July 21	Paid a portion of bank loan principal	$1,500
July 31	Paid salaries for the month with cash	$1,600
July 31	Purchased equipment – to be paid later	$1,900

Prepare the journal entries for the above transactions.

Date	Account Title and Explanation	Debit	Credit
3/1	Cash	10,000	
	PPE-Equipment	8,000	
	Owner Capital		18,000
3/3	Cash	1,000	
	P Rent Expense		1000
3/5	Shop tools	1200	
	Cash		1,200
3/7	Cash	2000	
	Service Revenue		2000
3/8	Shop tools	1000	
	A/P		1000
3/15	A/P	500	
	Cash		500
3/18	Advertising Expense	200	
	Cash		200
3/19	Salary Expense	1000	
	Cash		1000
3/20	Owner drawings	1500	
	Cash		1500
3/29	PPE-Equipment	1000	
	A/P		1000
3/31	PPE-Equipment	5000	
	Owner Capital		5000
3/31	Cash	3,000	
	Service Revenue		3,000

AP-8 (❷)

Noel Dy opened an automobile repair shop. The following are the transactions that occurred during the month of March 2013:

Mar 1	Noel Dy invested $10,000 cash and $8,000 worth of equipment in the business
Mar 3	Paid $1,000 cash to rent the shop space
Mar 5	Purchased $1,200 worth of shop tools using cash
Mar 7	Received $2,000 cash for repair work done for MJ Gonzales
Mar 8	Purchased additional shop tools from Adrian Cruz worth $1,000, on account
Mar 15	Paid half of the amount due to Adrian Cruz with cash
Mar 18	Paid $200 cash to local publication for advertising
Mar 19	Paid $1,000 of salaries to shop helpers with cash
Mar 20	Noel Dy withdrew $1,500 cash for personal use
Mar 29	Bought $1,000 worth of equipment for the shop on account
Mar 31	Invested additional equipment worth $5,000 for business use
Mar 31	Received $3,000 cash from various customers for repairs done on their automobiles

Noel Dy's bookkeeper established the following chart of accounts:

Account Description	Account #		Account Description	Account #
ASSETS			**REVENUE**	
Cash	101		Service Revenue	400
Accounts Receivable	105			
Prepaid Insurance	110		**EXPENSES**	
Shop Tools	115		Advertising Expense	500
PPE - Equipment	120		Bad Debt Expense	505
			Depreciation Expense	510
LIABILITIES			Insurance Expense	515
Accounts Payable	200		Interest Expense	520
Interest Payable	205		Maintenance Expense	525
Unearned Revenue	210		Office Supplies Expense	530
Bank Loan	215		Professional Fees Expense	535
			Rent Expense	540
OWNER'S EQUITY			Salaries Expense	545
Capital Account	300		Telephone Expense	550
Owner's Drawings	310		Travel Expense	555
Income Summary	315			

Required:

Using the given general journal, prepare journal entries for the above transactions.

Date	Account Title and Explanation	PR	Debit	Credit
Journal				

Date	Account Title and Explanation	PR	Debit	Credit

AP-9 (❷, ❸, ❹)

Thomas Topology provides surveying services to construction companies and municipalities. The closing balance at the end of March 2013 and their chart of accounts are given.

Thomas Topology Balance Sheet As at March 31, 2013			
Assets		**Liabilities**	
Cash	$22,000	Accounts Payable	$10,500
Accounts Receivable	9,000	Unearned Revenue	4,500
PPE - Equipment	8,000	Bank Loan	6,000
		Total Liabilities	21,000
		Owners' Equity	
		Capital Account	18,000
Total Assets	$39,000	**Total Liabilities & Owners' Equity**	$39,000

Account Description	Account #
ASSETS	
Cash	101
Accounts Receivable	105
Prepaid Insurance	110
Office Supplies	115
PPE - Equipment	120
LIABILITIES	
Accounts Payable	200
Interest Payable	205
Unearned Revenue	210
Bank Loan	215
OWNER'S EQUITY	
Capital Account	300
Owner's Drawings	310
Income Summary	315

Account Description	Account #
REVENUE	
Service Revenue	400
EXPENSES	
Advertising Expense	500
Bad Debt Expense	505
Depreciation Expense	510
Insurance Expense	515
Interest Expense	520
Maintenance Expense	525
Office Supplies Expense	530
Professional Fees Expense	535
Rent Expense	540
Salaries Expense	545
Telephone Expense	550
Travel Expense	555

During the month of April, Thomas Topology had the following transactions:

Apr 1	Purchased office equipment on account	$7,000
Apr 2	Received cash for services provided	$25,000
Apr 3	Paid cash for April's rent	$1,000
Apr 4	Prepaid insurance for one year	$1,200
Apr 10	Paid cash to reduce the balance of accounts payable	$200
Apr 14	Paid cash for employee's salaries	$8,000
Apr 20	Paid interest on bank loan	$50
Apr 22	Received telephone bill which will be paid next month	$250
Apr 24	Recorded travel expenses to be paid next month	$8,000
Apr 30	Paid portion of bank loan	$4,500

Required:

1) Prepare the journal entries for the month of April.
2) Post the journal entries to the ledger accounts.
3) Prepare a trial balance at the end of April.

Journal					Page 1
Date	**Account Title and Explanation**		**PR**	**Debit**	**Credit**

Account: Cash					GL No:	
Date	Description	PR	DR	CR	Balance	

Account:					GL No:	
Date	Description	PR	DR	CR	Balance	

Account:					GL No:	
Date	Description	PR	DR	CR	Balance	

Account:					GL No:	
Date	Description	PR	DR	CR	Balance	

Account:					GL No:	
Date	**Description**	**PR**	**DR**	**CR**	**Balance**	

Account:					GL No:	
Date	**Description**	**PR**	**DR**	**CR**	**Balance**	

Account:					GL No:	
Date	**Description**	**PR**	**DR**	**CR**	**Balance**	

Account:					GL No:	
Date	**Description**	**PR**	**DR**	**CR**	**Balance**	

Account:					GL No:		
Date	Description	PR	DR	CR	Balance		

Account:					GL No:		
Date	Description	PR	DR	CR	Balance		

Account:					GL No:		
Date	Description	PR	DR	CR	Balance		

Account:					GL No:		
Date	Description	PR	DR	CR	Balance		

Account:					GL No:	
Date	Description	PR	DR	CR	Balance	

Account:					GL No:	
Date	Description	PR	DR	CR	Balance	

Thomas Topology Trial Balance April 30, 2013		
Account Titles	DR	CR

AP-10 (❷, ❸, ❹)

High Flying Biplane provides sight-seeing tours in vintage biplanes. The closing balance at the end of May 2013 and their chart of accounts is shown below.

High Flying Biplane
Balance Sheet
As at May 31, 2013

Assets		Liabilities	
Cash	$8,000	Accounts Payable	$8,200
Accounts Receivable	6,000	Unearned Revenue	3,200
Prepaid Insurance	1,200	Bank Loan	20,000
PPE - Equipment	60,000	**Total Liabilities**	31,400
		Owners' Equity	
		Capital Account	43,800
Total Assets	$75,200	**Total Liabilities & Owners' Equity**	$75,200

Account Description	Account #
ASSETS	
Cash	101
Accounts Receivable	105
Prepaid Insurance	110
Office Supplies	115
PPE - Equipment	120
LIABILITIES	
Accounts Payable	200
Interest Payable	205
Unearned Revenue	210
Bank Loan	215
OWNER'S EQUITY	
Capital Account	300
Owner's Drawings	310
Income Summary	315

Account Description	Account #
REVENUE	
Service Revenue	400
EXPENSES	
Advertising Expense	500
Bad Debt Expense	505
Depreciation Expense	510
Insurance Expense	515
Interest Expense	520
Maintenance Expense	525
Office Supplies Expense	530
Professional Fees Expense	535
Rent Expense	540
Salaries Expense	545
Telephone Expense	550
Travel Expense	555

During the month of June, High Flying Biplane had the following transactions.

Jun 1	The owner invested cash into the business	$5,000
Jun 2	Received cash for tours that will be provided in August	$1,500
Jun 3	Received an advertising bill which will be paid next month	$400
Jun 4	Paid the telephone bill with cash	$200
Jun 10	Provided tours to customer who will pay later	$2,400
Jun 14	Purchased some equipment with cash	$4,000

Jun 20	Received payment from customers paying their account	$1,600
Jun 22	Paid part of accounts payable	$900
Jun 24	Paid bank loan principal	$1,000
Jun 30	The owner withdrew cash for personal use	$1,200

Required:

1) Prepare the journal entries for the month of June.
2) Post the journal entries to the ledger accounts.
3) Prepare a trial balance at the end of June.

Journal					Page 1
Date	Account Title and Explanation	PR	Debit	Credit	

Date	Account Title and Explanation	PR	Debit	Credit

Account: Cash   **GL No:**

Date	Description	PR	DR	CR	Balance	

Account: **GL No:**

Date	Description	PR	DR	CR	Balance	

Account:					GL No:	
Date	Description	PR	DR	CR	Balance	

Account:					GL No:	
Date	Description	PR	DR	CR	Balance	

Account:					GL No:	
Date	Description	PR	DR	CR	Balance	

Account:					GL No:	
Date	Description	PR	DR	CR	Balance	

Account:					GL No:	
Date	Description	PR	DR	CR	Balance	

Account:					GL No:	
Date	Description	PR	DR	CR	Balance	

Account:					GL No:	
Date	Description	PR	DR	CR	Balance	

Account:					GL No:	
Date	Description	PR	DR	CR	Balance	

Account:					GL No:	
Date	Description	PR	DR	CR	Balance	

Account:					GL No:	
Date	Description	PR	DR	CR	Balance	

High Flying Biplane Trial Balance June 30, 2013		
Account Titles	**DR**	**CR**
Cash	8,800	
Accounts Receivable	6,800	
Prepaid Insurance	1,200	
PPE - Equipment	64,000	
Accounts Payable		2,700
Unearned Revenue		4,700
Bank Loan		19,000
Capital Account		48,800
Owners drawings	1,200	
Service Revenue		2,400
Advertising Expense	400	
Telephone Expense	200	
Total	82,600	82,600

AP-11 (❷, ❸, ❹)

Limbo Lower provides acrobatic entertainment at children's parties and other events. The closing balance at the end of August 2013 and their chart of accounts are given.

Limbo Lower Balance Sheet As at August 31, 2013			
Assets		**Liabilities**	
Cash	$7,200	Accounts Payable	$3,400
Accounts Receivable	2,300	Unearned Revenue	1,400
Office Supplies	850	Bank Loan	5,600
PPE - Equipment	11,500	**Total Liabilities**	10,400
		Owners' Equity	
		Capital Account	11,450
Total Assets	$21,850	**Total Liabilities & Owners' Equity**	$21,850

Account Description	Account #
ASSETS	
Cash	101
Accounts Receivable	105
Prepaid Insurance	110
Office Supplies	115
PPE - Equipment	120
LIABILITIES	
Accounts Payable	200
Interest Payable	205
Unearned Revenue	210
Bank Loan	215
OWNER'S EQUITY	
Capital Account	300
Owner's Drawings	310
Income Summary	315

Account Description	Account #
REVENUE	
Service Revenue	400
EXPENSES	
Advertising Expense	500
Bad Debt Expense	505
Depreciation Expense	510
Insurance Expense	515
Interest Expense	520
Maintenance Expense	525
Office Supplies Expense	530
Professional Fees Expense	535
Rent Expense	540
Salaries Expense	545
Telephone Expense	550
Travel Expense	555

During the month of September, Limbo Lower had the following transactions.

Sep 1	Paid cash in advance for a one year insurance policy	$1,800
Sep 2	Received cash for services provided	$1,900
Sep 3	Paid cash for September's rent	$1,350
Sep 4	Purchased office supplies on account	$250
Sep 10	Paid interest on bank loan	$40
Sep 10	Paid bank loan principal	$960
Sep 20	Sold some equipment for its book value and received cash	$2,200
Sep 22	Received payment from customer paying their account	$850
Sep 24	Paid a portion of accounts payable	$600
Sep 30	The owner withdrew cash for personal use	$1,600

Required:

1) Prepare the journal entries for the month of September.
2) Post the journal entries to the ledger accounts.
3) Prepare a trial balance at the end of September.

| Journal | | | | Page 1 |
Date	Account Title and Explanation	PR	Debit	Credit
2013				
Sep 1	Prepaid insurance	110	1,800	
	Cash	101		1,800
	paid for a one year insurance policy			
Sep 2	Cash	101	1,900	
	Service Revenue	400		1,900
	Received cash for services			
Sep 3	Rent expense	540	1,350	
	Cash	101		1,350
	paid for rent			
Sep 4	Office Supplies	115	250	
	Accounts payable	200		250
	Purchased office supplies on account			
Sep 10	Interest Expense	520	40	
	Cash	101		40
	paid interest			
Sep 10	Bank loan	215	960	
	cash	101		960
	paid bank loan			
Sep 20	Cash	101	2,200	
	PPE - Equipment	120		2,200
	Sold equipment for cash			
Sep 22	Cash	101	850	
	Accounts Receivable	105		850
	Customers paid their account			
Sep 24	Accounts payable	200	600	
	Cash			600
	paid accounts payable			
Sep 30	Owners Drawings	310	1,600	
	Cash	101		1,600
	Owners withdrew cash personal use			

Account: Cash GL No:

Date	Description	PR	DR	CR	Balance	
2013						
Sep 1	Opening Balance				7,200	DR
Sep 1		J1		1,800	5,400	DR
Sep 2		J1	1,900		7,300	DR
Sep 3		J1		1,350	5,950	DR
Sep 10		J1		40	5,910	DR
Sep 10		J1		960	4,950	DR
Sep 20		J1	2,200		7,150	DR
Sep 22		J1				
Sep 24		J1	850		8,000	DR
Sep 30		J1		600	7,400	DR
		J1		1,600	5,800	DR

Account: Account Receivable GL No:

Date	Description	PR	DR	CR	Balance	
2013						
Sep 1	Opening Balance				2,300	Dr
Sep 22		J1		850	1,450	DR

Account: Prepaid Insurance GL No:

Date	Description	PR	DR	CR	Balance	
2013						
Sep 1	Opening Balance	J1		0		Pr
Sep 1		J1	1,800	1,800		Dr

Account: Office Supplies GL No:

Date	Description	PR	DR	CR	Balance	
2013						
Sep 1	Opening Balance				850	Dr
Sep 4		J1	250		1,100	Dr

Account: PPE - Equipment GL No:

Date	Description	PR	DR	CR	Balance	
2013						
Sep 1	Opening Balance				11,500	DR
Sep 20		J1		2,200	9,300	DR

Account: Accounts Payable   **GL No:** 200

Date	Description	PR	DR	CR	Balance
2013					
Sep 1	Opening Balance				3,400 CR
Sep 4		J1		250	3,650 CR
Sep 24		J1	600		3,050 CR

Account: Unearned Revenue   **GL No:** 210

Date	Description	PR	DR	CR	Balance
2013					
Sep 1	Opening Balance				1,400 CR

Account: Bank Loan   **GL No:** 215

Date	Description	PR	DR	CR	Balance
2013					
Sep 1	Opening Balance				5,000 CR
Sep 10		J1	960		4,040 CR

Account: Capital Account   **GL No:** 300

Date	Description	PR	DR	CR	Balance
2013					
Sep 1	Opening Balance				11,450 CR

Account: **GL No:** 310

Date	Description	PR	DR	CR	Balance
2013					
Sep 30		J1	1,600		1,600 DR

Account: Service Revenue — **GL No:**

Date	Description	PR	DR	CR	Balance
2013					
Sep 2		J1		1,900	1,900 CR

Account: Interest Expense — **GL No:**

Date	Description	PR	DR	CR	Balance
2013					
Sep 10		J1	40		40 DR

Account: Rent Expense — **GL No:**

Date	Description	PR	DR	CR	Balance
2013					
Sep 3		J1	1,350		1,350 DR

Limbo Lower
Trial Balance
September 30, 2013

Account Titles	DR	CR
Cash	5,800	
Account Receivable	1,450	
Prepaid Insurance	1,800	
Office Supplies	1,100	
PPE - Equipment	9,300	
Account Pee		3,050
Unearned Revenue		1,400
Bank Loan		4,640
Capital account		11,450
Owners drawings	1,600	
Service Revenue		1,900
Interest expense	40	
Rent Expense	1,350	
Total Expense	22,440	22,440

AP-12 (❶, ❹)

A part-time bookkeeper for Wombat Tours has created the trial balance at the end of the year and cannot get it to balance.

Wombat Tours Trial Balance December 31, 2013		
Account Titles	**DR**	**CR**
Accounts Payable	$3,150	
Accounts Receivable	2,350	
Advertising Expense		$2,100
Bank Loan		5,200
Capital Account		6,170
Cash	6,200	
Interest Expense	560	
Maintenance Expense	240	
Office Supplies		1,600
Owner's Drawings		2,300
Prepaid Insurance	1,200	
PPE - Equipment	13,500	
Rent Expense	6,200	
Salaries Expense	5,300	
Service Revenue		25,800
Telephone Expense	450	
Unearned Revenue	1,680	
Total	$40,830	$43,170

All the entries have been journalized and posted to the general ledger properly, and all the accounts should have normal balances.

Re-create the trial balance for Wombat Tours so that the accounts are listed in the order they would typically appear in a chart of accounts, and ensure that debits will equal credits.

Note: All accounts have normal balances.

Wombat Tours Trial Balance December 31, 2013		
Account Titles	**DR**	**CR**

Chapter 6

BUSINESS ACCOUNTING CYCLE PART II

──────── **Assessment Questions** ────────

AS-1 (❶)

What is the purpose of a worksheet?

_____

_____

AS-2 (❶)

Why must adjustments be made at the end of the accounting period?

_____

_____

AS-3 (❶)

When making an adjustment to record unearned revenue that is now earned, which accounts are used and how are they affected?

_____

_____

AS-4 (❶)

When making an adjustment to record depreciation on property, plant and equipment, which accounts are used and how are they affected?

_____

_____

AS-5 (❶)

What is the purpose of a contra account?

_____

_____

_____

AS-6 (❶)

True or False: All property, plant and equipment depreciates.

_____

_____

_____

AS-7 (❶)

When making an adjustment to record the used portion of prepaid insurance, which accounts are used and how are they affected?

_____

_____

AS-8 (❶)

When making an adjustment to record accrued interest on a bank loan, which accounts are used and how are they affected?

_____

_____

AS-9 (❷)

What is an adjusted trial balance?

_____

_____

AS-10 (❸)

What does the income statement report?

_____

_____

AS-11 (❸)

Which statement is prepared after the income statement but before the balance sheet?

_____

_____

AS-12 (❸)

What does the statement of owner's equity report?

_____

_____

AS-13 (❸)

What two items will cause owner's equity to increase and what two items will cause owner's equity to decrease?

_____

_____

_____

AS-14 (❸)

Which categories of accounts will be reported on the balance sheet?

_____

_____

AS-15 (3)

How does accumulated depreciation affect the value of property, plant and equipment?

_____

_____

AS-16 (5)

What does it mean to close the books?

_____

_____

_____

AS-17 (5)

What are the three steps to close directly to the capital account?

_____

_____

_____

AS-18 (5)

What are the four steps to close the accounts using the income summary?

_____

_____

_____

AS-19 (5)

If a company has a net income for the period and closes their books using the income summary account, will the income summary account have a debit or credit balance before it is closed to the capital account?

_____

_____

AS-20 (❺)

Which categories of accounts will appear on the post-closing trial balance?

_____

_____

AS-21 (❻)

Identify two benefits of a computerized accounting system.

_____

_____

_____

Application Questions

AP-1 (❶, ❷)

Swordfish Programming provides computer solutions to the security industry. At the end of April 2014, they had the following adjustments:

1) A count of office supplies showed that there was $550 remaining in the office.
2) The balance of prepaid insurance is for a 12 month policy, one month of insurance has been used.
3) During April, Swordfish Programming earned $900 of unearned revenue.
4) PPE - Computers depreciated $120 during April.

Required:

Using the following trial balance, complete the adjustments and the adjusted trial balance in the worksheet.

Swordfish Programming Worksheet April 30, 2014						
	Unadjusted Trial Balance		Adjustments		Adjusted Trial Balance	
Account	Debit	Credit	Debit	Credit	Debit	Credit
Cash	$4,200					
Accounts Receivable	2,300					
Prepaid Insurance	1,800					
Office Supplies	800					
PPE - Computers	10,400					
Accumulated Depreciation - Computers		$0				
Accounts Payable		1,640				
Unearned Revenue		1,950				
Bank Loan		3,200				
Capital Account		11,035				
Owner's Drawings	1,500					
Service Revenue		4,750				
Depreciation Expense	0					
Insurance Expense	0					
Office Supplies Expense	0					
Rent Expense	1,300					
Telephone Expense	275					
Total	$22,575	$22,575				

AP-2 (❶, ❷)

Chirp Hearing provides hearing aids and other auditory services. At the end of November 2013, they had the following adjustments:

1) Accrued $40 interest on the bank loan.
2) The balance of the prepaid insurance is for the remaining 10 months of the insurance policy. One month of insurance has been used.
3) One month of depreciation is $180.
4) Chirp Hearing completed $650 of work that was previously unearned.
5) Office supplies used during the month totaled $400.

Required:

Using the following trial balance, complete the adjustments and the adjusted trial balance in the worksheet.

Chirp Hearing Worksheet November 30, 2013						
	Unadjusted Trial Balance		Adjustments		Adjusted Trial Balance	
Account	**Debit**	**Credit**	**Debit**	**Credit**	**Debit**	**Credit**
Cash	$6,250					
Accounts Receivable	3,440					
Prepaid Insurance	2,200					
Office Supplies	1,140					
PPE - Equipment	15,400					
Accumulated Depreciation - Equipment		$360				
Accounts Payable		2,260				
Interest Payable		0				
Unearned Revenue		1,240				
Bank Loan		4,500				
Capital Account		13,220				
Owner's Drawings	2,100					
Service Revenue		12,500				
Depreciation Expense	0					
Insurance Expense	0					
Interest Expense	0					
Office Supplies Expense	0					
Rent Expense	1,650					
Salaries Expense	1,900					
Total	**$34,080**	**$34,080**				

AP-3 (❶, ❷, ❸, ❹)

Mr. Allan Poe operates an advertising business called A Advertising. He had the following transactions for the month of December 2013:

Dec 2   Invested $25,000 cash in the business

Dec 5   Paid $2,500 cash for two months of rent in advance

Dec 5   Prepaid $600 cash for a one-year subscription to Manila Bulletin, a monthly trade magazine that is left in the office for visitors to read

Dec 8   Bought equipment worth $26,000 on account

Dec 10   Received $6,000 cash as advertising income

Dec 11   Paid $13,000 cash as partial payment for the equipment bought on account

Dec 15   Paid $2,000 cash for salaries

Dec 27   Received $3,000 cash from Extreme Jockey Club for advertising services

Adjustments:

Dec 31   Recognized $1,250 rent expense for the month

Dec 31   One month of the annual subscription has been used. This will be expensed to office supplies expense

Dec 31   Depreciation for the month is $400

Chart of Accounts:

Account Description	Account #
ASSETS	
Cash	101
Accounts Receivable	105
Prepaid Rent	110
Prepaid Subscriptions	115
PPE - Equipment	120
Accumulated Depreciation - Equipment	125
LIABILITIES	
Accounts Payable	200
Interest Payable	205
Unearned Revenue	210
Bank Loan	215
OWNER'S EQUITY	
Capital Account	300
Owner's Drawings	310
Income Summary	315

Account Description	Account #
REVENUE	
Service Revenue	400
EXPENSES	
Advertising Expense	500
Bad Debt Expense	505
Depreciation Expense	510
Insurance Expense	515
Interest Expense	520
Maintenance Expense	525
Office Supplies Expense	530
Professional Fees Expense	535
Rent Expense	540
Salaries Expense	545
Telephone Expense	550
Travel Expense	555

Required:

Prepare the journal entries, post them to the general ledger, and complete the worksheet.

Journal				Page 1
Date	**Account Title and Explanation**	**PR**	**Debit**	**Credit**

Journal					Page 1
Date	**Account Title and Explanation**	**PR**	**Debit**	**Credit**	

Account: Cash					GL. No.	
Date	**Description**	**PR**	**Debit**	**Credit**	**Balance**	

Account:					GL. No.	
Date	**Description**	**PR**	**Debit**	**Credit**	**Balance**	

Account:					GL. No.	
Date	Description	PR	Debit	Credit	Balance	

Account:					GL. No.	
Date	Description	PR	Debit	Credit	Balance	

Account:					GL. No.	
Date	Description	PR	Debit	Credit	Balance	

Account:					GL. No.	
Date	Description	PR	Debit	Credit	Balance	

Account:					GL. No.	
Date	Description	PR	Debit	Credit	Balance	

Account:					GL. No.	
Date	Description	PR	Debit	Credit	Balance	

Account:					GL. No.	
Date	Description	PR	Debit	Credit	Balance	

Account:					GL. No.	
Date	Description	PR	Debit	Credit	Balance	

Account:					GL. No.	
Date	Description	PR	Debit	Credit	Balance	

Account:					GL. No.	
Date	Description	PR	Debit	Credit	Balance	

A ADVERTISING WORKSHEET DECEMBER 31, 2013										149
	Unadjusted Trial Balance		Adjustments		Adjusted Trial Balance		Income Statement		Balance Sheet	
ACCOUNT TITLES	Debit	Credit	Debit	Credit	Debit	Credit	Debit	Credit	Debit	Credit

AP-4 (❶, ❷, ❸, ❹)

Following is the list of transactions of MJ Sandblasting for the first month of operations during April 2014.

Apr 1	Owner invested $30,000 cash in the business
Apr 1	Purchased sandblasting equipment from Delta Company for $12,000. Paid $8,000 as a down payment with cash, and the remaining balance is payable in 60 days
Apr 2	Purchased a one year insurance policy, costing $3,600
Apr 5	Paid $3,000 cash for garage and office rent
Apr 8	Received $5,000 cash from Billed Server Realty Corp. and $3,500 from Angela Building Corp. for services provided
Apr 14	Paid $1,000 cash for utilities

Apr 20   Paid $2,500 for salaries to employees

Apr 25   Owner withdrew $2,000 cash for personal use

Adjustments:

Apr 30   Recognized $300 of insurance expense for the month

Apr 30   Depreciation for the month is $200

Chart of Accounts:

Account Description	Account #
ASSETS	
Cash	101
Accounts Receivable	105
Prepaid Insurance	110
Office Supplies	115
PPE - Equipment	120
Accumulated Depreciation - Equipment	125
LIABILITIES	
Accounts Payable	200
Interest Payable	205
Unearned Revenue	210
Bank Loan	215
OWNER'S EQUITY	
Capital Account	300
Owner's Drawings	310
Income Summary	315

Account Description	Account #
REVENUE	
Service Revenue	400
EXPENSES	
Advertising Expense	500
Bad Debt Expense	505
Depreciation Expense	510
Insurance Expense	515
Interest Expense	520
Maintenance Expense	525
Office Supplies Expense	530
Professional Fees Expense	535
Rent Expense	540
Salaries Expense	545
Telephone Expense	550
Utilities Expense	555

Required:

Prepare the journal entries, post them to the general ledger, and complete the trial balance worksheet.

Journal				Page 1
Date	Account Title and Explanation	PR	Debit	Credit

Journal					Page 1
Date	**Account Title and Explanation**		**PR**	**Debit**	**Credit**

Account:					GL. No.	
Date	Description	PR	Debit	Credit	Balance	

Account:					GL. No.	
Date	Description	PR	Debit	Credit	Balance	

Account:					GL. No.	
Date	Description	PR	Debit	Credit	Balance	

Account:					GL. No.	
Date	Description	PR	Debit	Credit	Balance	

Account:					GL. No.	
Date	Description	PR	Debit	Credit	Balance	

Account:					GL. No.	
Date	Description	PR	Debit	Credit	Balance	

Account:					GL. No.	
Date	Description	PR	Debit	Credit	Balance	

Account:					GL. No.	
Date	Description	PR	Debit	Credit	Balance	

Account:					GL. No.	
Date	Description	PR	Debit	Credit	Balance	

Account:					GL. No.	
Date	Description	PR	Debit	Credit	Balance	

Account:					GL. No.	
Date	Description	PR	Debit	Credit	Balance	

Account:					GL. No.	
Date	Description	PR	Debit	Credit	Balance	

Account:					GL. No.	
Date	Description	PR	Debit	Credit	Balance	

	MJ Sandblasting Worksheet April 30, 2014									
	Unadjusted Trial Balance		Adjustments		Adjusted Trial Balance		Income Statement		Balance Sheet	
Accounts	Debit	Credit	Debit	Credit	Debit	Credit	Debit	Credit	Debit	Credit

AP-5 (❶, ❷, ❸, ❹)

Sprig Gardening Service provides seasonal gardening services. At the end of August 2013, the company must make the following adjustments:

1) Depreciation for their property, plant and equipment is $120.
2) Interest due on a bank loan is $50. It will be paid next month.
3) Accrued salary expense for an employee at the end of the month. The company owes the employee $450.
4) One month of prepaid insurance at $70 per month has been used.
5) A physical count of office supplies shows that $300 was used during August.
6) Sprig Gardening earned $670 that was previously unearned.

Required:

Prepare the adjusting journal entries.

Answers:

Journal				Page 1
Date	Account Title and Explanation		Debit	Credit

AP-6 (❶, ❷, ❸, ❹, ❺, ❻)

Thomas Topology has completed all their journal entries for the month of April 2014 and posted them to the general ledger. Based on the ledger balances, an unadjusted trial balance has been prepared. Their chart of accounts and unadjusted trial balance are listed on the following page.

Account Description	Account #
ASSETS	
Cash	101
Accounts Receivable	105
Prepaid Insurance	110
Office Supplies	115
PPE - Equipment	120
Accumulated Depreciation - Equipment	125
LIABILITIES	
Accounts Payable	200
Interest Payable	205
Unearned Revenue	210
Bank Loan	215
OWNER'S EQUITY	
Capital Account	300
Owner's Drawings	310
Income Summary	315

Account Description	Account #
REVENUE	
Service Revenue	400
EXPENSES	
Advertising Expense	500
Bad Debt Expense	505
Depreciation Expense	510
Insurance Expense	515
Interest Expense	520
Maintenance Expense	525
Office Supplies Expense	530
Professional Fees Expense	535
Rent Expense	540
Salaries Expense	545
Telephone Expense	550
Travel Expense	555

Thomas Topology
Unadjusted Trial Balance
April 30, 2014

Account Titles	DR	CR
Cash	$32,050	
Accounts Receivable	9,000	
Prepaid Insurance	1,200	
PPE - Equipment	15,000	
Accounts Payable		$25,550
Unearned Revenue		4,500
Bank Loan		1,500
Capital Account		18,000
Service Revenue		25,000
Interest Expense	50	
Rent Expense	1,000	
Salaries Expense	8,000	
Telephone Expense	250	
Travel Expense	8,000	
Total	$74,550	$74,550

The following adjustments must be made at the end of April:

Apr 30	One month of prepaid insurance has been used	$100
Apr 30	Depreciation on PPE - Equipment	$120
Apr 30	Unearned revenue that has now been earned	$1,300

Required:

1) Fill in the unadjusted trial balance on the worksheet and complete the rest of the worksheet.
2) Prepare the income statement, statement of owner's equity and the balance sheet.
3) Create the journal entries for the adjustments from the worksheet and post the adjustments to the ledger accounts.
4) Create the closing entries using the income summary account and post the closing entries to the ledger accounts.
5) Prepare the post-closing trial balance.

Note: The daily transactions for the month of April have already been posted in the general ledger. You are only responsible for posting the adjusting and closing entries.

1) Worksheet

Thomas Topology
Worksheet
April 30, 2014

Account Titles	Unadjusted Trial Balance		Adjustments		Adjusted Trial Balance		Income Statement		Balance Sheet	
	Debit	Credit	Debit	Credit	Debit	Credit	Debit	Credit	Debit	Credit

2) Financial Statements

Thomas Topology Income Statement For the Month Ended April 30, 2014		

Thomas Topology Statement of Owner's Equity For the Month Ended April 30, 2014		

Thomas Topology Balance Sheet As at April 30, 2014		

3) Adjusting entries (the general ledger is at the end of this question).

Journal				Page 2
Date	**Account Title and Explanation**	**PR**	**DR**	**CR**
4.30	Insurance expense	515	100	100
	Prepaid insurance	710		100
4.30	one Month PP insurance used			
4.30	Depreciate expense	510	120	120
	Accumulation Depreciation	125		120
4.30	Recording Depreciation		1,300	
4.30	Unearned Rev	210	1,300	
	Service Rev	400		1,300

4) Closing entries (the general ledger is at the end of this question).

Journal				Page 3
Date	**Account Title and Explanation**	**PR**	**DR**	**CR**
Apr.30	Service Revenue	400	26,300	
	Income Summary			26,300
	Close Revenue account			
Apr 30	Income Summary	315	17,520	
	Depreciation expense			120
	Insurance expense			100
	Interest expense			50
	Rent expense			1,000
	Salaries expense			8,000
	Travel Expense			250
	Close Expense accounts			8,000
Apr 30	Income Summary	315	8,780	
	Capital account	300		8,780
	Close income summary account			

5) Post-closing trial balance.

Thomas Topology Post-Closing Trial Balance April 30, 2014		
Account Titles	DR	CR

General Ledger

Account:	Cash				GL. No: 101	
Date	Description	PR	DR	CR	Balance	
2014						
Apr 1	Opening Balance				22,000	DR
Apr 2		J1	25,000		47,000	DR
Apr 3		J1		1,000	46,000	DR
Apr 4		J1		1,200	44,800	DR
Apr 10		J1		200	44,600	DR
Apr 14		J1		8,000	36,600	DR
Apr 20		J1		50	36,550	DR
Apr 30		J1		4,500	32,050	DR

Account:	Accounts Receivable				GL No: 105	
Date	Description	PR	DR	CR	Balance	
2014						
Apr 1	Opening Balance				9,000	DR

Account:	Prepaid Insurance					GL No: 110	
Date	**Description**	**PR**	**DR**	**CR**	**Balance**	
2014						
Apr 1	Opening Balance				0	DR
Apr 4		J1	1,200		1,200	DR

Account:	PPE - Equipment					GL No: 120	
Date	**Description**	**PR**	**DR**	**CR**	**Balance**	
2014						
Apr 1	Opening Balance				8,000	DR
Apr 1		J1	7,000		15,000	DR

Account:	Accumulated Depreciation - Equipment					GL No: 125	
Date	**Description**	**PR**	**DR**	**CR**	**Balance**	

Account:	Accounts Payable					GL No: 200	
Date	**Description**	**PR**	**DR**	**CR**	**Balance**	
2014						
Apr 1	Opening Balance				10,500	CR
Apr 1		J1		7,000	17,500	CR
Apr 10		J1	200		17,300	CR
Apr 22		J1		250	17,550	CR
Apr 24		J1		8,000	25,550	CR

Account:	Unearned Revenue					GL No: 210	
Date	**Description**	**PR**	**DR**	**CR**	**Balance**	
2014						
Apr 1	Opening Balance				4,500	CR

Account:	Bank Loan				GL No: 215	
Date	**Description**	**PR**	**DR**	**CR**	**Balance**	
2014						
Apr 1	Opening Balance				6,000	CR
Apr 30		J1	4,500		1,500	CR

Account:	Capital Account				GL No: 300	
Date	**Description**	**PR**	**DR**	**CR**	**Balance**	
2014						
Apr 1	Opening Balance				18,000	CR

Account:	Income Summary				GL No: 315	
Date	**Description**	**PR**	**DR**	**CR**	**Balance**	

Account:	Service Revenue				GL No: 400	
Date	**Description**	**PR**	**DR**	**CR**	**Balance**	
2014						
Apr 2		J1		25,000	25,000	CR

Account:	Depreciation Expense				GL No: 510	
Date	**Description**	**PR**	**DR**	**CR**	**Balance**	

Account:	Insurance Expense				GL No: 515	
Date	Description	PR	DR	CR	Balance	

Account:	Interest Expense				GL No: 520	
Date	Description	PR	DR	CR	Balance	

Account:	Rent Expense				GL No: 540	
Date	Description	PR	DR	CR	Balance	
2014						
Apr 3		J1	1,000		1,000	DR

Account:	Salaries Expense				GL No: 545	
Date	Description	PR	DR	CR	Balance	
2014						
Apr 14		J1	8,000		8,000	DR

Account:	Telephone Expense				GL No: 550	
Date	Description	PR	DR	CR	Balance	
2014						
Apr 22		J1	250		250	DR

Account:	Travel Expense				GL No: 555	
Date	Description	PR	DR	CR	Balance	
2014						
Apr 24		J1	8,000		8,000	DR

AP-7 (❶, ❷, ❸, ❹, ❺, ❻)

High Flying Biplane has completed all their journal entries for the month of June 2013 and posted them to the general ledger. Based on the ledger balances, an unadjusted trial balance has been prepared. Their chart of accounts and unadjusted trial balance are listed below.

Account Description	Account #
ASSETS	
Cash	101
Accounts Receivable	105
Prepaid Insurance	110
Office Supplies	115
PPE - Equipment	120
Accumulated Depreciation - Equipment	125
LIABILITIES	
Accounts Payable	200
Interest Payable	205
Unearned Revenue	210
Bank Loan	215
OWNER'S EQUITY	
Capital Account	300
Owner's Drawings	310
Income Summary	315

Account Description	Account #
REVENUE	
Service Revenue	400
EXPENSES	
Advertising Expense	500
Bad Debt Expense	505
Depreciation Expense	510
Insurance Expense	515
Interest Expense	520
Maintenance Expense	525
Office Supplies Expense	530
Professional Fees Expense	535
Rent Expense	540
Salaries Expense	545
Telephone Expense	550
Travel Expense	555

High Flying Biplane Unadjusted Trial Balance June 30, 2013		
Account Titles	**DR**	**CR**
Cash	$8,800	
Accounts Receivable	6,800	
Prepaid Insurance	1,200	
PPE - Equipment	64,000	
Accounts Payable		$7,700
Unearned Revenue		4,700
Bank Loan		19,000
Capital Account		48,800
Owner's Drawings	1,200	
Service Revenue		2,400
Advertising Expense	400	
Telephone Expense	200	
Total	$82,600	$82,600

Note: During the month of June, the owner of High Flying Biplane invested $5,000 into the business.

The following adjustments must be made at the end of June:

Jun 30	One month of prepaid insurance has been used	$100
Jun 30	Depreciation on PPE - Equipment	$450
Jun 30	Unearned revenue that has now been earned	$620
Jun 30	Interest is accrued and owed on the bank loan	$75

Required:

1) Fill in the unadjusted trial balance on the worksheet and complete the rest of the worksheet.
2) Prepare the income statement, statement of owner's equity and the balance sheet.
3) Create the journal entries for the adjustments from the worksheet and post the adjustments to the ledger accounts.
4) Create the closing entries using the income summary account and post the closing entries to the ledger accounts.
5) Prepare the post-closing trial balance.

Note: The daily transactions for the month of June have already been posted in the general ledger. You are only responsible for posting the adjusting and closing entries.

1) Worksheet

High Flying Biplane
Worksheet
June 30, 2013

Account Titles	Unadjusted Trial Balance		Adjustments		Adjusted Trial Balance		Income Statement		Balance Sheet	
	Debit	Credit	Debit	Credit	Debit	Credit	Debit	Credit	Debit	Credit

2) Financial Statements

High Flying Biplane Income Statement For the Month Ended June 30, 2013		

High Flying Biplane Statement of Owner's Equity For the Month Ended June 30, 2013		

High Flying Biplane Balance Sheet As at June 30, 2013		

3) Adjusting entries (the general ledger is at the end of this question).

Journal					Page 2
Date	Account Title and Explanation	PR	DR	CR	

4) Closing entries (the general ledger is at the end of this question).

Journal					Page 3
Date	Account Title and Explanation	PR	DR	CR	

5) Post-closing trial balance.

Account Titles	DR	CR
High Flying Biplane Post-Closing Trial Balance June 30, 2013		

General Ledger

Account: Cash						GL. No: 101	
Date	Description	PR	DR	CR	Balance		
2013							
Jun 1	Opening Balance				8,000	DR	
Jun 1		J1	5,000		13,000	DR	
Jun 2		J1	1,500		14,500	DR	
Jun 4		J1		200	14,300	DR	
Jun 14		J1		4,000	10,300	DR	
Jun 20		J1	1,600		11,900	DR	
Jun 22		J1		900	11,000	DR	
Jun 24		J1		1,000	10,000	DR	
Jun 30		J1		1,200	8,800	DR	

Account: Accounts Receivable						GL No: 105	
Date	Description	PR	DR	CR	Balance		
2013							
Jun 1	Opening Balance				6,000	DR	
Jun 10		J1	2,400		8,400	DR	
Jun 20		J1		1,600	6,800	DR	

Account:	Prepaid Insurance				GL No: 110	
Date	Description	PR	DR	CR	Balance	
2013						
Jun 1	Opening Balance				1,200	DR

Account:	PPE - Equipment				GL No: 120	
Date	Description	PR	DR	CR	Balance	
2013						
Jun 1	Opening Balance				60,000	DR
Jun 14		J1	4,000		64,000	DR

Account:	Accumulated Depreciation - Equipment				GL No: 125	
Date	Description	PR	DR	CR	Balance	

Account:	Accounts Payable				GL No: 200	
Date	Description	PR	DR	CR	Balance	
2013						
Jun 1	Opening Balance				8,200	CR
Jun 3		J1		400	8,600	CR
Jun 22		J1	900		7,700	CR

Account:	Interest Payable				GL No: 205	
Date	Description	PR	DR	CR	Balance	

Account:	Unearned Revenue				GL No: 210	
Date	Description	PR	DR	CR	Balance	
2013						
Jun 1	Opening Balance				3,200	CR
Jun 2		J1		1,500	4,700	CR

Account:	Bank Loan				GL No: 215	
Date	**Description**	**PR**	**DR**	**CR**	**Balance**	
2013						
Jun 1	Opening Balance				20,000	CR
Jun 24		J1	1,000		19,000	CR

Account:	Capital Account				GL No: 300	
Date	**Description**	**PR**	**DR**	**CR**	**Balance**	
2013						
Jun 1	Opening Balance				43,800	CR
Jun 1		J1		5,000	48,800	CR

Account:	Owner's Drawings				GL No: 310	
Date	**Description**	**PR**	**DR**	**CR**	**Balance**	
2013						
Jun 30		J1	1,200		1,200	DR

Account:	Income Summary				GL No: 315	
Date	**Description**	**PR**	**DR**	**CR**	**Balance**	

Account:	Service Revenue				GL No: 400	
Date	**Description**	**PR**	**DR**	**CR**	**Balance**	
2013						
Jun 10		J1		2,400	2,400	CR

Account:	Advertising Expense					GL No: 500	
Date	Description	PR	DR	CR	Balance	
2013						
Jun 3		J1	400		400	DR

Account:	Depreciation Expense					GL No: 510	
Date	Description	PR	DR	CR	Balance	

Account:	Insurance Expense					GL No: 515	
Date	Description	PR	DR	CR	Balance	

Account:	Interest Expense					GL No: 520	
Date	Description	PR	DR	CR	Balance	

Account:	Telephone Expense					GL No: 550	
Date	Description	PR	DR	CR	Balance	
2013						
Jun 4		J1	200		200	DR

AP-8 (❶, ❷, ❸, ❹, ❺, ❻)

Limbo Lower has completed all their journal entries for the month of September 2013 and posted them to the general ledger. Based on the ledger balances, an unadjusted trial balance has been prepared. Their chart of accounts and unadjusted trial balance are listed on the following page.

Account Description	Account #
ASSETS	
Cash	101
Accounts Receivable	105
Prepaid Insurance	110
Office Supplies	115
PPE - Equipment	120
Accumulated Depreciation - Equipment	125
LIABILITIES	
Accounts Payable	200
Interest Payable	205
Unearned Revenue	210
Bank Loan	215
OWNER'S EQUITY	
Capital Account	300
Owner's Drawings	310
Income Summary	315

Account Description	Account #
REVENUE	
Service Revenue	400
EXPENSES	
Advertising Expense	500
Bad Debt Expense	505
Depreciation Expense	510
Insurance Expense	515
Interest Expense	520
Maintenance Expense	525
Office Supplies Expense	530
Professional Fees Expense	535
Rent Expense	540
Salaries Expense	545
Telephone Expense	550
Travel Expense	555

Limbo Lower
Unadjusted Trial Balance
September 30, 2013

Account Titles	DR	CR
Cash	$5,800	
Accounts Receivable	1,450	
Prepaid Insurance	1,800	
Office Supplies	1,100	
PPE - Equipment	9,300	
Accounts Payable		$3,050
Unearned Revenue		1,400
Bank Loan		4,640
Capital Account		11,450
Owner's Drawings	1,600	
Service Revenue		1,900
Interest Expense	40	
Rent Expense	1,350	
Total	$22,440	$22,440

The following adjustments must be made at the end of September:

Sep 30	One month of prepaid insurance has been used	$150
Sep 30	Depreciation on PPE - Equipment	$120
Sep 30	Unearned revenue that has now been earned	$360
Sep 30	Amount of office supplies used during the month	$450

Required:

1) Fill in the unadjusted trial balance on the worksheet and complete the rest of the worksheet.
2) Prepare the income statement, statement of owner's equity and the balance sheet.
3) Create the journal entries for the adjustments from the worksheet and post the adjustments to the ledger accounts.
4) Create the closing entries using the income summary account and post the closing entries to the ledger accounts.
5) Prepare the post-closing trial balance.

Note: The daily transactions for the month of September have already been posted in the general ledger. You are only responsible for posting the adjusting and closing entries.

1) Worksheet

Account Titles	Unadjusted Trial Balance		Adjustments		Adjusted Trial Balance		Income Statement		Balance Sheet	
	Debit	Credit	Debit	Credit	Debit	Credit	Debit	Credit	Debit	Credit

Limbo Lower
Worksheet
September 30, 2013

2) Financial Statements

Limbo Lower Income Statement For the Month Ended September 30, 2013		

Limbo Lower Statement of Owner's Equity For the Month Ended September 30, 2013		

Limbo Lower Balance Sheet As at September 30, 2013		

3) Adjusting entries (the general ledger is at the end of this question).

Journal				Page 2
Date	**Account Title and Explanation**	**PR**	**DR**	**CR**

4) Closing entries (the general ledger is at the end of this question).

Journal				Page 3
Date	**Account Title and Explanation**	**PR**	**DR**	**CR**

5) Post-closing trial balance.

<table>
<tr><td colspan="3" align="center">Limbo Lower
Post-Closing Trial Balance
September 30, 2013</td></tr>
<tr><td>Account Titles</td><td>DR</td><td>CR</td></tr>
<tr><td></td><td></td><td></td></tr>
<tr><td></td><td></td><td></td></tr>
<tr><td></td><td></td><td></td></tr>
<tr><td></td><td></td><td></td></tr>
<tr><td></td><td></td><td></td></tr>
<tr><td></td><td></td><td></td></tr>
<tr><td></td><td></td><td></td></tr>
<tr><td></td><td></td><td></td></tr>
<tr><td></td><td></td><td></td></tr>
<tr><td></td><td></td><td></td></tr>
<tr><td></td><td></td><td></td></tr>
<tr><td></td><td></td><td></td></tr>
</table>

General Ledger

Account: Cash GL. No: 101

Date	Description	PR	DR	CR	Balance	
2013						
Sep 1	Opening Balance				7,200	DR
Sep 1		J1		1,800	5,400	DR
Sep 2		J1	1,900		7,300	DR
Sep 3		J1		1,350	5,950	DR
Sep 10		J1		40	5,910	DR
Sep 10		J1		960	4,950	DR
Sep 20		J1	2,200		7,150	DR
Sep 22		J1	850		8,000	DR
Sep 24		J1		600	7,400	DR
Sep 30		J1		1,600	5,800	DR

Account: Accounts Receivable GL No: 105

Date	Description	PR	DR	CR	Balance	
2013						
Sep 1	Opening Balance				2,300	DR
Sep 22		J1		850	1,450	DR

Account:	Prepaid Insurance				GL No: 110	
Date	**Description**	**PR**	**DR**	**CR**	**Balance**	
2013						
Sep 1	Opening Balance				0	DR
Sep 1		J1	1,800		1,800	DR

Account:	Office Supplies				GL No: 115	
Date	**Description**	**PR**	**DR**	**CR**	**Balance**	
2013						
Sep 1	Opening Balance				850	DR
Sep 4		J1	250		1,100	DR

Account:	PPE - Equipment				GL No: 120	
Date	**Description**	**PR**	**DR**	**CR**	**Balance**	
2013						
Sep 1	Opening Balance				11,500	DR
Sep 20		J1		2,200	9,300	DR

Account:	Accumulated Depreciation - Equipment				GL No: 125	
Date	**Description**	**PR**	**DR**	**CR**	**Balance**	

Account:	Accounts Payable				GL No: 200	
Date	**Description**	**PR**	**DR**	**CR**	**Balance**	
2013						
Sep 1	Opening Balance				3,400	CR
Sep 4		J1		250	3,650	CR
Sep 24		J1	600		3,050	CR

Account:	Unearned Revenue				GL No: 210	
Date	Description	PR	DR	CR	Balance	
2013						
Sep 1	Opening Balance				1,400	CR

Account:	Bank Loan				GL No: 215	
Date	Description	PR	DR	CR	Balance	
2013						
Sep 1	Opening Balance				5,600	CR
Sep 10		J1	960		4,640	CR

Account:	Capital Account				GL No: 300	
Date	Description	PR	DR	CR	Balance	
2013						
Sep 1	Opening Balance				11,450	CR

Account:	Owner's Drawings				GL No: 310	
Date	Description	PR	DR	CR	Balance	
2013						
Sep 30		J1	1,600		1,600	DR

Account:	Income Summary				GL No: 315	
Date	Description	PR	DR	CR	Balance	

Account:	Service Revenue				GL No: 400	
Date	Description	PR	DR	CR	Balance	
2013						
Sep 2		J1		1,900	1,900	CR

Account:	Depreciation Expense				GL No: 510	
Date	Description	PR	DR	CR	Balance	

Account:	Insurance Expense				GL No: 515	
Date	Description	PR	DR	CR	Balance	

Account:	Interest Expense				GL No: 520	
Date	Description	PR	DR	CR	Balance	
2013						
Sep 10		J1	40		40	DR

Account:	Office Supplies Expense				GL No: 530	
Date	Description	PR	DR	CR	Balance	

Account:	Rent Expense				GL No: 540	
Date	Description	PR	DR	CR	Balance	
2013						
Sep 3		J1	1,350		1,350	DR

AP-9 (⑤)

Keynote Consulting has journalized their adjusting entries and prepared their adjusted trial balance. Using the adjusted trial balance, prepare the closing entries using the income summary account for the month of August and create the post-closing trial balance.

Keynote Consulting Adjusted Trial Balance August 31, 2013		
Account	**Debit**	**Credit**
Cash	$6,200	
Accounts Receivable	1,750	
Prepaid Insurance	1,650	
Office Supplies	1,150	
PPE - Equipment	10,650	
Accumulated Depreciation - Equipment		$320
Accounts Payable		1,640
Interest Payable		50
Unearned Revenue		1,420
Bank Loan		3,000
Capital Account		14,290
Owner's Drawings	2,000	
Service Revenue		4,100
Depreciation Expense	150	
Insurance Expense	170	
Interest Expense	50	
Rent Expense	800	
Telephone Expense	250	
Total	$24,820	$24,820

a) Closing entries.

Date	Account Title and Explanation	DR	CR

b) Post-closing trial balance

Keynote Consulting Post-Closing Trial Balance August 31, 2013		
Account	**Debit**	**Credit**

AP-10 (❺)

Frank's Custom Framing has journalized their adjusting entries and prepared their adjusted trial balance. Using the adjusted trial balance, prepare the closing entries using the income summary account for the month of October and create the post-closing trial balance.

Frank's Custom Framing Adjusted Trial Balance October 31, 2013		
Account	**Debit**	**Credit**
Cash	$8,620	
Accounts Receivable	2,340	
Prepaid Insurance	2,650	
Office Supplies	1,840	
PPE - Equipment	23,400	
Accumulated Depreciation - Equipment		$1,640
Accounts Payable		3,540
Interest Payable		120
Unearned Revenue		2,110
Bank Loan		5,500
Capital Account		24,080
Owner's Drawings	3,200	
Service Revenue		8,750
Depreciation Expense	260	
Insurance Expense	185	
Interest Expense	120	
Rent Expense	1,200	
Telephone Expense	275	
Salaries Expense	1,650	
Total	**$45,740**	**$45,740**

a) Closing entries.

Date	Account Title and Explanation	DR	CR

b) Post-closing trial balance

Frank's Custom Framing Post-Closing Trial Balance October 31, 2013		
Account	**Debit**	**Credit**

AP-11 (❺)

Home Protector has journalized their adjusting entries and prepared their adjusted trial balance. Using the adjusted trial balance, prepare the closing entries directly to the capital account for the month of December and create the post-closing trial balance.

Home Protector Adjusted Trial Balance December 31, 2013		
Account	**Debit**	**Credit**
Cash	$12,650	
Accounts Receivable	5,420	
Prepaid Insurance	2,820	
Office Supplies	2,240	
PPE - Equipment	25,600	
Accumulated Depreciation - Equipment		$2,340
Accounts Payable		6,250
Salaries Payable		650
Unearned Revenue		4,250
Bank Loan		7,500
Capital Account		21,645
Owner's Drawings	4,300	
Service Revenue		16,875
Depreciation Expense	320	
Insurance Expense	220	
Interest Expense	160	
Rent Expense	1,890	
Telephone Expense	350	
Salaries Expense	3,540	
Total	$59,510	$59,510

a) Closing entries.

Date	Account Title and Explanation	DR	CR

b) Post-closing trial balance

Home Protector Post-Closing Trial Balance December 31, 2013		
Account	Debit	Credit

AP-12 (⑤)

Luminary Electric has journalized their adjusting entries and prepared their adjusted trial balance. Using the adjusted trial balance, prepare the closing entries directly to the capital account for the month of March and create the post-closing trial balance.

Luminary Electric Adjusted Trial Balance March 31, 2013		
Account	**Debit**	**Credit**
Cash	$10,420	
Accounts Receivable	6,350	
Prepaid Insurance	2,350	
Office Supplies	1,860	
PPE - Equipment	32,500	
Accumulated Depreciation - Equipment		$5,480
Accounts Payable		4,870
Salaries Payable		840
Unearned Revenue		5,340
Bank Loan		9,000
Capital Account		23,745
Owner's Drawings	5,200	
Service Revenue		17,850
Depreciation Expense	410	
Insurance Expense	195	
Interest Expense	210	
Office Supplies Expense	670	
Rent Expense	2,150	
Telephone Expense	450	
Salaries Expense	4,360	
Total	$67,125	$67,125

a) Closing entries.

Date	Account Title and Explanation	DR	CR

b) Post-closing trial balance

Luminary Electric Post-Closing Trial Balance March 31, 2013		
Account	**Debit**	**Credit**

Case Study

CS-1 (❶, ❷, ❸, ❹, ❺)

Grindstone Paving provides residential and commercial paving services. Their balance sheet at the end of June 2013 is shown below, along with their chart of accounts.

Grindstone Paving Balance Sheet As at June 30, 2013			
Assets		**Liabilities**	
Cash	$7,580	Accounts Payable	$15,800
Accounts Receivable	6,000	Unearned Revenue	6,200
Prepaid Insurance	1,800	Bank Loan	22,000
PPE - Equipment	55,000	Total Liabilities	44,000
		Owners' Equity	
		Capital Account	26,380
Total Assets	$70,380	**Total Liabilities & Owners' Equity**	$70,380

Account Description	Account #
ASSETS	
Cash	101
Accounts Receivable	105
Prepaid Insurance	110
Office Supplies	115
PPE - Equipment	120
Accumulated Depreciation - Equipment	125
LIABILITIES	
Accounts Payable	200
Interest Payable	205
Salary Payable	210
Unearned Revenue	215
Bank Loan	220
OWNER'S EQUITY	
Capital Account	300
Owner's Drawings	310
Income Summary	315

Account Description	Account #
REVENUE	
Service Revenue	400
EXPENSES	
Advertising Expense	500
Bad Debt Expense	505
Depreciation Expense	510
Insurance Expense	515
Interest Expense	520
Maintenance Expense	525
Office Supplies Expense	530
Professional Fees Expense	535
Rent Expense	540
Salaries Expense	545
Telephone Expense	550
Travel Expense	555

For the month of July 2013, Grindstone Paving had the following transactions:

Jul 1	The owner invested cash into the business	$8,000
Jul 2	Received cash for work that will be provided in August	$2,530
Jul 5	Received an advertising bill which will be paid next month	$600
Jul 8	Paid the telephone bill with cash	$350

Jul 10	Provided services to customers who will pay later	$4,680
Jul 14	Purchase equipment with cash	$8,200
Jul 20	Received payment from customers paying their account	$2,350
Jul 22	Paid part of accounts payable	$1,970
Jul 24	Paid bank loan principal	$1,300
Jul 28	Paid salary to an employee	$2,400
Jul 30	The owner withdrew cash for personal use	$2,200

At the end of July, the following adjustment had to be journalized to properly report the balances of the company's accounts:

Jul 31	One month of prepaid insurance has been used	$100
Jul 31	Depreciation on PPE - Equipment	$450
Jul 31	Unearned revenue that has now been earned	$620
Jul 31	Interest is accrued and owed on the bank loan	$75
Jul 31	Accrued salary expense for an employee	$500

Required:

1) Enter the opening balances from the June 2013 balance sheet into the general ledger accounts (the ledger accounts are presented at the end of this question).
2) Prepare the journal entries for the month of July and post them to the appropriate general ledger accounts.
3) Create the trial balance in the worksheet, and then complete the remaining section of the worksheet.
4) Create the income statement, statement of owner's equity and the balance sheet.
5) Prepare the journal entries for the adjustments and post them to the appropriate general ledger accounts.
6) Prepare the journal entries to close the books for the month of July 2013 (use the income summary account), and post the journal entries to the appropriate general ledger accounts.
7) Create the post-closing trial balance.

Answers:

1) Journal entries

Journal				Page 1
Date	Account Title and Explanation	PR	DR	CR

Journal					Page 1
Date	Account Title and Explanation	PR	DR	CR	

2) Worksheet

Account Titles	Grindstone Paving Worksheet July 31, 2013											
	Unadjusted Trial Balance		Adjustments		Adjusted Trial Balance		Income Statement		Balance Sheet	
	Debit	Credit	Debit	Credit	Debit	Credit	Debit	Credit	Debit	Credit

3) Financial statements

<table>
<tr><td colspan="3">Grindstone Paving
Income Statement
For the Month Ended July 31, 2013</td></tr>
<tr><td></td><td></td><td></td></tr>
<tr><td></td><td></td><td></td></tr>
<tr><td></td><td></td><td></td></tr>
<tr><td></td><td></td><td></td></tr>
<tr><td></td><td></td><td></td></tr>
<tr><td></td><td></td><td></td></tr>
<tr><td></td><td></td><td></td></tr>
<tr><td></td><td></td><td></td></tr>
<tr><td></td><td></td><td></td></tr>
<tr><td></td><td></td><td></td></tr>
<tr><td></td><td></td><td></td></tr>
</table>

<table>
<tr><td colspan="3">Grindstone Paving
Statement of Owner's Equity
As at July 31, 2013</td></tr>
<tr><td></td><td></td><td></td></tr>
<tr><td></td><td></td><td></td></tr>
<tr><td></td><td></td><td></td></tr>
<tr><td></td><td></td><td></td></tr>
<tr><td></td><td></td><td></td></tr>
<tr><td></td><td></td><td></td></tr>
<tr><td></td><td></td><td></td></tr>
<tr><td></td><td></td><td></td></tr>
</table>

<table>
<tr><td colspan="3">Grindstone Paving
Balance Sheet
For the Month Ended July 31, 2013</td></tr>
<tr><td></td><td></td><td></td></tr>
<tr><td></td><td></td><td></td></tr>
<tr><td></td><td></td><td></td></tr>
<tr><td></td><td></td><td></td></tr>
<tr><td></td><td></td><td></td></tr>
<tr><td></td><td></td><td></td></tr>
<tr><td></td><td></td><td></td></tr>
<tr><td></td><td></td><td></td></tr>
<tr><td></td><td></td><td></td></tr>
<tr><td></td><td></td><td></td></tr>
<tr><td></td><td></td><td></td></tr>
<tr><td></td><td></td><td></td></tr>
<tr><td></td><td></td><td></td></tr>
<tr><td></td><td></td><td></td></tr>
<tr><td></td><td></td><td></td></tr>
<tr><td></td><td></td><td></td></tr>
<tr><td></td><td></td><td></td></tr>
</table>

4) Adjusting entries

Journal					Page 2
Date	Account Title and Explanation	PR	DR	CR	

5) Closing entries

Journal					Page 3
Date	Account Title and Explanation	PR	DR	CR	

6) Create the post-closing trial balance.

Grindstone Paving		
Post-Closing Trial Balance		
July 31, 2013		
Account Titles	**DR**	**CR**

General Ledger

Account:	Cash					GL. No.	
Date	**Description**	**PR**	**Debit**	**Credit**	**Balance**		

Account:						GL. No.	
Date	**Description**	**PR**	**Debit**	**Credit**	**Balance**		

Account:					GL. No.	
Date	**Description**	**PR**	**Debit**	**Credit**	**Balance**	

Account:					GL. No.	
Date	**Description**	**PR**	**Debit**	**Credit**	**Balance**	

Account:					GL. No.	
Date	**Description**	**PR**	**Debit**	**Credit**	**Balance**	

Account:					GL. No.	
Date	**Description**	**PR**	**Debit**	**Credit**	**Balance**	

Account:					GL. No.	
Date	**Description**	**PR**	**Debit**	**Credit**	**Balance**	

Account:					GL. No.	
Date	Description	PR	Debit	Credit	Balance	

Account:					GL. No.	
Date	Description	PR	Debit	Credit	Balance	

Account:					GL. No.	
Date	Description	PR	Debit	Credit	Balance	

Account:					GL. No.	
Date	Description	PR	Debit	Credit	Balance	

Account:					GL. No.	
Date	Description	PR	Debit	Credit	Balance	

Account:					GL. No.	
Date	Description	PR	Debit	Credit	Balance	

Account:					GL. No.	
Date	Description	PR	Debit	Credit	Balance	

Account:					GL. No.	
Date	Description	PR	Debit	Credit	Balance	

Account:					GL. No.	
Date	Description	PR	Debit	Credit	Balance	

Account:					GL. No.	
Date	Description	PR	Debit	Credit	Balance	

Account:					GL. No.	
Date	Description	PR	Debit	Credit	Balance	

Account:					GL. No.	
Date	Description	PR	Debit	Credit	Balance	

Account:					GL. No.	
Date	Description	PR	Debit	Credit	Balance	

Chapter 7

MERCHANDISING CORPORATION

—————————— **Assessment Questions** ——————————

AS-1 (❶)

What is a merchandising business?

_____

_____

_____

AS-2 (❶)

What does contributed capital in a corporation represent?

_____

_____

_____

AS-3 (❷)

What does retained earnings in a corporation represent?

_____

_____

_____

AS-4 (❸)

In a perpetual inventory system, how often are inventory levels updated?

_____

_____

AS-5 (❸)

In a periodic inventory system, how often are inventory levels updated?

_____

_____

AS-6 (❹)

Define inventory in the context of a merchandising corporation.

_____

_____

_____

AS-7 (❺)

What does gross profit equal?

_____

_____

AS-8 (❷)

Define operating expenses.

_____

_____

_____

AS-9 (❻)

Define current assets.

_____

_____

AS-10 (6)

Define long-term assets.

_____

_____

_____

AS-11 (6)

What are current liabilities? Provide two examples of current liabilities.

_____

_____

_____

AS-12 (6)

What are long-term liabilities? Provide two examples of long-term liabilities.

_____

_____

_____

AS-13 (6)

What is one difference between a non-classified balance sheet and a classified balance sheet?

_____

_____

_____

AS-14 (6)

How do you calculate the current ratio and what does it measure?

_____

_____

_____

AS-15 (❻)

What is one difference between a non-multistep income statement and a multistep income statement?

_____

_____

_____

AS-16 (❻)

What are administrative expenses?

_____

_____

_____

AS-17 (❻)

In a typical multistep income statement, which category will items such as interest revenue and loss from a lawsuit fall under?

_____

_____

_____

--------------- **Application Questions** ---------------

AP-1 (6)

Empowered Inc. has the following balances as at May 31, 2013:

Cash	$22,000
Accounts Receivable	15,000
Inventory	12,000
PPE - Equipment	73,000
Accounts Payable	13,000
Unearned Revenue	8,000
Current Portion of Bank Loan	10,000
Long Term Portion of Bank Loan	20,000
Common Stock	20,000
Retained Earnings	51,000

Required: Prepare a classified balance sheet using the balances listed above.

Empowered Inc. Balance Sheet As At May 31, 2013	

AP-2 (❶, ❷)

The following information is taken from the financial statements of Gray Company during its third year of operations:

	Jan 1, 2013	Dec 31, 2013
Total Assets	$77,000	$89,000
Total Stockholders' Equity	61,000	?
2013 Revenue		22,000
2013 Expenses		15,000
Dividend paid		18,000

Additional information:
Total Stockholders' Equity as at January 1, 2013 is composed of:

Common Stock	$30,000
Retained Earnings	$31,000

Required: Calculate the stockholders' equity on December 31, 2013. Assume no shares are issued or re-purchased during the year.

_____

_____

_____

_____

AP-3 (❶, ❷)

Jordan Manufacturing reports the following financial structure for the year ended December 2013:

Current Assets	$105,000
Long-Term Assets	150,000
Current Liabilities	30,000
Long-Term Liabilities	40,000

Calculate stockholders' equity.

_____

_____

_____

AP-4 (⑥)

The following information is taken from the records of Ginger Corporation:

Accounts Payable	$19,000
Short-term Investment	12,000
Land	52,000
Cash	23,000
Factory Equipment	29,000
Loans Payable	30,000
Office Furniture	18,000
Prepaid Expense	9,000
Unearned Revenue	6,000

a) Calculate total current assets.

_____

_____

_____

_____

b) Calculate total long-term assets.

_____

_____

_____

c) Calculate total assets.

_____

_____

_____

AP-5 (⑥)

Suppose a corporation has a $400,000 bank loan on December 31, 2013. The borrowing arrangement requires the corporation to pay $100,000 of this debt by September 2014. Show how the corporation will report both current and long-term liabilities on its December 31, 2013 balance sheet.

AP-6 (⦿)

ABC Corporation borrowed a $1,000,000 interest-free bank loan on January 1, 2013. Payment is agreed to be made in four years in four equal annual installments on January 1 of each year. Calculate the current and long-term liabilities as at December 31 for the following years.

	December 31			
	2013	2014	2015	2016
Current portion of loan payable				
Long-term loan payable				

AP-7 (⦿)

Renegade Corporation's general ledger includes the following account balances on December 31, 2013.

Accounts Payable	$12,000
Interest Payable	3,000
Salaries Payable	2,000
Bank Loan:	
Current Portion	10,000
Long-Term Portion	20,000

a) Calculate current liabilities.

b) Calculate long-term liabilities.

AP-8 (❻)

For the following independent transactions, determine the amount of current and long-term liabilities.

	Transaction	Current	Long-Term
a)	On December 31, 2013, Frankie Co. borrowed $300,000 from the bank. The entire amount is due on December 30, 2014.		
b)	KLM Company purchased a small building at a cost of $190,000. The down payment is $100,000. The remaining balance is payable in 3 years with an annual payment of $30,000, starting next year.		
c)	During June 2013, a business owner obtained an interest-free loan from a financing company. The loan amount was $60,000. The agreed terms of payment is four annual installments of $15,000.		
d)	A business owner borrowed $20,000 from his close friend for a business expansion. They both signed an agreement that the payment will be made after two years.		

AP-9 (❻)

Milward Inc. is a new corporation that was established in April 2013. The corporation had the following transactions for the month of April:

Apr 1   Ray Merck and Jessie Tolley, the owners of the company, invested $50,000 and $70,000 cash into the business, respectively. They will both receive stock in exchange for their investment.

Apr 2   Purchased a building that will be used in business operations for $40,000 cash.

Apr 5   Purchased office furniture worth $7,000, on account.

Apr 10   Borrowed $100,000 cash from the bank. The amount is to be paid in five years with annual principal payments of $20,000.

Apr 11   Purchased two automobiles worth $30,000 for business use. The amount was fully paid with cash.

Apr 14   Purchased $10,000 of inventory with cash.

Apr 19   Made $20,000 of sales during the first month; $15,000 cash and $5,000 on credit.

Apr 28   Paid cash for the following expenses during the month:

Advertising	$850
Gas	500
Water	400
Electricity	700
	$2,450

Apr 30   Paid $2,000 in salaries for the month

a) Record the journal entries for the above transactions.

Date	Account Title and Explanation	Debit	Credit

b) Prepare a classified balance sheet.

Milward Inc. Balance Sheet As at April 30, 2013	

AP-10 (⑥)

The following information is taken from the accounting records of Eternity Corp. for the year ended December 31, 2012.

Current Liabilities:	
Accounts Payable	$20,000
Current portion of bank loan	25,000
Long-Term Liabilities:	
Long-term portion of bank loan	50,000
Stockholders' Equity	80,000

Additional information:
1. Long-term bank loan is payable in annual installments of $25,000 every December 31st.
2. During 2013, the company was able to generate a net income of $15,000 and reduce accounts payable to $7,000.
3. Investors made additional investments of $30,000 cash in 2013.

a) Calculate total liabilities as at December 31, 2013.

_____

_____

_____

_____

b) Calculate stockholders' equity as at December 31, 2013.

_____

_____

_____

_____

AP-11 (❶, ❹)

a) On January 1, 2013, William M. Wilcoxen, an investor, contributed $50,000 to a new business operating as a corporation called W-B Limited. Jerry Bryant, a second investor contributed another $50,000. Prepare the journal entry for W-B Limited to record the new investment.

Date	Account Title and Explanation	Debit	Credit

b) On January 10, W-B Limited purchased $10,000 worth of inventory with cash. Prepare the journal entry to record the inventory purchase.

Date	Account Title and Explanation	Debit	Credit

c) At the end of the first year of operation, W-B Limited generated sales of $390,000 and their expenses amounted to $380,000 (assume zero taxes). Calculate the following: (1) the net income amount for the first year; and (2) the amount of owners' equity at the end of the first year. Assume the beginning equity was $100,000.

AP-12 (❶, ❹)

Prepare the journal entry for each of the following transactions for Cosea Limited. These transactions occurred during the month of January 2013.

a) Sylvia Seaberg and Deanna Colin, in return for common stock, contributed $100,000 to a new business operating as a corporation called Cosea Limited.

Date	Account Title and Explanation	Debit	Credit

b) Sylvia and Deanna negotiated a bank loan in the amount of $50,000, payable in equal annual installments over the next five years.

Date	Account Title and Explanation	Debit	Credit

c) The company purchased equipment for $20,000 cash.

Date	Account Title and Explanation	Debit	Credit

d) The company also purchased inventory in the amount of $60,000 with cash.

Date	Account Title and Explanation	Debit	Credit

e) Made sales of $80,000 on account. The cost of the inventory is $60,000.

Date	Account Title and Explanation	Debit	Credit

Date	Account Title and Explanation	Debit	Credit

f) Their insurance company asked the company to pay $1,200 in advance for insurance coverage for one year. The insurance premium is $100 per month. Prepare the journal entry to record the initial prepayment.

Date	Account Title and Explanation	Debit	Credit

During the month, various expenses were incurred. Record the following transactions:

g) Travel expenses were incurred in the amount of $3,000 to be paid next month.

Date	Account Title and Explanation	Debit	Credit

h) Wages were paid with cash in the amount of $18,000.

Date	Account Title and Explanation	Debit	Credit

i) Rent was paid with cash in the amount of $5,000.

Date	Account Title and Explanation	Debit	Credit

At the end of the month, various adjustments were made. Record the following transactions:

j) Recognized $100 of prepaid insurance as an expense.

Date	Account Title and Explanation	Debit	Credit

There were a few more transactions for the month relating to the payment of outstanding debts and the collection of accounts receivable. Record the following transactions:

k) Cosea has extra cash available and decides to pay a portion of the bank loan ahead of schedule. Cosea pays $10,000 of principal and $500 of interest.

Date	Account Title and Explanation	Debit	Credit

l) Accounts receivable were collected in the amount of $30,000.

Date	Account Title and Explanation	Debit	Credit

m) Accounts payable were reduced by $3,000.

Date	Account Title and Explanation	Debit	Credit

AP-13 (❻)

Prepare a classified balance sheet using the results of the transactions recorded in AP-12 as at January 31, 2013. Assume that all beginning balances were $0.

Cosea Limited Balance Sheet As at January 31, 2013	

AP-14 (❷)

A company's beginning retained earnings for a period is $2,400. Net income for the period was $3,000. The company did not pay any dividends during this period. Calculate ending retained earnings.

_____

_____

_____

_____

AP-15 (❷)

House Audio Shop is a retailer of high quality audio equipment. It is currently the end of May 2013. The company's retained earnings balance as of May 1, 2013 was $56,000. During May, House Audio Shop earned $10,000 in revenue and incurred $7,500 in expenses. On May 30, 2013, the company declared and paid dividends in the amount of $3,500. What is the balance of retained earnings as at May 31, 2013?

_____

_____

_____

_____

AP-16 (❺)

If sales are $300,000 and cost of goods sold is $180,000, what is the gross profit and gross margin percentage?

_____

_____

_____

_____

AP-17 (❺)

If the gross profit margin is 25% and the sales are $500,000. What would be the cost of goods sold?

_____

_____

_____

_____

_____

_____

_____

AP-18 (❸, ❹)

Cost Retailor Inc. purchased inventory costing $45,000 with cash on March 20, 2013. The company sold 75% of the inventory for $36,000 cash on July 21. Complete down the journal entries for both dates. Assume Cost Retailor uses the perpetual inventory system.

a) March 20, 2013

Date	Account Title and Explanation	Debit	Credit

b) July 21, 2013

Date	Account Title and Explanation	Debit	Credit

Case Study

CS-1 (④, ⑤, ⑥)

George K. Connor operates a company that sells goods. During its first month of operations, the following transactions occurred.

Date	Transaction Details	Amount
Feb 1	Purchased inventory - to be paid later	$36,000
Feb 1	Received a deposit from a customer for products to be provided later	6,000
Feb 1	Prepaid insurance for one year with cash	3,600
Feb 5	Sold products for cash	13,000
Feb 5	Recorded COGS for products sold	6,000
Feb 11	Paid miscellaneous cash expenses	200
Feb 16	Received an advertising bill which will be paid later	3,000
Feb 21	Sold products on account	31,000
Feb 21	Recorded COGS for products sold	14,000
Feb 22	Paid wages and benefits	6,000
Feb 25	Purchased new computers - to be paid later	4,000
Feb 26	Incurred maintenance expense - to be paid next month	2,000
Feb 27	Customers paid their outstanding account balances owing	3,000
Feb 28	Recognized prepaid insurance for one month	300

The company uses the following chart of accounts to implement its accounting system:

Account Description	Account #
ASSETS	
Cash	101
Accounts Receivable	105
Prepaid Insurance	110
Inventory	115
PPE - Computers	120
Accumulated Depreciation	125
LIABILITIES	
Accounts Payable	200
Interest Payable	205
Salary Payable	210
Unearned Revenue	215
Bank Loan	220
STOCKHOLDERS' EQUITY	
Common Stock	300
Retained Earnings	310
Income Summary	315

Account Description	Account #
REVENUE	
Sales Revenue	400
Sales Returns & Allowances	405
Sales Discount	410
EXPENSES	
Cost of Goods Sold	500
Advertising Expense	505
Depreciation Expense	510
Insurance Expense	515
Maintenance Expense	520
Miscellaneous Expense	525
Office Supplies Expense	530
Professional Fees Expense	535
Rent Expense	540
Salaries Expense	545
Utilities Expense	550
Travel Expense	555

Required:

Prepare the journal entries for the period.

Post the entries to the general ledger.

Prepare a trial balance.

Prepare a multistep income statement for the period.

Prepare a classified balance sheet for the period.

Calculate the gross profit margin on product sales.

Calculate the current ratio of the company for the period.

Journal					Page 1
Date	Account Title and Explanation		PR	Debit	Credit

Journal				Page 1
Date	**Account Title and Explanation**	**PR**	**Debit**	**Credit**

ACCOUNT:					No.
Date	**Description**	**PR**	**Debit**	**Credit**	**Balance**

ACCOUNT:					No.
Date	**Description**	**PR**	**Debit**	**Credit**	**Balance**

ACCOUNT:					No.
Date	**Description**	**PR**	**Debit**	**Credit**	**Balance**

ACCOUNT:					No.
Date	**Description**	**PR**	**Debit**	**Credit**	**Balance**

ACCOUNT:					No.
Date	**Description**	**PR**	**Debit**	**Credit**	**Balance**

ACCOUNT:					No.	
Date	**Description**	**PR**	**Debit**	**Credit**	**Balance**	

ACCOUNT:					No.	
Date	**Description**	**PR**	**Debit**	**Credit**	**Balance**	

ACCOUNT:					No.	
Date	**Description**	**PR**	**Debit**	**Credit**	**Balance**	

ACCOUNT:					No.	
Date	**Description**	**PR**	**Debit**	**Credit**	**Balance**	

ACCOUNT:					No.	
Date	**Description**	**PR**	**Debit**	**Credit**	**Balance**	

ACCOUNT:					No.
Date	**Description**	**PR**	**Debit**	**Credit**	**Balance**

ACCOUNT:					No.
Date	**Description**	**PR**	**Debit**	**Credit**	**Balance**

ACCOUNT:					No.
Date	**Description**	**PR**	**Debit**	**Credit**	**Balance**

ACCOUNT:					No.
Date	**Description**	**PR**	**Debit**	**Credit**	**Balance**

	Trial Balance		Income Statement		Balance Sheet	
Account	**Debit**	**Credit**	**Debit**	**Credit**	**Debit**	**Credit**
Cash						
Accounts Receivable						
Prepaid Insurance						
Inventory						
PPE - Computers						
Accounts Payable						
Unearned Revenue						
Sales Revenue						
Cost of Goods Sold						
Advertising Expense						
Insurance Expense						
Maintenance Expense						
Miscellaneous Expenses						
Salaries Expense						
Totals						
NET INCOME (LOSS)						
TOTAL						

George K. Connor
Worksheet
February 28, 2013

George K. Connor
Income Statement
For the Month Ended February 28, 2013

George K. Connor Balance Sheet As at February 28, 2013	

Calculation of the gross profit margin on product sales:

_____

_____

Calculation of the current ratio:

_____

_____

Chapter 8

ACCOUNTING INFORMATION SYSTEMS

─────────── **Assessment Questions** ───────────

AS-1 (❶)

What are the features of an effective accounting information system?

_____

_____

_____

_____

_____

_____

AS-2 (❶)

Describe the paper trail in a manual accounting system.

_____

_____

_____

_____

_____

_____

_____

_____

_____

_____

AS-3 (❶)

How do the elements in a computerized system differ from those in a manual system?

_____

_____

_____

_____

_____

_____

_____

_____

_____

AS-4 (❶)

Will the owner using a computerized accounting system be able to extract journals, ledgers and reports to manage their business? Explain.

_____

_____

_____

_____

_____

_____

_____

_____

_____

AS-5 (❶)

What fields of information should the database contain?

_____

_____

_____

_____

_____

_____

AS-6 (❶)

List some examples of the kind of reports that could be generated from the accounting information system.

_____

_____

_____

_____

_____

_____

_____

_____

AS-7 (❷)

What are special journals used for?

_____

_____

_____

AS-8 (❷)

What type of information would be found in the sales journal?

_____

_____

_____

AS-9 (❷)

What are general journals used for?

_____

_____

AS-10 (❸)

Why are subsidiary ledgers used?

_____

_____

_____

AS-11 (❸)

What is the relationship between a control account and its corresponding subledgers?

_____

_____

_____

AS-12 (❸)

What type of information can be found in an accounts payable subsidiary ledger?

_____

_____

_____

_____

AS-13 (❹)

Is allowing a client list to be viewed by unauthorized people an ethical issue? Explain.

_____

_____

_____

_____

Application Question

AP-1 (❷, ❸)

Gherry Inc. is a small shoe retailer. The following is a list of transactions for the month of May.

May 4	Received $6,000 from a cash sale to Teamster Inc. (sold sport shoes costing $700)
May 5	Received a bill (Invoice #5780) for $800 worth of supplies from BZDepot Inc.
May 6	Received $840 from Jo-Ann regarding her outstanding accounts receivable
May 9	Received $650 for the cash sale of 5 pairs of shoes (costing a total of $85) to Sgt. Pepper
May 9	Received a bill from ComTech Inc. (Invoice #167) for $150 for telephone services
May 10	Received $325 in interest from loan to Lance Livestrong
May 12	Paid amount owing (Invoice #5780) to BZDepot Inc. (Check #201)
May 15	The company received a loan of $1,000
May 18	Made a sale on account (Invoice #2341) to Keith Ricardo, for $250 (with inventory costing $200)
May 21	Handed over check #202 to Nikel Inc for $2,000 worth of inventory
May 22	Paid amount owing (Invoice #167) to ComTech Inc. for telephone services with check # 203
May 25	Paid $205 to BFG Inc., for maintenance expenses (Check #204)
May 26	Received bill from Adibas Inc. (Invoice #113) for $5,500 worth of inventory
May 28	Made a sale, on account (Invoice #2342), to Gary Lineker for $2,000 worth of shoes (shoes cost $1,700)

Part 1

Record these transactions in the Cash Receipts, Sales, Purchases and Cash Payments Journal. Use the following headings:

Cash Receipts Journal								Page 1
Date	Account	PR	Cash (DR)	Sales (CR)	Accounts Receivable (CR)	Interest Revenue (CR)	Loans Payable (CR)	Other (CR)	COGS/ Inventory (DR/CR)

Sales Journal						Page 1
Date	Account	Invoice #	PR	Accounts Receivable (DR)	Sales (CR)	COGS/Inventory (DR/CR)

Purchases Journal						Page 1
Date	Account	Invoice #	PR	Telephone Expense (DR)	Office Supplies (DR)	Inventory (DR)	Accounts Payable (CR)

Cash Payments Journal							Page 1
Date	Account	Check #	PR	Other (DR)	Inventory (DR)	Accounts Payable (DR)	Cash (CR)

Part 2

Post from the special journals in part 1 to the accounts receivable sub-ledger and then to the general ledger control account at the end of the month. Assume opening sub-ledger balances of:

- Jo-Ann : $940 (DR)
- Keith Ricardo. : $600 (DR)
- Gary Lineker : $800 (DR)

Note that Gherry's accounts receivable records consist of only these three sub-ledgers. Assume no entries were made directly to accounts receivable through the general journal. Update the PR columns in both the subledgers and special journals.

Use the following headings:

Accounts Receivable Subsidiary Ledger Jo-Ann				
Date	PR	Debit	Credit	Balance

Accounts Receivable Subsidiary Ledger Keith Ricardo				
Date	PR	Debit	Credit	Balance

Accounts Receivable Subsidiary Ledger Gary Lineker				
Date	PR	Debit	Credit	Balance

General Ledger Accounts Receivable				
Date	PR	Debit	Credit	Balance

Part 3

Post from the special journals in part 1 to the accounts payable sub-ledger and then to the general ledger control account at the end of the month. Assume opening sub-ledger balances of:

- BZDepot Inc.: $1,000 (CR)
- ComTech Inc.: $1,200 (CR)
- The Adibas Inc.: $1,400 (CR)

Note that Gherry's accounts payable records consist of only these three sub-ledgers. Assume no entries were made directly to accounts payable through the general journal. Update the PR columns in both the subledgers and special journals.

Use the following headings:

Accounts Payable Subsidiary Ledger BZDepot Inc.				
Date	PR	Debit	Credit	Balance

Accounts Payable Subsidiary Ledger ComTech Inc.				
Date	PR	Debit	Credit	Balance

Accounts Payable Subsidiary Ledger Adibas Inc.				
Date	PR	Debit	Credit	Balance

General Ledger Accounts Payable				
Date	PR	Debit	Credit	Balance

Part 1

					Cash Receipts Journal					Page 1
Date	Account	PR	Cash (DR)	Sales (CR)	Accounts Receivable (CR)	Interest Revenue (CR)	Loans Payable (CR)	Other (CR)	COGS/ Inventory (DR/CR)

			Sales Journal			Page 1
Date	Account	Invoice #	PR	Accounts Receivable (DR)	Sales (CR)	COGS/Inventory (DR/CR)

			Purchases Journal				Page 1
Date	Account	Invoice #	PR	Telephone Expense (DR)	Office Supplies (DR)	Inventory (DR)	Accounts Payable (CR)

			Cash Payments Journal			Page 1
Date	Account	Check #	PR	Other (DR)	Inventory (DR)	Accounts Payable (DR)	Cash (CR)

Part 2

Accounts Receivable Subsidiary Ledger Jo-Ann				
Date	PR	Debit	Credit	Balance

Accounts Receivable Subsidiary Ledger Keith Ricardo				
Date	PR	Debit	Credit	Balance

Accounts Receivable Subsidiary Ledger Gary Lineker				
Date	PR	Debit	Credit	Balance

Post to general ledger.

General Ledger Accounts Receivable				
Date	PR	Debit	Credit	Balance

Part 3

Accounts Payable Subsidiary Ledger BZDepot Inc.				
Date	PR	Debit	Credit	Balance

Accounts Payable Subsidiary Ledger ComTech Inc.				
Date	PR	Debit	Credit	Balance

Accounts Payable Subsidiary Ledger Adibas Inc.				
Date	PR	Debit	Credit	Balance

Post to general ledger.

General Ledger Accounts Payable				
Date	PR	Debit	Credit	Balance

AP-2 (❷)

Hidson Inc. is a small retailer. The following is a list of sales transactions for the month of April.

Apr 2   Made a sale on account (Invoice # 5703) to B. Fager for $450 (cost $300)

Apr 5   Made a sale on account (Invoice # 5704) to J. Dryer for $1,150 (cost $900)

Apr 10   Made a sale on account (Invoice # 5705) to T. Burton for $550 (cost $450)

Apr 12   Made a sale on account (Invoice # 5706) to JB Inc. for $670 (cost $500)

Required:

Record these transactions in the sales journal.

Sales Journal						Page 1
Date	Account	Invoice #	PR	Accounts Receivable (DR)	Sales (CR)	COGS/ Inventory (DR/CR)

AP-3 (❷)

Smart Inc. has provided you with the following information about its sales transactions during the month of September:

Sep 1	Made a sale on account (Invoice # 1122) to Fat Inc. for $1,450 (cost $1,200)
Sep 5	Made a sale on account (Invoice # 1123) to Charisma Ltd. for $2,150 (cost $1,900)
Sep 9	Made a sale on account (Invoice # 1124) to Hidendsa Inc. for $750 (cost $600)
Sep 11	Made a sale on account (Invoice # 1125) to Henry Inc. for $1,270 (cost $1,080)
Sep 14	Made a sale on account (Invoice # 1126) to Snoob Inc. for $970 (cost $800)
Sep 20	Made a sale on account (Invoice # 1127) to Lime&Lemon for $ 1,150 (cost $1,020)

Required:

Record these transactions in the sales journal.

Sales Journal						Page 1
Date	Account	Invoice #	PR	Accounts Receivable (DR)	Sales (CR)	COGS/ Inventory (DR/CR)

AP-4 (❷)

F. Benjuman owns a small clothing store. The following is the list of prices he charges for different types of products:

Product	Price	Cost
Blue cotton	$6 per sheet	$4 per sheet
Black silk	$20 per meter	$15 per meter
white tape	$10 per roll	$6 per roll
Green felt	$4 per meter	$2 per meter

During the month of July, the company made the following sales:

Jul 1   Sold 3 rolls of white tape, 5 sheets of blue cotton, and 1 meter of black silk to F. Grey, on account (Invoice # 5739)

Jul 5   Sold 6 rolls of white tape and 30 meters of green felt to A. Gray, on account (Invoice # 5740)

Jul 9   Sold 1 meter of black silk to E. Hines, on account (Invoice # 5741)

Jul 11   Sold 10 rolls of white tape, 6 sheets of blue cotton, 3 meters of black silk and 11 meters of green felt to M. Allen, on account (Invoice # 5742)

Jul 14   Made a sale on account (Invoice # 5743) to B. Cooper: 12 rolls of white tape, 14 sheets of blue cotton and 9 meters of green felt

Required:

Record these transactions in the sales journal.

Sales Journal						Page 1
Date	Account	Invoice #	PR	Accounts Receivable (DR)	Sales (CR)	COGS/ Inventory (DR/CR)

AP-5 (❷)

Jane Fisher is selling the following items at the prices listed below:

Product	Price	Cost
Plastic tubing	$1 per meter	$0.5 per meter
Polythene sheeting	$2 per meter	$1 per meter
Vinyl Padding	$5 per box	$3 per box
Foam rubber	$3 per sheet	$2 per sheet

She has provided you the following data about sales transactions incurred during the month of August:

Aug 2   Sold 22 meters of plastic tubing, 6 sheets of foam rubber and 4 boxes of vinyl padding to A. Portsmouth, on account (Invoice # 1240)

Aug 4   Sold 50 meters of polythene sheeting, 6 sheets of foam rubber and 4 boxes of vinyl padding to B.Butler, on account (Invoice # 1241)

Aug 6   Sold 4 meters of plastic tubing to A. Gate, on account (Invoice # 1242)

Aug 10   Sold 29 meters of plastic tubing to L. Makeson, on account (Invoice # 1243)

Aug 12   Made a sale on account (Invoice # 1244) to M. Alison: 32 meters of plastic tubing, 24 meters of polythene sheets and 20 boxes of vinyl padding

Required:

Record these transactions in the sales journal.

Sales Journal						Page 1
Date	Account	Invoice #	PR	Accounts Receivable (DR)	Sales (CR)	COGS/ Inventory (DR/CR)

AP-6 (❷)

Bob123 Inc., a household items retailer, made the following purchases during the month of March:

Mar 2   Received a bill (Invoice # 305) from D. Pope for the purchase of 4 DVDs, worth $240 each

Mar 4   Received a bill (Invoice # 426) from F. Lolyd for the purchase of 2 washing machines worth $560 each and 5 vacuum cleaners worth $400 each

Mar 6   Received a bill (Invoice # 765) from B. Sankey for the purchase of 1 internet modem worth $600 and 2 washing machines worth $320 each

Mar 10   Received a bill (Invoice # 2132) from J. Wilson for the purchase of 6 CD/Radios worth $45 each

Mar 12   Received a bill (Invoice # 1234) from R. Freer for the purchase of 4 dishwashers worth $240 each

Required:

Record these transactions in the purchase journal.

Purchase Journal					Page 1
Date	Account	Invoice #	PR	Inventory (DR)	Accounts Payable (CR)

AP-7 (❷)

J. Glen, a sports retailer, made the following purchases during the month of May:

May 2   Received a bill (Invoice # 125) from F. Day for the purchase of 2 basketballs worth $100 each and 6 footballs worth $45 each

May 4   Received a bill (Invoice # 135) from G. Smith for the purchase of 7 cricket bats worth $65 each, 5 ice skates worth $32 each and 4 rugby balls worth $32 each

May 10   Received a bill (Invoice # 145) from L. Todd for the purchase of 6 cricket bats worth $55 each

May 12   Received a bill (Invoice # 222) from M. Moore for the purchase of 9 golf balls at $45 each

Required:

Record these transactions in the purchase journal.

Purchase Journal					Page 1
Date	Account	Invoice #	PR	Inventory (DR)	Accounts Payable (CR)

AP-8 (❷)

Philips Inc., a clothing store, has the following purchases for the month of September:

Sep 2   Received a bill (Invoice # 723) from Smith Inc. for the purchase of $80 worth of silk, and $100 worth of cotton

Sep 7   Received a bill (Invoice # 657) from Grantley store for the purchase of Lycra goods worth $38 and woolen items worth $64

Sep 12   Received a bill (Invoice # 498) from Henry Inc. for the purchase of silk worth $45, cotton worth $130 and lycra worth $135

Sep 17   Received a bill (Invoice # 342) from Kelly Inc. for the purchase of $98 worth of cotton and $56 worth of Lycra goods

Sep 22   Received a bill (Invoice # 290) of $380 from Hamilton Inc. for the purchase of Lycra goods

Required:

Record these transactions in the purchase journal.

Purchase Journal					Page 1
Date	Account	Invoice #	PR	Inventory (DR)	Accounts Payable (CR)

AP-9 (❷)

Vina Duckworth has provided the following information relating to her activities in the month of June:

Jun 2	Paid amount owing $650 (Invoice #780) to SK Depot (Check #195)
Jun 6	Paid back loan of $800 to Crystal Inc. (Check #196)
Jun 10	Handed over check #197 to Nektel Inc. for $3,000 worth of inventory
Jun 13	Received the telephone bill for $350 and paid the amount owing to CasTech Inc. for telephone services (Check #198)
Jun 25	Paid $205 to SFC Inc. for general expenses (Check #199)

Required:

Record these transactions in the cash payment journal.

Cash Payments							Page 1
Date	Account	Check #	PR	Other (DR)	Inventory (DR)	Accounts Payable (DR)	Cash (CR)

AP-10 (❷)

Ambassador Inc. uses a cash payment journal to record all the payments made by the company. Ambassador Inc. has provided you with the following information about the transactions incurred in the month of August:

Aug 2	Paid salary to Amanda Black, $1,600 cash (Check # 241)
Aug 12	Paid $2,400 owing (Invoice # 543) to Hargrave Inc. (Check # 242)
Aug 14	Paid insurance premium of $300 (Check # 243)
Aug 20	Paid newspaper bill of $150 to News & Paper (Check # 244)
Aug 26	Handed over check # 245 to JKL Company for $2,000 worth of inventory

Required:

Record these transactions in the cash payment journal.

Cash Payments							Page 1
Date	Account	Check #	PR	Other (DR)	Inventory (DR)	Accounts Payable (DR)	Cash (CR)

AP-11 (❷)

Medicines World, a medical store, makes all transactions in cash only. It has provided you with the following information about the transactions for the month of May.

May 2	Paid $1,000 rent for the month of May to Mrs. Elizabeth (Check #23)
May 4	Paid salary to James Jones for the month of April, $800. (Check #24)
May 6	Paid repair and maintenance charges amounting $300 to Building Services Inc. (Check #25)
May 10	Paid $200 of internet charges to Castech. (Check #26)
May 12	Bought medicine costing $8,000 from Medicines Inc. (Check #27)

Required:

Record these transactions in the cash payment journal.

Cash Payments							Page 1
Date	Account	Check #	PR	Other (DR)	Inventory (DR)	Accounts Payable (DR)	Cash (CR)

AP-12 (❷)

Riya Cosmetics has provided you with the following information about the transactions the company incurred during the month of June:

Jun 2   Received $2,000 from a cash sale to Faces Inc. (cost $1,500)

Jun 6   Received $840 from Beauty Breeze regarding outstanding accounts receivable

Jun 10   Received $650 for the cash sale of 5 facial scrubs (cost $540) to Seizers Salon

Jun 13   Received $325 in interest earned from bank deposit

Jun 25   Took out a loan of $3,000 from a bank

Required:

Record these transactions in the cash receipt journal.

			Cash (DR)	Sales (CR)	Accounts Receivable (CR)	Interest Revenue (CR)	Other (CR)	COGS/ Inventory (DR/CR)
Date	Account	PR						

AP-13 (❷)

Book World is a dealer for stationery items. The company has provided you the following information about the transactions incurred in the month of March:

Mar 2   Received $3,500 from cash sale to Books n Books (cost $ 3,000)

Mar 9   Received $300 in interest earned from bank deposit

Mar 14   Received bank loan of $500

Mar 19   Received $700 from cash sale to Book Ocean (cost $500)

Mar 21   Received $900 from cash sale to Beacon Books (cost $700)

Required:

Record these transactions in the cash receipt journal.

					Cash Receipts Journal			**Page 1**
Date	**Account**	**PR**	**Cash (DR)**	**Sales (CR)**	**Accounts Receivable (CR)**	**Interest Revenue (CR)**	**Other (CR)**	**COGS/ Inventory (DR/CR)**

AP-14 (❷)

Lin Z is an owner operated sporting goods retailer. The following is a list of the company's transactions for the month of June:

Jun 2 Received a tax refund of $165.

Jun 6 Received a loan of $1,000 from the bank

Jun 10 Received $150 of interest earned on the savings account

Jun 13 Received $2,000 from cash sales to Dawn Sports (sold sports items costing $1,500)

Jun 25 Received $800 from AD Sports regarding outstanding accounts receivable

Required:

Record these transactions in the cash receipt journal.

					Cash Receipts Journal			**Page 1**
Date	**Account**	**PR**	**Cash (DR)**	**Sales (CR)**	**Accounts Receivable (CR)**	**Interest Revenue (CR)**	**Other (CR)**	**COGS/ Inventory (DR/CR)**

AP-15 (❷, ❸)

Highway Interchange sells clothing to retailers. During the month of July 2013, the following transactions occurred:

Jul 7   Sold inventory to Fashion House for $5,600 cash. The inventory had a cost of $2,400. The invoice number was #526.

Jul 10   Received a loan from the bank for $5,000.

Jul 15   Sold inventory to Stella Lanes on account for $8,500. The inventory had a cost of $3,400. The invoice number was #527.

Jul 17   Sold inventory to Cover Me for $7,500 on account. The inventory had a cost of $3,100. The invoice number was #528.

Jul 24   Received full payment from Stella Lanes for the sale on July 15.

Jul 31   Received $50 of interest earned on a savings account.

Required:

a) Record the above transactions in the sales journal and the cash receipts journal.

b) Post the appropriate transactions from the journals to the subledger accounts.

c) At the end of the month, total the journals and update the accounts receivable control account.

Assume zero opening balances for the subledger and general ledger accounts. Assume no entries were made directly to the A/R general ledger from the general journal.

Sales Journal						Page 1
Date	Account	Invoice #	PR	Accounts Receivable	Sales	COGS/ Inventory
				(DR)	(CR)	(DR/CR)

Cash Receipts Journal							Page 1
			Cash	Accounts Receivable	Sales	Bank Loan	Other	COGS/ Inventory
Date	Account	PR	(DR)	(CR)	(CR)	(CR)	(CR)	(DR/CR)

Account:	Accounts Receivable				GI. No.	110	
Date	Description	PR	Debit	Credit	Balance		

Account:		Stella Lanes				
Date	PR	Debit	Credit	Balance		

Account:		Cover Me				
Date	PR	Debit	Credit	Balance		

AP-16 (❷, ❸)

Peter's Pewter sells figurines. During the month of August 2013, the following transactions occurred:

Aug 3	Peter invested $4,000 into his business.
Aug 7	Sold inventory to Joyce Fontane for $500 cash. The inventory had a cost of $240.
Aug 16	Sold inventory to Carol Balsdon for $750 on account. The inventory had a cost of $310.
Aug 17	Sold inventory to James Stewart for $820 on account. The inventory had a cost of $420.
Aug 24	Received full payment from Carol Balsdon from the Aug 16 transaction.

Required:

a) Record the above transactions in the sales journal and the cash receipts journal.

b) Post the appropriate transactions from the journals to the subledger accounts.

c) At the end of the month, total the journals and update the accounts receivable control account.

Assume zero opening balances for the subledger and general ledger accounts. Assume no entries were made directly to the A/R general ledger from the general journal.

Sales Journal						Page 1
				Accounts Receivable	Sales	COGS/ Inventory
Date	Account	Invoice #	PR	(DR)	(CR)	(DR/CR)

Cash Receipts Journal								Page 3
			Cash	Accounts Receivable	Sales	Bank Loan	Other	COGS/ Inventory
Date	Account	PR	(DR)	(CR)	(CR)	(CR)	(CR)	(DR/CR)

Account:	Accounts Receivable				110	
Date	Description	PR	Debit	Credit	Balance	

Account:	Carol Balsdon			
Date	PR	Debit	Credit	Balance

Account:	James Stewart			
Date	PR	Debit	Credit	Balance

AP-17 (❷, ❸)

Put-A-Wrench-In-It sells hand tools. During the month of October 2013, the following transactions occurred:

Oct 3	Purchased inventory for $6,300 on account from Block and Deck.
Oct 7	Paid salaries for $2,100 with check #256.
Oct 10	Purchased inventory for $4,100 cash from Malida Inc. with check #257.
Oct 17	Paid the full amount owing to Block and Deck from the Oct 3 transaction.
Oct 24	Purchased inventory for $7,700 on account from Debolt Inc.

Required:

a) Record the above transactions in the purchases journal and the cash payments journal.

b) Post the appropriate transactions from the journals to the subledger accounts.

c) At the end of the month, total the journals and update the accounts payable control account.

Assume zero opening balances for the subledger and general ledger accounts. Assume no entries were made directly to the A/P general ledger from the general journal.

Purchases Journal							Page 6
				Inventory	Office Supplies	Other	Account Payable
Date	Account	Invoice	PR	(DR)	(DR)	(DR)	(CR)

Cash Payments Journal							Page 4
				Accounts Payable	Other	Inventory	Cash
Date	Account	Check #	PR	(DR)	(DR)	(DR)	(CR)

Account:	Accounts Payable				GL. No	200
Date	Description	PR	Debit	Credit	Balance	

Account:	Block and Deck				
Date	PR	Debit	Credit	Balance	

Account:	Debolt Inc.				
Date	PR	Debit	Credit	Balance	

AP-18 (❷, ❸)

Blossoming Gardens sells landscaping materials. During the month of May 2013, the following transactions occurred:

May 3	Purchased office supplies for $800 on account from Office Supply Shop.
May 7	Purchased inventory for $1,200 cash from Rock Bottom with check #456.
May 10	Paid telephone bill for $350 cash with check #457
May 17	Paid the amount owing to Office Supply Shop with check #458
May 24	Purchased inventory for $3,500 from Paving Stones on account.

Required:

a) Record the above transactions in the purchases journal and the cash payments journal.

b) Post the appropriate transactions from the journals to the subledger accounts.

c) At the end of the month, total the journals and update the accounts payable control account.

Assume zero opening balances for the subledger and general ledger accounts. Assume no entries were made directly to the A/P general ledger from the general journal.

Purchases Journal							Page 6
				Inventory	Office Supplies	Other	Account Payable
Date	Account	Invoice	PR	(DR)	(DR)	(DR)	(CR)

Cash Payments Journal							Page 4
				Accounts Payable	Other	Inventory	Cash
Date	Account	Check #	PR	(DR)	(DR)	(DR)	(CR)

Account:	Accounts Payable				GL. No	200	
Date	Description	PR	Debit	Credit	Balance		

Account:	Office Supply Shop				
Date	PR	Debit	Credit	Balance	

Account:	Paving Stones				
Date	PR	Debit	Credit	Balance	

AP-19 (❶)

TR Retailer has the following unadjusted trial balance at their year end, December 31, 2013.

Account	Trial Balance Debit	Trial Balance Credit
Cash	$12,800	
Accounts Receivable	32,400	
Inventory	41,500	
Prepaid Insurance	2,400	
Property, Plant & Equipment	65,000	
Accumulated Depreciation		$3,000
Accounts Payable		39,500
Interest Payable		0
Unearned Revenue		7,600
Bank Loan		20,000
Capital Account		32,660
Owner's Drawings	8,500	
Sales Revenue		164,800
Cost of Goods Sold	74,160	
Depreciation Expense	0	
Insurance Expense	0	
Interest Expense	0	
Rent Expense	26,000	
Telephone Expense	4,800	
Total	**$267,560**	**$267,560**

Regarding the bank loan, $10,000 will be paid by December 31, 2014.

TR Retailer also had the following adjusting entries that had to be entered into the books.

1. Interest accrued on the bank loan was $80.

2. Insurance used as of December 31, 2013 was $400.

3. TR Retailer had earned $1,000 of unearned revenue. Assume no accompanying COGS entry.

4. Depreciation for the year was $600.

Required:

a) Complete the worksheet provided.

	TR Retailer					
	Worksheet					
	December 31, 2013					
	Unadjusted Trial Balance		Adjustments		Adjusted Trial Balance	
Account	Debit	Credit	Debit	Credit	Debit	Credit
Total						

b) Based on the values from the adjusted trial balance from part a), complete a multistep income statement and a classified balance sheet.

TR Retailer		
Income Statement		
For the Year Ended December 31, 2013		

TR Retailer		
Balance Sheet		
As at December 31, 2013		

Case Study

CS-1 (❸, ❹)

Easy Riser sells pre-fabricated stair cases to builders for new homes and renovations. Lately, the owner has been receiving calls from suppliers regarding late payments. The owner is aware of the late payments because he has been holding back payments due to a shortage of cash. The company is having excellent sales, and earning a very good profit even though they have a cash shortfall.

After asking the bookkeeper about the cash shortage problem, the bookkeeper informed the owner about the accounting process. All transactions are entered into the general journal and posted to the general ledger. The supplier invoices were stored in one folder and the sales invoices in another folder in the bookkeeper's desk. When the owner asked to see a sales invoice from last month (to see if the amount had been collected), the bookkeeper had trouble finding it. When it was finally found, it was determined that it had not been paid yet.

a) What ethical and control issues does this company have?

b) What would you suggest to improve the bookkeeping for this company?

Critical Thinking

CT-1 (❶, ❷, ❹)

John Swann is the CEO of Galapagos Systems. One of John's close buddies told him that he should be concerned about his employees expensing non business related events (e.g. meals with family members rather than clients). He advised John to regularly review the company's cash payments journal for anomalies. John is happy to have learned about this procedure but wonders if it is sufficient. Can you make any suggestions?

_____

_____

_____

_____

_____

_____

_____

Chapter 9

CASH CONTROLS

—————— **Assessment Questions** ——————

AS-1 (❶)

What is a bank reconciliation?

_____

_____

_____

AS-2 (❶)

List three typical reasons for the bank making additional deductions from the company's cash account.

_____

_____

_____

AS-3 (❶)

What are two typical reasons for the bank making additional deposits to the company's cash account?

_____

_____

_____

AS-4 (❶)

In a typical bank reconciliation, what are the titles of the two column headers?

_____

_____

_____

AS-5 (❶)

What are non-sufficient funds (NSF) checks?

_____

_____

_____

AS-6 (❶)

What is an outstanding deposit?

_____

_____

_____

AS-7 (❶)

When is a journal entry required during a bank reconciliation?

_____

_____

_____

AS-8 (❶)

How are outstanding checks recorded on the bank reconciliation?

_____

_____

_____

AS-9 (❷)

What is an imprest system (in the context of petty cash)?

_____

_____

_____

AS-10 (❷)

Briefly describe the responsibilities of the petty cash custodian.

_____

_____

_____

AS-11 (❷)

What does an employee that requires petty cash need to present to the petty cash custodian?

_____

_____

_____

AS-12 (❷)

What is a petty cash summary sheet?

_____

_____

_____

AS-13 (❷)

Why do petty cash overages or shortages occur?

_____

_____

_____

AS-14 (❷)

When does the cash over and short account behave like an expense account?

_____

_____

_____

AS-15 (❷)

What are the only two times that the petty cash account in the ledger is debited or credited?

_____

_____

_____

AS-16 (❸)

List two general controls that can be used for petty cash.

_____

_____

_____

AS-17 (❸)

List two controls that can be used to prevent the misuse of cash?

_____

_____

_____

—————————— **Application Questions** ——————————

AP-1 (❶)

Quality Electronic Corporation is preparing a bank reconciliation and has identified the following potential reconciling items. For each item, indicate if it is (i) added to the balance of the ledger, (ii) deducted from the balance of the ledger, (iii) added to the balance of the bank statement, or (iv) deducted from the balance of the bank statement.

a) Deposits that are not shown on the bank statement

b) Interest deposited to the company's account

c) Bank service charges

d) Outstanding checks

e) NSF checks returned

_____

_____

_____

_____

AP-2 (❶)

The following data represents information necessary to assist in preparing the June 30th bank reconciliation for Trimore Company Inc.

a) The June 30th bank balance was $5,300

b) The bank statement indicated a deduction of $30 for bank service charges

c) A customer deposited $1,200 directly into the bank account to settle an outstanding accounts receivable bill

d) Check number 850 for $600 and check number 857 for $420 have been recorded in the company ledger but did not appear on the bank statement

e) A customer paid an amount of $4,534 to Trimore on the 30th of June but the deposit did not appear on the bank statement

f) The accounting clerk made an error and recorded a $200 check as $2,000. The check was written to pay outstanding accounts payable account

g) Check number 9574 for $100 was deducted from Trimore's account by the bank. This check was not written by Trimore and needs to be reversed by the bank.

h) The bank included an NSF check in the amount of $820 relating to a customer's payment.

i) The general ledger cash account showed a balance of $6,764 on June 30th

Required:

1. Complete the bank reconciliation for Trimore Company
2. Write the necessary journal entries to correct Trimore's records

Ref.	Explanation	Ledger	Bank

Date	Account Title and Explanation	Debit	Credit

Date	Account Title and Explanation	Debit	Credit

Date	Account Title and Explanation	Debit	Credit

Date	Account Title and Explanation	Debit	Credit

AP-3 (❶)

a) Prepare the July 2013 bank reconciliation statement for World's Computer Inc. using the following information

- Cash balance per general ledger is $2,219
- Bank statement balance is $2,478.80
- These checks were recorded in the ledger but did not appear on the bank statement. They are: Check #186 for $100; Check #193 for $57; Check #199 for $143.
- A deposit for $368 dated July 31 was recorded in the ledger but did not appear on the bank statement
- Service charges of $18 are shown on the bank statement
- A check for $37.50 has been cashed (correctly) by the bank but was incorrectly recorded in the company's ledger as $375.50. The check was issued for the purchase of office supplies.
- The bank automatically deposited interest of $7.80 at the end of the month.

b) Record any journal entries required to bring the company records up to date.

a)

World's Computer Inc. Bank Reconciliation Statement July 31, 2013		
Explanation	**Ledger**	**Bank**

b)

Date	Account Title and Explanation	Debit	Credit

AP-4 (❶)

Mike's Cleaning Service received its monthly bank statement for its business bank account, with a balance of $55,062 for the month of July 2013. The total for the ledger account as at July 31, 2013 was $59,461. After a comparison of the checks written by the company and those deducted from the bank account, Mike's accountant determined that three checks, totaling $2,806 (No. 256 - $606, No. 261 - $1,200, No. 262 - $1,000), were outstanding on July 31. A review of the deposits showed that a deposit on July 1 for $12,610 was actually recorded in the company's ledger on June 30 and a July 31 deposit of $9,760 was recorded in the company's ledger on the date but had not been recorded by the bank yet. The July bank statement showed a service fee of $18, a customer's check in the amount of $70 that had been returned NSF, a loan payment of $857 that was deducted automatically by the bank, and a customer automatically made a $3,500 payment which was deposited into Mike's Cleaning bank account.

Required:

a) Prepare bank reconciliation as at July 31.

b) How much cash does Mike's Cleaning Service actually have in its cash account on July 31?

c) Prepare adjusting journal entries to record all necessary adjustments to bring the cash account to its adjusted balance.

a)

Mike's Cleaning Service Bank Reconciliation Statement July 31, 2013		
Explanation	Ledger	Bank

b) _____

c)

Date	Account Title and Explanation	Debit	Credit

AP-5 (❶)

The following T-Account contains information about RJ Cosmetics' cash account:

Cash

Opening Balance Feb 1	4,000	Feb 3	800
Feb 12	2,500	Feb 21	1,200
Feb 28	1,000	Feb 26	950
		Feb 27	600
Ending Balance Feb 28	**3,950**		

This is RJ Cosmetics' bank statement for the month of February.

Date	Explanation	Withdrawal	Deposit	Balance
Feb 01	Opening Balance			4,000
Feb 03	Check # 1	800		3,200
Feb 12	Deposit		2,500	5,700
Feb 14	NSF Check	500		5,200
Feb 14	NSF Charge	15		5,185
Feb 21	Check # 2	1,200		3,985
Feb 25	EFT - Monthly Rent expense	1,000		2,985
Feb 28	Service Charges	25		2,960
Feb 28	Interest on Bank Account		20	2,980
		3,540	2,520	

a) Prepare a bank reconciliation for RJ Cosmetics.

RJ Cosmetics Bank Reconciliation February 28, 2013		
Explanation	Ledger	Bank

b) Prepare the required journal entries for the corrections made in the bank reconciliation.

Date	Account Title and Explanation	Debit	Credit

c) Prepare a reconciled cash T-Account.

Cash

AP-6 (❶)

Shine Laundry's bank reconciliation is provided for the month of September. However, due to some errors on the bank reconciliation, the reconciled balance for the ledger and the bank are different from each other.

Shine Laundry Bank Reconciliation September 30, 2013		
	Ledger	Bank
Balance as per records	5,100	3,820
Add: Outstanding deposit - Sep 29	400	
Outstanding deposit - Sep 30	1,220	
Less: Outstanding check # 3 - Sep 8		(1,000)
Outstanding check # 4 - Sep 10	(600)	
EFT - Insurance - Sep 15		(400)
EFT - Monthly rent - Sep 18		(600)
NSF check - Sep 19		(250)
Charges for NSF check - Sep 19		(5)
Service charges - Sep 30	(15)	
Interest on bank account - Sep 30	(10)	
Reconciled Balance	6,095	1,565

Required:

a) Prepare a reconciled bank reconciliation. Assume the dollar amounts of the individual items on the bank reconciliation are correct.

Shine Laundry Bank Reconciliation September 30, 2013		
Explanation	Ledger	Bank

b) Prepare all journal entries that would be required by Shine Laundry.

Date	Account Title and Explanation	Debit	Credit

AP-7 (❶)

For the month of September 2013, Jared Anitco has noticed that the bank has processed a check that he was not aware of. As a result, he calls the bank and determines that the check belongs to another account. The following is the general ledger report for cash in the bank and bank statement for Jared Anitco for the month of September.

GENERAL LEDGER - CASH				
Date	Explanation	Debit	Credit	Balance
Sep 1	Opening Balance			7,000
Sep 6	CandyMan Check # 200		500	6,500
Sep 6	Supply Store - Check # 201		754	5,746
Sep 10	Jordan Lo - Check # 1000	800		6,546
Sep 25	Book Store - Check # 202		200	6,346

BANK STATEMENT				
Date	Explanation	Withdrawal	Deposit	Balance
Sep 1	Opening Balance			7,000
Sep 10	CandyMan Check # 200	500		6,500
Sep 10	Supply Store - Check # 201	754		5,746
Sep 14	Jordan Lo - Check # 1000		800	6,546
Sep 20	Mooris Mo - Check # 1107	820		5,726
Sep 30	Book Store - Check # 202	200		5,526

Required:

Identify the check that does not belong to Jared. If necessary, prepare the required journal entries.

Date	Account Title and Explanation	Debit	Credit

AP-8 (❶)

Consider the following general ledger and bank statement for Meena Salon.

GENERAL LEDGER - CASH				
Date	**Explanation**	**Debit**	**Credit**	**Balance**
Apr 1	Opening Balance			8,000
Apr 6	Jimmy Supplies - Check # 101		500	7,500
Apr 10	HitHit Supplies - Check # 102		1,000	6,500
Apr 11	Mary Malony	250		6,750
Apr 14	Inner Beauty Inc. - Check # 103		757	5,993
Apr 19	Shona Care Ltd. - Check # 104		840	5,153
Apr 29	Deposit	2,500		7,653

BANK STATEMENT				
Date	**Explanation**	**Withdrawal**	**Deposit**	**Balance**
Apr 1	Opening Balance			8,000
Apr 6	Check # 101	500		7,500
Apr 10	Check # 102	1,000		6,500
Apr 10	EFT - Monthly Rent	800		5,700
Apr 11	Mary Malony		250	5,950
Apr 11	NSF Check	250		5,700
Apr 11	NSF Charge	5		5,695
Apr 14	Check # 103	575		5,120
Apr 21	Check # 1520	3,000		2,120
Apr 30	Service Charges	25		2,095
Apr 30	Interest on Bank Account		20	2,115
		6,155	270	

Additional Information:

1. On April 14, Meena Salon purchased $575 worth of salon supplies from Inner Beauty Inc.

2. The salon's check numbers are always three-digits in length.

Required:

a) Prepare a bank reconciliation for Meena Salon on April 30, 2014.

Meena Salon Bank Reconciliation April 30, 2014		
Explanation	**Ledger**	**Bank**

b) Prepare the necessary journal entries.

Date	Account Title and Explanation	Debit	Credit

AP-9 (❶)

The bank statement for Fashion Fly Inc. had an ending cash balance of $1,500 on December 31, 2013. On this date the cash balance in their general ledger was $2,000. After comparing the bank statement with the company records, the following information was determined:

- The bank returned an NSF check in the amount of $320 that Fashion Fly Inc. deposited on December 20th.
- Direct deposit received from a customer on December 30th in payment of their accounts totaling $3,850. This has not yet been recorded by the company.
- On December 30th the bank deposited $10 for interest earned.
- The bank withdrew $20 for bank service charges
- Deposits in transit on December 31st totaled $4,020

Required: Reconcile the ledger and bank statement and prepare the required journal entries.

Fashion Fly Inc. Bank Reconciliation December 31, 2013		
Explanation	**Ledger**	**Bank**

Date	Account Title and Explanation	Debit	Credit

AP-10 (❷)

On June 7, Mary decided to use a petty cash fund for her small business. A check of $125 was issued and cashed. The $125 cash was given to the store supervisor who was to act as petty cashier. The petty cashier was told to obtain authorized vouchers for all payments. Petty cash was to be replenished when the balance in the cash box reached $23.

a) Record the establishment of the fund on June 7.

b) On June 19, this summary was prepared:

Delivery Expense	$50.90
Miscellaneous Expense	20.40
Office Expense	24.10
Postage Expense	6.60
Total	102

Prepare the entry to replenish the petty cash.

c) On June 23, it was decided to increase the amount of the petty cash fund from $125 to $175. A check of $50 was issued. Record the transaction.

a)

Date	Account Title and Explanation	Debit	Credit

b)

Date	Account Title and Explanation	Debit	Credit

c)

Date	Account Title and Explanation	Debit	Credit

AP-11 (❷)

The petty cash fund was established on August 12, 2013 in the amount of $250.00. Expenditures from the fund by the custodian as of August 31, 2013, were evidenced by approved receipts for the following:

Postage expense	$30.00
Supplies expense	65.00
Maintenance expense	42.00
Delivery expense	58.20
Newspaper advertising	21.95
Miscellaneous expense	15.75

On August 31, 2013, the petty cash fund was replenished and increased to $300.00; currency and coin in the fund at that time totaled $15.60.

Required:

Prepare the journal entries to record the transactions related to the petty cash fund for the month of August.

Date	Account Title and Explanation	Debit	Credit

Date	Account Title and Explanation	Debit	Credit

AP-12 (❷, ❸)

Last year, Holtzman Company established a petty cash fund of $100. The custodian complained that she had to reimburse the fund on a weekly basis, and suggested that the fund be increased to $400. That way, she would only have to summarize payouts and get a check from the cashier once per month.

Management agreed with the custodian, and on April 1 advised the cashier to increase the fund to $400.

    a) Write the journal entry to increase the fund to $400.

    b) List five internal controls that should be established around the use of petty cash.

a)

Date	Account Title and Explanation	Debit	Credit

b)

_____

_____

_____

_____

_____

_____

_____

_____

AP-13 (❷)

On March 20th, Skyline Enterprises established a $300 petty cash fund.

    a) Prepare the entry to record the establishment of the fund.

    b) At the end of the month, the petty cash custodian analyzed all the monthly transactions. She opened the petty cash box and counted $100 cash remaining. There were also two receipts in the petty cash box: receipt # 1: $100 – Entertainment and receipt #2: $98 – Travel. Record the journal entries for this month's expenses and replenish the fund.

    c) At the end of the month, Skyline Enterprises wanted to increase the petty cash fund by $100. Prepare the journal entry to record the increase in petty cash fund.

a)

Date	Account Title and Explanation	Debit	Credit

b)

Date	Account Title and Explanation	Debit	Credit

c)

Date	Account Title and Explanation	Debit	Credit

AP-14 (❷)

On January 1, 2014, Hit Design Inc. set up a petty cash fund for $250.
At the end of the first week, the petty cash fund contains the following:

Cash on hand	$50
Receipt for the purchase of office supplies	40
Receipt for delivery charges	10
Receipt for the purchase of stamps	20
Receipt for travel to a client meeting	50
Receipt for the payment of newspaper advertising	75

Required:

a) Calculate any cash overage or shortage.

_____

_____

_____

b) Prepare the journal entries for setting up and replenishing the petty cash fund.

Date	Account Title and Explanation	Debit	Credit

AP-15 (❷)

The following information was taken from the records of the JoJo Store.

Apr 14	Paid $25 for public transit
Apr 16	Paid $20 for food
Apr 17	Purchased stamps for $5
Apr 17	Paid $50 for window washing
Apr 19	Paid $15 for the delivery of packages
Apr 20	Purchased office supplies for $30

JoJo is the owner of the store and he established a petty cash fund of $200 on April 12, 2014. All the transactions listed above were paid using petty cash. Petty cash needs to be replenished when $50 is left in the petty cash box. On April 21, there was $50 left in the petty cash box.

Required: Prepare the journal entries for setting up and replenishing the petty cash fund.

Date	Account Title and Explanation	Debit	Credit

AP-16 (❷)

On April 1, 2014, Clayton Company established a petty cash fund of $200.

During the month the custodian paid out the following amounts:

April 6	Purchased stamps	$40
April 8	Delivery charge on outgoing package	20
April 10	Public transit fares for employees on company business	25
April 14	Coffee and donuts for clients during a meeting	8
April 15	Package of paper for the copy machine	7

The custodian counted the fund on April 16th and found $105 in the petty cash box.

Required:

a) Prepare the journal entry to record the establishment of the fund.

Date	Account Title and Explanation	Debit	Credit

b) Prepare the journal entry to record the reimbursement of the fund on April 16, 2014.

Date	Account Title and Explanation	Debit	Credit

Case Study

CS-1 (❸)

M & G Block (M & G) is an incorporated tax preparation company. Most of its clients pay for the completion of their tax returns with either a debit or a credit card. The rest pay with actual cash.

At the office in Miami, M & G has employed 20 tax preparers, two supervisors and a manager. The office collects thousands of dollars in cash every day. After a tax return is prepared by one of the 20 tax preparers, a supervisor is responsible for recording information (i.e. customer name, amount charged, payment method) related to the return in a log.

The receipt of cash is recorded immediately when it is received. Receipts are issued immediately in numerical order. Copies of the receipts are also kept with the logs. The cash is kept in the drawer of the employee who prepared the tax return. At the end of the day, the cash being kept by the various employees are pooled together and then passed on to the supervisor, who will keep it in his drawer. The cash is deposited into the bank at the end of each work week.

Over the past few weeks, the manager has noted that the amount of cash on hand in the office has consistently been less than the amount recorded in the logs. In fact, the difference between the actual cash on hand and the recorded amount is increasing little by little over time.

Required:

a) Is M & G exhibiting any positive aspects in its system of cash controls? Explain.

_____

_____

_____

_____

_____

_____

_____

b) What are the negatives in M & G's cash control system? Explain. (You can refer to
    controls that do not exist, or controls that exist but are ineffective).

_____

_____

_____

_____

_____

_____

_____

_____

_____

_____

_____

_____

_____

_____

_____

_____

_____

_____

Chapter 10

ACCOUNTS AND NOTES RECEIVABLE

——————— **Assessment Questions** ———————

AS-1 (❶)

Define accounts receivable.

_____

_____

_____

_____

AS-2 (❶)

Describe the presentation of accounts receivable on the balance sheet.

_____

_____

_____

_____

AS-3 (❶)

How can the subsidiary ledger assist in managing a company's accounts receivable?

_____

_____

_____

_____

AS-4 (❶)

Explain the relationship between the accounts receivable control account and individual customer accounts in the accounts receivable sub-ledger.

_____

_____

_____

_____

AS-5 (❷, ❸)

List the names of the alternative methods for accounting for bad debt. Are both methods allowed under GAAP?

_____

_____

_____

_____

AS-6 (❷)

Briefly outline the direct write-off method for dealing with bad debt.

_____

_____

_____

_____

AS-7 (❹, ❺)

Name two different approaches for estimating the bad debt expense when using the AFDA method.

_____

_____

_____

_____

_____

AS-8 (❻)

Name two ratios used to assess accounts receivable, and state the formulas used to calculate the ratios.

_____

_____

_____

_____

_____

AS-9 (❽)

What are the risks involved when selling on credit?

_____

_____

_____

_____

_____

AS-10 (❷, ❸)

Which method of accounting for bad debt (direct method or allowance method) is more preferable? Support your answer.

_____

_____

_____

_____

AS-11 (❸, ❹, ❺)

If a company uses the allowance method to account for bad debt, which method is best for estimating the allowance: income statement method or balance sheet method?

_____

_____

_____

_____

_____

_____

_____

_____

_____

_____

AS-12 (❽)

What are the advantages and disadvantages to a company which sells on credit?

_____

_____

_____

_____

AS-13 (❹)

What pitfalls exist for a company that uses the income statement method for recording bad debt expense?

_____

_____

_____

_____

AS-14 (❻)

How do you assess the DSO number? The ART ratio?

_____

_____

_____

_____

AS-15 (❽)

Give two examples of accounting reports that can be generated involving accounts receivable.

_____

_____

_____

_____

_____

_____

_____

_____

AS-16 (❽)

What internal controls are important for accounts receivable? Is there any one control that is absolutely necessary?

_____

_____

_____

_____

_____

_____

_____

_____

AS-17 (8)

What ethical problems are related to accounts receivable? Can they be avoided?

_____

_____

_____

_____

_____

_____

Application Questions

AP-1 (❷)

On June 15, you discover that your customer, Tyrone Huntzinger, has gone bankrupt. He owes you $1,000. Prepare the appropriate journal entry assuming the direct method is used.

Date	Account Title and Explanation	Debit	Credit

AP-2 (❸)

Refer to AP-1. Assuming that $5,000 had been credited to the allowance account for the year, prepare the journal entry for the write-off assuming the allowance method is used.

Date	Account Title and Explanation	Debit	Credit

AP-3 (❸)

Your company decides that an allowance for doubtful accounts is required in the amount of $6,000. There is a zero balance in the account. Prepare the journal entry to set up the required allowance.

Date	Account Title and Explanation	Debit	Credit

AP-4 (❷, ❸)

On December 31, 2013, Mann Company's accounts receivable ledger showed an ending balance of $40,000. The company realized that $2,000 of accounts receivable was deemed uncollectible. Prepare a journal entry to demonstrate the treatment of $2,000 uncollectible amount using (a) direct method and (b) allowance method.

a) Direct Method

Date	Account Title and Explanation	Debit	Credit

b) Allowance Method

Date	Account Title and Explanation	Debit	Credit

AP-5 (❸)

Your company decides that an allowance for doubtful accounts is required in the amount of $6,000. There is a $4,000 credit balance in the account. Prepare the journal entry to set up the required allowance.

Date	Account Title and Explanation	Debit	Credit

AP-6 (❷)

Jane Lee is the owner of a small consulting firm called Lee Solutions. She uses the direct method to account for uncollectible receivables. On April 14, 2013, Lee Solution's accounts receivable account balance was $10,000. A week later, it was discovered that Mr. Joe Black, who owed the firm $1,500, will not be able to make the payment.

Required:

a) Prepare a journal entry to account for the amount deemed uncollectible.

Date	Account Title and Explanation	Debit	Credit

b) On May 26, 2013, Mr. Joe Black was able to repay 50% of the amount he owed, which had been previously written-off. Prepare the journal entries required to record this transaction.

Date	Account Title and Explanation	Debit	Credit

AP-7 (❸)

Your company decides that an allowance for doubtful accounts is required in the amount of $6,000. There is a $1,000 debit balance in the account. Prepare the journal entry to set up the required allowance.

Date	Account Title and Explanation	Debit	Credit

AP-8 (❸)

A customer's account in the amount of $2,000 was previously written off. Amazingly, on December 31, you receive a check in the mail from the customer with a letter of apology for not paying sooner (the account is 2 years old). Prepare the journal entry by using the allowance method.

Date	Account Title and Explanation	Debit	Credit

Date	Account Title and Explanation	Debit	Credit

AP-9 (❹)

Your company uses the income statement approach for estimating bad debt. Last year, credit sales amounted to $1 million. The estimated bad debt is 0.5% of sales. Prepare the journal entry to record bad debt expense for the year.

Date	Account Title and Explanation	Debit	Credit

AP-10 (❸, ❹)

B&B Inc. uses the allowance method to account for uncollectible receivables. During 2013, the company made total credit sales of $1,250,000, of which $300,000 was currently owed by customers. According to the company's historical sales, 1.5% of the amount will be uncollected. B&B Inc. uses an income statement approach to estimate the amount of uncollectible receivables.

Required: Prepare the journal entry to account for the amount deemed uncollectible.

Date	Account Title and Explanation	Debit	Credit

AP-11 (❸, ❺)

The following chart is prepared by the accountant of Happy Shoes Inc. The percentages are based on historical performance.

Aging Category	Bad Debt %	Balance
30 days	1%	$80,000
31 - 60 days	3%	40,000
over 60 days	5%	20,000
Total		140,000

Happy Shoes Inc. uses the balance sheet approach to estimate uncollectible receivables.

Required:

a) Calculate the company's bad debt.

b) Assume that allowance for doubtful accounts has a credit balance of $1,000. Calculate the amount of bad debt expense the company will record.

AP-12 (❸, ❺)

Fishy Inc. uses the balance sheet approach to estimate uncollectible receivables. Use the following table to determine the amount of bad debt expense, and prepare the journal entry to record the bad debt expense. The allowance account currently has a zero balance.

Aging Category	Bad Debt %	Balance
30 days	2%	$25,000
31 - 60 days	3%	10,000
over 60 days	4%	2,000
Total		$37,000

Aging Category	Bad Debt %	Balance	Estimated Bad Debt

Date	Account Title and Explanation	Debit	Credit

AP-13 (⑤)

Your company uses the balance sheet approach to estimate bad debt. Details of the accounts receivable balances owing on December 31, 2013 are shown below:

Aging Category	Bad debt % (probability of being uncollectible)	Balance
Under 30 days	1%	$90,000
31-60 days	20%	90,000
Over 60 days	50%	30,000
Total		$210,000

a)   Calculate the required allowance.

Aging Category	Bad debt % (probability of being uncollectible)	Balance	Required allowance
Under 30 days	1%	$90,000	
31-60 days	20%	90,000	
Over 60 days	50%	30,000	
Total		$210,000	

b)   Write the journal entry to record bad debt expense for the year, assuming that the allowance account has a $20,000 credit balance.

Date	Account Title and Explanation	Debit	Credit

AP-14 (③, ④)

During the year 2013, Jaime Corporation made total credit sales of $500,000, of which $25,000 was currently owed by customers. On the basis of historical sales, 1% of that amount will be uncollectible. Jaime Corporation uses the allowance method to account for uncollectible receivables, and uses an income statement approach to estimate the amount of receivables that will not be collected.

Required:

a) Prepare the journal entry to account for the amount deemed uncollectible.

Date	Account Title and Explanation	Debit	Credit

b) On January 20, 2014, Mrs. L. Green who owes the company $500 informs that she will be unable to pay the amount. Prepare the necessary journal entry.

Date	Account Title and Explanation	Debit	Credit

c) On February 14, 2014, Mrs. L. Green wins a lottery and decides to repay the full amount owing to Jaime Corporation. Prepare the necessary journal entries.

Date	Account Title and Explanation	Debit	Credit

AP-15 (❸)

On January 1, 2013, Jay Company's allowance for doubtful accounts had a credit balance of $30,000. During 2013, Jay charged $64,000 to bad debt expense, and wrote off $46,000 of uncollectible accounts receivable. What is the balance of allowance for doubtful accounts on December 31, 2013?

AP-16 (❻)

Wechsler Company has net accounts receivable opening balance of $250,000 and ending balance of $300,000. The total sales amount for the year is $1,700,000, of which 80% are on credit. Normal credit terms are 30 days. Calculate the day sales outstanding and the accounts receivable turnover. Comment on the calculated ratios.

_____

_____

_____

_____

_____

_____

_____

_____

_____

AP-17 (❼)

Lakisha Ogata operates a proprietorship selling machinery. Because of the high value of the machinery sold, Lakisha often requires customers to sign a note. Lakisha originally sold a Gadget machine to Neil Marcin for $10,000 on November 14. The sale was initially recorded as an account receivable, but now Lakisha decides to ask Neil to sign a note. On December 1, Neil signs a one-year note to be paid in quarterly installments, plus 5% interest on the balance outstanding. Lakisha's company has a year end of April 30.

Required:

Prepare an amortization schedule showing the interest and payments due on the note. Use the following format:

Date	Opening balance	Interest	Total	Payment	Closing balance
Dec 1					
Mar 1					
Jun 1					
Sep 1					
Dec 1					

Prepare the journal entries to reflect the transactions related to the receivable and note.

Date	Account Title and Explanation	Debit	Credit

AP-18 (❼)

Larry Jim owns a toy shop called Larry's Toys. The total accounts receivable balance of Larry's Toys on December 31, 2012 was $100,000. On January 1, 2013, Mr. L. Smith who owes the company $15,000 informs that he will be unable to pay the amount owing in the present year. However, he agrees to sign a two-year note to be paid in semi-annual installments, plus 3% interest on the balance outstanding.

Required: Calculate the interest revenue and payment amounts.

Date	Opening Balance	Interest	Total	Payment	Closing Balance

AP-19 (❸)

In 2013, Upper Machine Sales Company sold equipment on credit in the amount of $950,000. Total cash collections during the year were $820,000. The company determined that $7,000 of accounts receivable would not be collected and wrote them off. At the end of 2013, management decided to increase its allowance percentage to 1% of credit sales from 0.5% last year because of the amount of accounts receivable that proved to be uncollectible during the year. At the end of 2012, the company had $135,000 in accounts receivable and a credit balance of $6,000 in allowance for doubtful accounts. Assume the company has a year end of December 31.

Required:

a) Prepare the necessary journal entries to record all 2013 transactions including sales, collection, the write-off, and the new allowance amount. Disregard the dates when recording the transactions.

Date	Account Title and Explanation	Debit	Credit

b) Show the amount of net accounts receivable on the balance sheet as at December 31, 2013.

AP-20 (❸)

The 2012 and 2013 sales and accounts receivable information for Velcary Company are shown below:

At the beginning of 2012, the AFDA account had a $0 balance. During 2012, sales for the year totaled $1,200,000 with 60% on credit. At December 31 year end, the accounts receivable had a debit balance of $55,000. The management estimated that 0.5% of all credit sales would be uncollectible. The company wrote off $3,100 worth of accounts receivable at the end of the year.

During the year 2013, sales totaled $1,630,000 with 60% on credit. At the end of 2013, accounts receivable has a debit balance of $76,000. During the year, the company wrote off a number of accounts receivable, leaving the allowance for doubtful accounts with a debit balance of $4,500. The estimate for bad debt expense for the year has not been determined or recorded. After reviewing the write-offs, the company decided that the estimated percentage for AFDA should be increased from 0.5% to 0.75%.

Required:

a) Prepare the journal entry to record the bad debt expense for 2013.

Date	Account Title and Explanation	Debit	Credit

b) Prepare a T-Account for the Allowance for Doubtful Accounts and enter all related transactions for year 2012 and 2013.

c) What are the net accounts receivable at the end of 2013?

AP-21 (❽)

Suppose a company has a bonus plan that rewards managers for achieving a certain level of reported net income. What incentives might management have to influence the estimated amount of uncollectible accounts receivable?

_____

_____

_____

_____

_____

AP-22 (❺)

Nortelle Canada operates in an industry that has a high rate of bad debt. Before the year end adjustments, Nortelle Canada's accounts receivable has a debit balance of $536,000 and the allowance for doubtful accounts had a credit balance of $20,000. The year-end balance reported on the balance sheet for the allowance for doubtful accounts will be based on the aging schedule shown below:

Aging Category	Bad Debt %	Balance
Less than 16 days	2%	$300,000
16 – 30 days	3%	100,000
31 – 45 days	5%	75,000
46 – 60 days	10%	32,000
61 – 75 days	20%	18,000
Over 75 days	40%	11,000

Required:

a)   What is the balance for the Allowance for Doubtful Accounts at year end?

Aging Category	Bad Debt %	Balance	Estimated Amount of Bad Debt
Less than 16 days	2%	$300,000	
16 – 30 days	3%	100,000	
31 – 45 days	5%	75,000	
46 – 60 days	10%	32,000	
61 – 75 days	20%	18,000	
Over 75 days	40%	11,000	

b)   Prepare the journal entry to record bad debt expense for the year

Date	Account Title and Explanation	Debit	Credit

AP-23 (❻)

A company's relevant accounts receivable information for year 2012 and 2013 is provided below:

	2013	2012
Average Net Accounts Receivable	$1,486,739	$1,769,032
Net Credit Sales	23,075,635	22,107,539

Required:

a) Calculate the accounts receivable turnover ratio for year 2012 and 2013.

_____

_____

_____

_____

b) Calculate the days-sales-outstanding for year 2012 and 2013.

_____

_____

_____

_____

c) Compare and discuss the results from part a) and b).

_____

_____

_____

_____

AP-24 (❻)

The following information relevant to accounts receivable is presented for Dommar Company (in thousands of dollars):

	2014	2013	2012
Accounts Receivable	$319	$422	$501
Allowance for Doubtful Accounts	19	18	20
Net Credit Sales	$4,377	$3,598	$2,937

Required:

a) Calculate the Accounts Receivable Turnover Ratio for the years 2013 and 2014.

_____

_____

_____

_____

b) Calculate the Day Sales Outstanding for the years 2013 and 2014.

_____

_____

_____

_____

c) At the 2013 year end, Dommar Company agreed to sell some of its accounts receivable with a fee paid to the purchaser. Why do you think a company would pay a fee to sell its accounts receivable?

_____

_____

_____

_____

d) Dommar Company sold the accounts receivable on a limited recourse basis. Research and define the meaning of selling on a limited recourse basis.

_____

_____

_____

_____

AP-25 (❼)

On May 1, 2013, People's Networks sold computer networking supplies to American Autos for $36,000. The cost of the supplies is $15,000. Instead of paying immediately, American Autos signed a note receivable with 11% annual interest, payable in eight months with the principle amount. People's Networks has a year end of October 31.

Required:

a) Record the journal entry when the sale is made; assume People's Networks uses the perpetual inventory system.

Date	Account Title and Explanation	Debit	Credit

b) Prepare the journal entry for the year end adjustment.

Date	Account Title and Explanation	Debit	Credit

c) Prepare the journal entry for receipt of payment from American Autos on January 1, 2014.

Date	Account Title and Explanation	Debit	Credit

d) What items would be included on the balance sheet and income statement of People's Networks as at October 31, 2013 with respect to this note?

_____

_____

_____

_____

AP-26 (❼)

On January 1, 2013, Beta Company determined that it would not be able to pay the account receivable that was owed to Star Inc. Beta Company was confident that it would have sufficient cash one year later, therefore signed a one-year notes receivable for the $10,000 that was owed. The annual interest rate is 9%, payable on July 1 and January 1. Star Inc. has a year end of June 30.

Required:

a) Record journal entries for Star Inc. when the note is signed.

Date	Account Title and Explanation	Debit	Credit

b) Prepare journal entries for the year end adjustment.

Date	Account Title and Explanation	Debit	Credit

c) Prepare journal entries for the receipt of first interest payment.

Date	Account Title and Explanation	Debit	Credit

d) Prepare journal entries for receipt of payment from Beta Company on January 1, 2014.

Date	Account Title and Explanation	Debit	Credit

─────────────── **Case Study** ───────────────

CS-1 (❶, ❷, ❸, ❼)

You are the Chief Financial Officer for Stanton Feery and Company. Mr. Stanton's friend, Shad Baxtor, is starting up a new company, and needs some advice on accounts receivable and bad debt accounting practices. Mr. Stanton has asked you to meet with Mr. Baxtor, and answer a few questions. He hands you a list of things that Shad Baxtor wants clarified.

Here is the handwritten list:

- What are accounts receivable?
- What are bad debts?
- When are amounts considered bad debt?
- Are there different ways of accounting for bad debt expenses?
- How is bad debt shown on the financial statements?
- Which method is best for accounting for bad debt?
- What type of reports are important for accounts receivable?
- What is an aging list?
- What is the difference between a credit sale and a cash sale?
- How can you assess the quality of accounts receivable?
- Should I sell on credit? Are there risks involved?

a) What are accounts receivable?

_____

_____

_____

_____

b) What are bad debts?

_____

_____

_____

_____

c) When are amounts considered bad debt?

_____

_____

_____

_____

d) Are there different ways of accounting for bad debt expenses?

_____

_____

_____

_____

e) How is bad debt shown on the financial statements?

_____

_____

_____

_____

f) Which method is best for accounting for bad debt?

_____

_____

_____

_____

g) Which reports are helpful in analyzing a company's accounts receivable?

_____

_____

_____

h) What is an aging list?

_____

_____

_____

_____

i)   What is the difference between a credit sale and a cash sale?

_____

_____

_____

_____

j)   How can you assess the quality of accounts receivable?

_____

_____

_____

_____

k) What is the impact of selling on credit and what is the potential risk involved?

_____

_____

_____

_____

Chapter 11

INVENTORY

--- **Assessment Questions** ---

AS-1 (❷)

Explain the difference between a purchase return and a purchase allowance.

_____

_____

_____

AS-2 (❷)

Explain the difference between a sales allowance and a sales discount.

_____

_____

_____

_____

AS-3 (❸)

List the different ways of valuing inventory.

_____

_____

_____

AS-4 (❸)

In times of rising prices, which inventory valuation method results in the highest closing inventory? Explain your answer.

_____

_____

_____

AS-5 (❸)

Different inventory valuation methods result in different inventory values. What factors may cause a company to select FIFO, LIFO, weighted average or specific identification?

_____

_____

_____

_____

_____

_____

_____

_____

_____

AS-6 (❺)

The use of lower of cost or market is based on what GAAP principle?

_____

_____

_____

AS-7 (❹, ❽)

What are the causes of a misstated inventory balance?

_____

_____

_____

_____

_____

_____

_____

_____

AS-8 (❻)

Name two methods which can be used to estimate inventory for interim statement purposes.

_____

_____

_____

AS-9 (❶)

What is the benefit to a company of using a perpetual inventory system?

_____

_____

_____

_____

_____

_____

_____

AS-10 (❷, ❾)

Differentiate the journal entries required for sales when using a perpetual inventory system from the entries required when using a periodic inventory system.

AS-11 (❽)

List three reports that are useful for managing inventory.

AS-12 (❽)

List five internal controls that are useful for controlling and managing inventory.

_____

_____

_____

_____

_____

_____

_____

_____

_____

_____

_____

_____

_____

_____

_____

_____

_____

_____

_____

_____

_____

_____

AS-13 (❶)

You, being an accountant of Bask Retailers, are beginning the adjusting and closing process at the end of the fiscal year. Does the trial balance contain the correct ending balance of inventory if the business uses the perpetual inventory system? Why or why not?

_____

_____

_____

_____

AS-14 (❶)

Explain how costs of goods available for sale is calculated in a periodic inventory system.

_____

_____

_____

AS-15 (❸)

Describe the principles a company may follow while choosing an inventory valuation method.

_____

_____

_____

_____

_____

_____

_____

_____

_____

AS-16 (❹)

Describe the impacts of inventory errors.

_____

_____

_____

_____

_____

_____

_____

_____

_____

_____

AS-17 (❸)

Which of the inventory valuation method can be used by the companies for showing better results in case of rising prices?

_____

_____

_____

_____

_____

_____

_____

_____

_____

AS-18 (❽)

How can a company monitor and prevent inventory shrinkage?

_____

_____

_____

_____

_____

_____

_____

_____

AS-19 (❽)

List two safety measures that can be taken to avoid inventory losses through theft.

_____

_____

_____

_____

AS-20 (❺)

Describe the reason for applying the principle of lower of cost or market (LCM) to inventory.

_____

_____

_____

_____

AS-21 (❽)

What is the impact of inflating inventory on financial statements? What is the ethical responsibility of management in this regard?

_____

_____

_____

_____

_____

_____

Application Questions

AP-1 (❷)

Hip Top Shirt Retailers bought $15,000 worth of shirts from Super Shirt Wholesalers Ltd. on March 15th. Payment was due in April. Prepare the journal entry at the time of purchase. Assume they use the perpetual inventory system.

Date	Account Title and Explanation	Debit	Credit

AP-2 (❷)

Referring to the purchase made in AP-1 above, prepare the journal entry for Hip Top Shirt Retailers for the payment of $15,000 made to Super Shirt Wholesalers on April 15th.

Date	Account Title and Explanation	Debit	Credit

AP-3 (❾)

Refer to AP-1 above and, assuming Hip Top Shirt uses the *periodic inventory system*, record the journal entries at time of purchase and at time of payment.

Date	Account Title and Explanation	Debit	Credit

AP-4 (❷)

JB Supermarkets bought $3,000 worth of groceries on account from a produce supplier on May 10th. On May 11th, JB's bookkeeper was informed that $200 worth of tomatoes was substandard and returned to the supplier. Prepare the journal entry to record the purchase return. Assume they use the perpetual inventory system.

Date	Account Title and Explanation	Debit	Credit

AP-5 (❷)

Refer to AP-4 above and record the purchase return assuming JB uses a periodic inventory system.

Date	Account Title and Explanation	Debit	Credit

AP-6 (❷)

On January 12th, Corner-Mart received a shipment of T-shirts from Promo Novelties for an event. The invoice amounted to $5,000 and was recorded in the accounting system. Soon after the delivery was made, the marketing manager discovered that the logo was printed incorrectly. The goods were returned to Promo Novelties on January 31st. Prepare the journal entry that would be recorded on January 31st. Assume Corner-Mart uses the perpetual inventory system.

Date	Account Title and Explanation	Debit	Credit

AP-7 (❷)

Refer to AP-6 above. Record the purchase return assuming Corner-Mart uses a periodic inventory system.

Date	Account Title and Explanation	Debit	Credit

AP-8 (❷)

Signs Unlimited received a shipment of plastic sheets on April 3rd. The value of the plastic was $8,000, plus $100 of freight charges. Prepare the journal entry to record the receipt of goods by Signs Unlimited, assuming the payment would be made in May. Assume they use the perpetual inventory system.

Date	Account Title and Explanation	Debit	Credit

AP-9 (❷)

Referring to AP-8 above, several of the plastic sheets delivered to Signs Unlimited were in the wrong color. After some negotiation, the manager agreed to keep the products with a 10% discount of the price of the plastic sheets. Prepare the entry on April 10th to record the purchase allowance. (Assume all plastic sheets were still in inventory.) Continue to assume they use the perpetual inventory system.

Date	Account Title and Explanation	Debit	Credit

AP-10 (❷)

Refer to AP-8 and AP-9 above and journalize the transaction for Signs Unlimited when the payment is made on May 3rd. Continue to assume they use the perpetual inventory system.

Date	Account Title and Explanation	Debit	Credit

AP-11 (❾)

Boards Unlimited received a shipment of plastic sheets on April 3rd. The value of the plastic was $8,000, plus $100 of freight charges. Prepare the journal entry to record the receipt of goods by Boards Unlimited, assuming the payment would be made in May. Assume they use the periodic inventory system.

Date	Account Title and Explanation	Debit	Credit

AP-12 (❾)

Referring to AP-11 above, several of the plastic sheets delivered to Boards Unlimited were in the wrong color. After some negotiation, the manager agreed to keep the products with a 10% discount of the price of the plastic sheets. Prepare the entry on April 10th to record the purchase allowance. (Assume all plastic sheets were still in inventory.) Continue to assume they use the periodic inventory system.

Date	Account Title and Explanation	Debit	Credit

AP-13 (❾)

Referring to AP-11 and AP-12 above, journalize the transaction for Boards Unlimited when the payment is made on May 3rd. Continue to assume they use the periodic inventory system.

Date	Account Title and Explanation	Debit	Credit

AP-14 (❶)

The following is written on an invoice relating to goods that were purchased: 5/10, n/30. What does it mean?

_____

_____

_____

_____

AP-15 (❶)

Shoe Retailers purchased $10,000 worth of shoes from Runner Wear Supplies on March 1st. Since Shoe Retailers has good cash reserves, the accountant took advantage of the early payment discount that Runner Wear offers. Runner Wear's invoice shows terms of 2/10, n/30. What is the latest date that Shoe Retailers could pay the bill to take advantage of the discount?

AP-16 (❷)

Refer to AP-15 above. As the bookkeeper for Shoe Retailers, prepare the journal entry to record the purchase on March 1st. Assume they use the perpetual inventory system.

Date	Account Title and Explanation	Debit	Credit

AP-17 (❷)

Referring to AP-15 above, journalize the transaction for payment of the invoice, assuming the payment was made on March 5th. Continue to assume they use the perpetual inventory system.

Date	Account Title and Explanation	Debit	Credit

AP-18 (❷)

Referring to AP-15 above, journalize the transaction for payment of the invoice, assuming the payment was made on March 30th. Continue to assume they use the perpetual inventory system.

Date	Account Title and Explanation	Debit	Credit

AP-19 (❶)

Socks Retailers purchased $10,000 worth of shoes from Jogger Wear Supplies on March 1st. Since Socks Retailers has good cash reserves, the accountant took advantage of the early payment discount that Jogger Wear offers. Jogger Wear's invoice shows terms of 2/15, n/60. What is the latest date that Socks Retailers could pay the bill to take advantage of the discount?

_____

_____

AP-20 (❷)

Refer to AP-19 above. As the bookkeeper for Sock Retailers, prepare the journal entry to record the purchase on March 1st. Assume they use the periodic inventory system.

Date	Account Title and Explanation	Debit	Credit

AP-21 (❷)

Referring to AP-19 above, journalize the transaction for payment of the invoice, assuming the payment was made on March 5th. Continue to assume they use the periodic inventory system.

Date	Account Title and Explanation	Debit	Credit

AP-22 (❷)

Referring to AP-19 above, journalize the transaction for payment of the invoice, assuming the payment was made on March 30th. Continue to assume they use the periodic inventory system.

Date	Account Title and Explanation	Debit	Credit

AP-23 (❷)

On March 20th, Cup-A-Java received a shipment of gift mugs for resale from Cup Makers Inc. in the amount of $5,000, plus $200 shipping charges. The terms stated on the invoice from Cup Makers Inc. were as follows: 3/15, n/60. Assume Cup-A-Java uses the perpetual inventory system. Journalize the following scenarios:

a) As the bookkeeper for Cup-A-Java, complete the original invoice transaction.

Date	Account Title and Explanation	Debit	Credit

b) If Cup-A-Java decided to take advantage of the early payment cash discount, by when should the payment be made to qualify for the discount?

_____

_____

c) The payment by Cup-A-Java to Cup Makers Inc. was made on March 31st. Prepare the journal entry for the payment of goods. Continue to assume they use the perpetual inventory system.

Date	Account Title and Explanation	Debit	Credit

d) Journalize the entry if payment was made on May 20th. Continue to assume they use the perpetual inventory system.

Date	Account Title and Explanation	Debit	Credit

e) Suppose 20% of the shipment was returned on March 25th because they were in the wrong color. Cup Makers Inc. agreed to apply the same percentage deduction to the freight charges. The invoice has not been paid. Prepare the journal entry to record this transaction. Continue to assume they use the perpetual inventory system.

Date	Account Title and Explanation	Debit	Credit

f) Continue from part e, journalize the entry if Cup-A-Java took advantage of the early payment cash discount when paying for the balance of the cups on March 31st. Round off to the nearest dollar. Continue to assume they use the perpetual inventory system.

Date	Account Title and Explanation	Debit	Credit

AP-24 (❶)

If a computer company bought computers for $10,000 and sold them for $14,000, how much would the gross profit be on the entire shipment if the business took advantage of the early cash payment terms of 2/15, n/30 from their supplier?

_____

_____

_____

AP-25 (❷)

On May 1st, Food Wholesalers purchased $3,000 worth of dried fruit inventory plus $100 freight charges on account. On May 15th, Food Wholesalers sold the entire dried fruit inventory to Retail Grocers for $4,000 on account. As the bookkeeper for Food Wholesalers, journalize the transactions. Assume they use the perpetual inventory system.

Date	Account Title and Explanation	Debit	Credit

AP-26 (❷)

Referring to AP-25 above, if operating expenses were $500:

   a)   How much was Food Wholesalers' gross profit?

_____

_____

_____

   b)   How much was Food Wholesalers' net income?

_____

_____

_____

AP-27 (❷)

Macks is a maker of cotton garments that sells to various retailers. On June 1st, Cory's Retailers sent back a shipment of goods that was unsatisfactory. As a gesture of goodwill, Macks agreed to the return of the goods. The goods were sold on account for $6,000 originally and cost $4,000. Assume Macks uses the perpetual inventory system. Complete the following:

a) As Mack's bookkeeper prepare the journal entries to reflect the return.

Date	Account Title and Explanation	Debit	Credit

b) Journalize the entry if Cory's only returned half of the shipment. Continue to assume they use the perpetual inventory system.

Date	Account Title and Explanation	Debit	Credit

c) What happened to the value of Macks' owner's equity when Cory's returned the merchandise? Did it increase, decrease or stay the same? Explain your answer.

_____

_____

_____

_____

d) Explain the logic behind debiting the sales returns and allowances as a contra-account instead of debiting the revenue account directly.

_____

_____

_____

_____

AP-28 (❷)

Assume you are the bookkeeper for Moira's Wholesalers, a distributor of kitchen furniture. Your sales manager informed you that Ted's Retailers were unhappy with the quality of some tables delivered on August 12th, and they will be shipping back all the goods. The original invoice amounted to $1,500 and the goods cost Moira's $1,000. Assume they use the perpetual inventory system. Complete the journal entries for each of the following scenarios:

a) Rather than taking the tables back, your sales manager agreed to allow Ted's Retailers a 10% discount if they agreed to keep the goods. On August 14, Moira recorded the sales discount and reduced the balance owed by Ted. Record Ted's payment in settlement of the invoice on September 12th.

Date	Account Title and Explanation	Debit	Credit

b) Suppose that Ted's shipped back all the goods on August 15th. Journalize the transactions. Continue to assume they use the perpetual inventory system.

Date	Account Title and Explanation	Debit	Credit

c) Suppose that Ted's shipped back half the goods on August 15th and kept the other half with 10% allowance. Journalize the transactions that took place on August 15th. Continue to assume they use the perpetual inventory system.

Date	Account Title and Explanation	Debit	Credit

d) Continue from part b. Since all the goods were sold and returned in the same period, what happened to Moira's gross profit? (Disregard the additional shipping and administration costs). Explain your answer.

_____

_____

_____

_____

AP-29 (❷)

Pete's Wholesalers imports and distributes towels. They sell their products to various retailers throughout the country and offer payment terms of 2/10, n/30. On October 1st, Pete's made a large sale to Ernie's Bathroom Retailers in the amount of $15,000, which cost Pete's $9,000. Pete's uses a perpetual inventory system. Complete the following:

a) Journalize the sale that was made on account.

Date	Account Title and Explanation	Debit	Credit

b) By what date must Ernie's pay the invoice to qualify for the early cash payment discount?

_____

_____

_____

c) Assume Ernie's paid the bill on October 5th. Record the journal entries. Continue to assume they use the perpetual inventory system.

Date	Account Title and Explanation	Debit	Credit

d) If Ernie's had returned half the shipment and paid for the balance owing on October 5th, how would the transaction be journalized? Continue to assume they use the perpetual inventory system.

Date	Account Title and Explanation	Debit	Credit

e) Suppose Ernie's found the goods unsatisfactory and agreed to keep the goods with a 10% discount. Prepare the journal entry to record the sales allowance and Ernie's payment on October 20th. Continue to assume they use the perpetual inventory system.

Date	Account Title and Explanation	Debit	Credit

AP-30 (❷)

Assume you are the bookkeeper for Joe The Printer. The company buys ink cartridges from various suppliers, refills them and sells them to customers. All purchases and sales are made on account. Assume they use the perpetual inventory system. Complete the following for Joe The Printer.

a) Record the purchase on December 15th of $3,000 for ink cartridges from Inkster Supplies, whose payment terms are 3/10, n/45.

Date	Account Title and Explanation	Debit	Credit

b) When must Joe pay the account to qualify for the discount?

_____

_____

_____

c) Prepare the journal entry to record Joe's payment on December 20th. Continue to assume they use the perpetual inventory system.

Date	Account Title and Explanation	Debit	Credit

d) If Joe's made the payment on December 31st instead, journalize the transaction. Continue to assume they use the perpetual inventory system.

Date	Account Title and Explanation	Debit	Credit

e) If Joe's returned one-third of the products and paid the balance, how would both of these transactions be journalized? Assume both transactions occurred on December 20th. Continue to assume they use the perpetual inventory system.

Date	Account Title and Explanation	Debit	Credit

f) If on January 5th, Joe's sold all $3,000 worth of inventory for $5,000 to Smith printers on account, how would the transactions be journalized? Continue to assume they use the perpetual inventory system.

Date	Account Title and Explanation	Debit	Credit

g) Continue from the previous question. If Joe's selling terms were 4/7, n/30, prepare the journal entry to record receipt of payment on January 12th. Continue to assume they use the perpetual inventory system.

Date	Account Title and Explanation	Debit	Credit

AP-31 (❸)

Fill in the missing numbers on the perpetual inventory record. The company uses the weighted average cost for inventory. Assume beginning inventory is zero.

		Purchase / Sales		Quantity on Hand	
Date	Description	Quantity	Amount	Quantity	Amount
	Purchase from AAA Co.	200	$2,000		
	Sale to SSS Co.			100	1,000
	Sale to TTT Co.	-50		50	500
	Purchase from BBB	60	720		
	Sale to UUU Co.	-20		90	

AP-32 (❸)

Use the information from your completed answer to AP-31. What is the cost of each unit sold to UUU Co. using the FIFO method?

_____

_____

_____

_____

_____

AP-33 (❸)

Use the information from your completed answer to AP-31. What is the cost of each unit sold to UUU Co. using the LIFO method?

_____

_____

_____

_____

AP-34 (❸)

Use the information from your completed answer to AP-31. What is the total cost of the units sold to UUU Co. using Specific Identification? 10 of the units sold to UUU were purchased from AAA, and 10 units were purchased from BBB.

_____

_____

_____

_____

_____

AP-35 (❸)

Complete the following table, based on the information in your completed AP-31, AP-32, AP33 and AP-34.

	Specific Identification	Average Cost	FIFO	LIFO
Balance Before Sale to UUU				
COGS on Sale to UUU				
Closing inventory Balance				

AP-36 (❺)

A company has three types of products: gadgets, widgets and gizmos. The cost of each type is listed below. Complete the table by applying the lower of cost or market method.

Description	Category	Cost	Market	Lower of Cost or Market Applied to... Individual	Category	Total
Gadget Type 1	Gadgets	$1,000	$900			
Gadget Type 2	Gadgets	5,000	5,200			
Total Gadgets						
Widget A	Widgets	100	100			
Widget B	Widgets	20	200			
Total Widgets						
Gizmo 1	Gizmos	1,500	1,450			
Gizmo 2	Gizmos	1,750	2,000			
Total Gizmos						
Total						

AP-37 (❹)

A company reported ending inventory of $100,000 in year 1. It was discovered in year 2 that the correct value of the ending inventory was $90,000 for year 1. Complete the following table, based on this information. Assume the company uses perpetual inventory.

Item	Reported	Correct Amount
Inventory	$100,000	
Current Assets	$150,000	
Total Assets	$500,000	
Owner's Equity year 1	$200,000	
Sales	$1,000,000	
Cost of Goods Sold	$500,000	
Profit for year 1	$6,000	

AP-38 (❻)

Assume that you have to prepare quarterly financial statements, and the following information is available from the General Ledger:

Required:

Sales	$200,000
Opening Inventory	$67,000
Purchases	$90,000
Gross Profit Margin (from examination of prior years' statements) = 30%	

Calculate the estimated closing inventory using the gross profit method.

AP-39 (◉)

Shown below is the current information for a company.

Required:

Calculate the estimated closing inventory at cost by using the retail method.

	At Cost	At Retail
Cost of Goods Sold		
Opening Inventory	2,000	4,000
Purchases	42,000	90,000
Cost of Goods Available for Sale	44,000	94,000
Sales at Retail		50,000
Closing Inventory at Retail		44,000

AP-40 (❷, ❾)

A company purchases 1,000 units of inventory at $12 per unit on account. The company subsequently sells 25 units for $50 per unit on account. The company uses a perpetual inventory system.

Required:

    a) Write the journal entries to record the above transactions.

    b) Write the journal entries as if the company used a periodic inventory system.

Date	Account Title and Explanation	Debit	Credit

AP-41 (❼)

The following is a list of relevant inventory numbers from ABC Company for the 2013 fiscal year:

ABC Company	$ Millions
Inventory - December 31, 2012	$108.5
Inventory - December 31, 2013	169.7
Cost of Goods Sold	$1,452.5

A list of relevant inventory numbers from XYZ Company for the 2013 fiscal year:

XYZ Company	$ Millions
Inventory - December 31, 2012	$221.7
Inventory - December 31, 2013	209.6
Cost of Goods Sold	$1,432.0

Required:

a) Calculate the Inventory Turnover Ratio and Inventory Days on Hand for ABC Company.

b) Calculate the Inventory Turnover Ratio and Inventory Days on Hand for XYZ Company.

c) Compare the results between two companies. What conclusion can we draw about the performance of these two companies comparatively?

AP-42 (❼)

Delta Corporation reported the following amounts for ending inventory and cost of goods sold in the financial statements:

Ending Inventory		Cost of Goods Sold	
2013	$799,000	2013	$25,927,000
2012	$1,365,000	2012	$36,479,000
2011	$3,205,000	2011	$47,025,000

Required:

a) Calculate the Inventory Turnover Ratio and Inventory Days on Hand for the year 2013 and 2012.

b) Compare and discuss the results between two years.

c) Delta Corporation is a software company in a rapidly changing industry. Evaluate the results from part (a) by using this information and considering the amount of cost of goods sold.

_____

_____

_____

_____

_____

_____

_____

_____

_____

_____

_____

_____

_____

_____

AP-43 (❸, ⑩)

Simplex Inc. has a fiscal year end on December 31. Below is an inventory purchase and sales record for the year 2013. The company has only one product in inventory, and all units of that product are identical (homogenous).

Date	Units Purchased	Units Sold	Units Balance
January 1			15 @ $10 each
February 13	20 @$12 each		
March 26	15 @ 13 each		
April 17		40 @ $20 each	
July 25	50 @$14 each		
September 28		35 @ $20 each	
November 3		20 @ $20 each	
December 31			5

Required:

a) Assume that Simplex Inc. uses the periodic inventory system and values inventory by using the weighted average method. Calculate the value of ending inventory at December 31.

b) Assume that Simplex Inc. uses the perpetual inventory system and values inventory by using the First-In-First-Out (FIFO) method. Calculate the value of cost of goods sold (COGS) for the year.

c) Assume that Simplex Inc. uses the perpetual inventory system and values inventor by using the Last-In-First-Out (LIFO) method. Calculate the value of cost of goods sold (COGS) for the year.

_____

_____

_____

_____

_____

_____

_____

_____

_____

_____

_____

_____

_____

_____

_____

AP-44 (❷, ❾)

Refer to AP-43 and answer the following:

a) Assume that Simplex Inc. uses the periodic inventory system and values inventory using the First-In-First-Out (FIFO) method during 2013. Prepare journal entries for recognizing the sale of 40 units at $20 per unit (recognizing COGS if applicable) on April 17. Assume that the sale is made on account. For each component of the journal entries, clearly state whether the debit/credit is made to an income statement (I/S) account or a balance sheet (B/S) account. (For example, Dr. Cash (B/S) $10; Cr. Revenue (I/S) $10)

b) Assume that Simplex Inc. uses the perpetual inventory system and values inventory using the First-In-First-Out (FIFO) method during 2013. Prepare journal entries for recognizing the sale of 35 units at $20 per unit (recognizing COGS if applicable) on September 28. Assume that the sale is made on account. For each component of the journal entries, clearly state whether the debit/credit is made to an income statement (I/S) account or a balance sheet (B/S) account. (For example, Dr. Cash (B/S) $10; Cr. Revenue (I/S) $10)

c) Assume that Simplex Inc. uses the perpetual inventory system and values inventory using the Last-In-First-Out (LIFO) method during 2013. Prepare journal entries for recognizing the sale of 20 units at $20 per unit (recognizing COGS if applicable) on November 3. Assume that the sale is made on account. For each component of the journal entries, clearly state whether the debit/credit is made to an income statement (I/S) account or a balance sheet (B/S) account. (For example, Dr. Cash (B/S) $10; Cr. Revenue (I/S) $10)

Your Answers:

a)

Date	Account Title and Explanation	Debit	Credit

b)

Date	Account Title and Explanation	Debit	Credit

c)

Date	Account Title and Explanation	Debit	Credit

AP-45 (❺)

Garden Inc. uses the perpetual inventory system and its inventory consists of four products as at December 31, 2013. Selected information is provided below.

Required:

a) Calculate the inventory value that should be reported on December 31, 2013, using the lower of cost or market approach applied on an individual-item basis.

Product	Number of units	Cost (per unit)	Expected selling price (per unit)	LCM (Individual)
1	15	$80	$120	
2	20	$80	$60	
3	40	$60	$50	
4	5	$120	$180	

_____

_____

_____

b) Using the results from a), prepare the journal entry to adjust inventory to LCM (at individual-item level).

Date	Account Title and Explanation	Debit	Credit

_____

_____

AP-46 (⑥)

Refer to AP-45. It is now March 31, 2013 and Garden Inc. needs to present a set of financial statements showing the performance of the first quarter of 2013 to a local bank for a loan. To prepare the statements in a timely manner, Garden Inc. decided to estimate the inventory amount instead of doing a physical count. The following information is provided:

Accounts Receivable, January 1, 2013	$1,500
Accounts Receivable, March 31, 2013	2,200
Collections of accounts from January 1 to March 31	5,300
Inventory, January 1, 2013	1,200
Purchases from January 1 to March 31	6,800

Assume all sales are made on account. The sale prices of the products are determined by marking up costs by 25%.

Required:

Calculate the estimated cost of the inventory on March 31, 2013 using the gross profit method.

AP-47 (⑩)

Good Life Corporation sells medical support products and records purchases at net amounts. They account for their inventory using the periodic system. In 2013, the following information was available from the company's inventory records for ankle support products.

	Units	Unit Cost
January 1, 2013 (beginning inventory)	1,600	$18.00
Purchases		
January 5, 2013	2,600	$20.00
January 25, 2013	2,400	$21.00
February 16, 2013	1,000	$22.00
March 15, 2013	1,800	$23.00

A physical count was taken on March 31, 2013 and showed 2,000 units on hand.

Required:

a) Prepare schedules to calculate the ending inventory at March 31, 2013 under the FIFO valuation method.

b) Prepare schedules to calculate the ending inventory at March 31, 2013 under the weighted average valuation method.

c) Prepare schedules to calculate the ending inventory at March 31, 2013 under the LIFO valuation method.

a)

	Units	Unit Cost	Total Cost

b)

	Units	Unit Cost	Total Cost

c)

	Units	Unit Cost	Total Cost

AP-48 (❷, ❾)

For each business transaction in the table below, identify which accounts are debited and credited. Do this for both the perpetual and periodic inventory system.

	Transaction	Perpetual Inventory System		Periodic Inventory System	
		DR	CR	DR	CR
(a)	Purchased inventory on account.				
(b)	Returned a portion of the inventory purchased in transaction (a).				
(c)	Paid for remaining invoice balance after taking advantage of the early payment discount.				
(d)	Sold inventory on account.				
(e)	Customer found that a portion of goods sold in transaction (d) were of lower quality. However, he agreed to keep them at 10% discount.				
(f)	Customer paid the remaining invoice balance after taking the advantage of an early payment discount.				

AP-49 (❷, ❽)

AB Retailers had the following business transactions during the month of April:

Apr 10   AB Retailers bought $3,500 worth of T- shirts from Unique Designers. The invoice showed payment terms of 2/10, n/30.

Apr 10   Soon after AB Retailers received the products, it was discovered that some of the T- shirts (worth $500) did not meet quality standards. These goods were returned to the supplier.

Apr 20   AB Retailers made payment for the remaining invoice balance.

Apr 22   AB Retailers sold *all* the goods for $4,500 to SK Stores on terms 3/10, n/45.

Apr 28   SK Stores paid for the goods purchased and took advantage of the early payment discount.

Required:

a) Prepare the journal entries to record the above transactions. Assume the company uses the perpetual inventory system.

Date	Account Title and Explanation	Debit	Credit

b) Calculate April's ending inventory based on the above transactions. Assume that inventory at the beginning of April amounted to $1,500.

_____

_____

_____

c) At the end of April, an inventory count was performed. The balance of inventory according to the count was $1,300. Management deemed that the difference between the ledger account and physical inventory account is due to theft (shrinkage). Prepare the journal entry to adjust the inventory balance on April 30.

Date	Account Title and Explanation	Debit	Credit

d) Describe some inventory controls that could be implemented to help prevent inventory shrinkage.

_____

_____

_____

_____

_____

_____

AP-50 (❷)

AA Booksellers are in the business of buying and selling books, stationary and related items. They had the following transactions during the month of January:

Jan 6   AA Booksellers purchased papers worth $6,000 from SK Publishers. The invoice showed payment terms of 2/10 n/45.

Jan 7   AA Booksellers found that 5% of the papers were of inferior quality. After negotiations with the suppliers, AA Booksellers received a 10% discount on the inferior quality papers.

Jan 10   AA Booksellers paid SK Publishers' invoice and took advantage of the early payment discount.

Jan 20   AA Booksellers sold paper costing $5,377 for $6,500 to a major customer, Cathedral High School. The invoice terms were 3/10 n/30.

Jan 23   Cathedral High School paid the invoice on time, taking advantage of the early payment discount.

AA Booksellers uses the perpetual inventory system. The opening inventory on January 1 was $200 and the closing inventory on January 31st was $674. The opening balance for accounts receivable was $500 and the opening balance for accounts payable was $600 on January 1.

Required:

Record the transactions on the following T-Accounts:

INVENTORY

ACCOUNTS PAYABLE

SALES REVENUE

SALES DISCOUNT

ACCOUNTS RECEIVABLE

AP-51 (❾)

Refer to AP-50 and assume that AA Booksellers uses the periodic inventory system.

a) Prepare the journal entries to record the transactions.

Date	Account Title and Explanation	Debit	Credit

b) Prepare the cost of goods sold section for the month of January.

_____

_____

_____

_____

_____

_____

_____

_____

_____

_____

_____

_____

AP-52 (❾)

Crystal Crockery has provided you with the following information about the transactions occurring in March:

Mar 2   Crystal Crockery received a shipment of gift mugs for resale from Cup Makers Inc. The amount on the invoice is $7,000 and the stated terms are: 2/15, n/45.

Mar 2   Crystal Crockery paid $400 cash for shipping charges.

Mar 5   The manager of Crystal Crockery performed a check on the shipped cups and found that goods worth $700 were defective. The defective goods were returned to the supplier.

Mar 13   Crystal Crockery paid the remaining invoice balance and, in doing so, took advantage of the early payment discount.

Mar 20   Crystal Crockery sold the goods costing $6,227 to AS Supermarket for $9,500.

Mar 22   AS Supermarket found 10% of items to be defective and returned these to Crystal Crockery.

Mar 28   The invoice showed terms 2/10, n/60. AS Supermarket paid the remaining invoice balance after taking advantage of the early settlement discount.

Opening inventory balance was $500 and the closing inventory balance was $847.

Required:

Assume Crystal Crockery uses the periodic inventory system:

a) Prepare the journal entries to record the purchase and sales transactions.

Date	Account Title and Explanation	Debit	Credit

b) Prepare the journal entries to record the end of period adjustments.

Date	Account Title and Explanation	Debit	Credit

Date	Account Title and Explanation	Debit	Credit

c) Prepare the cost of goods sold section of the income statement.

AP-53 (❺)

MJ Corporation sells three categories of products – Alpha, Beta and Gamma. The company uses a perpetual inventory system. The following information was available at year end:

	Alpha	Beta	Gamma
	$ per unit	$ per unit	$ per unit
Original cost	10	13	15
Estimated selling price (Market)	15	12	14
Inventory: number of units held	300	380	240

Required:

a) Calculate the value of inventory (apply the LCM principle at the category level).

_____

_____

_____

_____

_____

b) Using the results from a), prepare the journal entry to adjust inventory to LCM (at category level). Assume the perpetual inventory system.

Date	Account Title and Explanation	Debit	Credit

_____

_____

AP-54 (❸)

An inventory record card for item A – 903 shows the following details:

March 1	60 units in opening inventory at a cost of $70 per unit
March 9	130 units purchased at a cost of $65 per unit
March 18	70 units sold
March 24	40 units purchased at a cost of $80 per unit
March 29	100 units sold

Required:

The company uses the perpetual inventory method. Calculate the value of inventory at each of the above dates and determine the ending inventory at the end of March using the following methods:

    (a) FIFO

    (b) Weighted average cost method

    (c) LIFO

(a) FIFO

_____

_____

_____

_____

_____

_____

_____

_____

_____

(b) Weighted average cost method

_____

_____

_____

_____

_____

_____

_____

_____

_____

(c) LIFO

_____

_____

_____

_____

_____

_____

_____

_____

_____

AP-55 (❹)

Trevor and Arkady run Squash Stuff Inc. The net income earned by their business during the year ended December 31, 2013 is $250,000. However, an inventory clerk realized that the ending inventory for 2013 was overstated by $10,000.

Required:

a) If the error is not corrected for, what would be the effect on 2013 net income?

_____

_____

_____

b) If the error is not corrected for, what would be the effect on the 2013 equity balance?

_____

_____

_____

c) Record journal entries to correct the overstatement of inventory assuming that error was discovered in 2013.

Date	Account Title and Explanation	Debit	Credit

d) If the error is not corrected for, how would the sum of 2013 and 2014 net income be affected?

_____

_____

_____

_____

_____

e) There have been cases where companies who are applying for bank loans have intentionally overstated their closing inventory. Why would companies overstate their closing inventory? and what are some of the methods of overstating closing inventory?

_____

_____

_____

_____

_____

_____

AP-56 (❻)

Fine Grocery Store has been buying and selling grocery items for many years. During the month of January, some inventory was lost due to an accidental fire in the store. The following amounts have been extracted from the accounts of Fine Grocery Store:

Sales		$280,000
Beginning Inventory	$210,000	
Purchases	340,000	
Inventory in good condition after fire	300,000	
Gross Profit Margin		30%

Calculate the amount of inventory lost due to the fire by calculating the amount of COGS using the gross profit method.

_____

_____

_____

_____

_____

AP-57 (❻)

The following information has been provided by AS Retailers for the month of August.
Calculate the estimated closing inventory at cost using the retail method.

	At Cost	At Retail
Cost of Goods sold		
Opening inventory	3,000	6,000
Purchases	32,000	80,000
Goods available for sale	35,000	86,000
Sales at retail		50,000
Closing inventory at retail		36,000

_____

_____

_____

_____

_____

AP-58 (❸)

GB, a bookseller, had the following transactions during the month of August and uses the
perpetual inventory system:

Aug 1	Novels	Bought 10 novels at $30 each
Aug 2	College bags	Bought 10 bags at $45 each
Aug 5	Novels	Sold 5 novels
Aug 10	Pencil case	Bought 15 at $5 each
Aug 21	College bags	Sold 3 bags

Required:

a) Calculate the value of inventory at each date using the specific identification method.
   Clearly show August ending inventory.

_____

_____

_____

_____

_____

_____

b) Calculate the COGS.

_____

_____

_____

_____

AP-59 (❼)

A list of relevant inventory numbers from SI Company for the year ended December 31, 2013 is provided below:

Average inventory – December 31, 2012	$90,000
Average inventory – December 31, 2013	110,000
Cost of Goods Sold – 2012	920,000
Cost of Goods Sold - 2013	980,000

Required:

a) Calculate the following ratios for SI company for the two years.

- Inventory turnover ratio
- Inventory days on hand ratio

_____

_____

_____

b) Compare the results between two years. What conclusion can be drawn about the performance of the company regarding both years?

_____

_____

_____

_____

_____

Case Study

CS-1 (❷, ❸, ❺, ❻)

1. Record the following for a company using a perpetual inventory system (using FIFO).

   a) Purchase of 1,000 widgets at $20 each on credit
   b) Sale of 900 widgets at $55 each for cash
   c) Purchase of 500 widgets at $25 each on credit
   d) Sale of 100 widgets at $60 on credit
   e) Sale of 300 widgets at $50 each for cash

2. Prepare the perpetual inventory record for the preceding transactions. The company uses FIFO inventory methods. The company has no widgets in its opening inventory.

3. Prepare a statement showing Sales, Cost of Sales and Gross Profit.

4. The company physically counted and valued the inventory, and prepared the following table. Complete the table using individual item LCM methods.

5. Record the journal entry to adjust the value of inventory to lower of cost or market based on individual items using the results from #4 above.

6. Sales for the following interim period are $100,000 and purchases were $68,500. Calculate the gross profit margin and prepare an interim statement for the period, using the gross profit method to estimate inventory. (Use the information from your previous answers.)

1.

Date	Account Title and Explanation	Debit	Credit

2.

Inventory Sub Ledger Account					
		Purchase / Sales		Quantity on Hand	
Date	Description	Quantity	Amount	Quantity	Amount

3.

_____

_____

_____

_____

4.

Description	Category	Cost	Market	Lower of Cost or Market Applied to...		
				Individual	Category	Total
Widget A	Widgets	3,000	2,700			
Widget B	Widgets	2,000	3,300			
Total Widgets						
Total						

5.

Date	Account Title and Explanation	Debit	Credit

6.

_____

_____

_____

_____

_____

_____

_____

_____

_____

_____

_____

_____

_____

Critical Thinking

CT-1 (⑤, ⑥, ⑦)

1. Lower of cost and market may be calculated using one of three methods. Which method is best? Support your answer.

2. Inventory can be estimated using the gross profit method or the retail method. Counting and valuing inventory can be an expensive process (labor cost, closing retail stores while count is underway, etc.) Is it necessary to count and value inventory when it can be estimated? Explain your answer.

3. Profits can be easily manipulated by management by misstating the amount of inventory. Discuss the methods by which management can report incorrect inventory amounts, and the means by which such errors can be eliminated, or at least, reduced.

_____

_____

_____

_____

_____

_____

_____

_____

Notes

Chapter 12

LONG-TERM ASSETS

────────────── **Assessment Questions** ──────────────

AS-1 (❶)

Where would one expect to find capital assets listed on the Balance Sheet?

_____

_____

_____

AS-2 (❶)

Define capital assets. Give an example of a capital asset.

_____

_____

_____

_____

AS-3 (❶)

When deciding whether or not to classify an amount as a capital asset, what criteria are used?

_____

_____

_____

_____

AS-4 (❷)

What is meant by a lump sum purchase of assets? How are costs allocated when the purchase of assets is a lump sum purchase?

_____

_____

_____

_____

_____

AS-5 (❷)

After the initial purchase of a capital asset, additional costs may be incurred. What criteria are used to assess whether this cost is regarded as an expense or an addition to assets?

_____

_____

_____

_____

_____

_____

_____

AS-6 (❸)

What is the residual value of a capital asset? By what other name is residual value known?

_____

_____

_____

AS-7 (❸)

Name three different methods of calculating depreciation.

_____

_____

_____

_____

AS-8 (❹)

Does a company always receive the estimated salvage value of an asset on disposal? Assuming the asset is fully depreciated, how is the difference between the estimated and actual salvage value treated?

_____

_____

_____

_____

AS-9 (❹)

What does the net book value of a capital asset represent? Does the net book value represent the market value of the asset?

_____

_____

_____

AS-10 (❻)

In which section of the balance sheet are intangible assets found?

_____

_____

_____

AS-11 (❻)

Discuss the differences between intangible assets and other long-term assets (i.e. Property, Plant and Equipment).

_____

_____

_____

_____

AS-12 (❻)

Define intangible assets and describe the costs that are included in calculating its value.

_____

_____

_____

_____

AS-13 (❻)

Define goodwill.

_____

_____

_____

_____

AS-14 (❻)

How do you calculate the value of goodwill?

_____

_____

_____

AS-15 (⑥)

What is the major difference between goodwill and other intangible assets?

_____

_____

_____

AS-16 (⑤)

What method is usually used to record the depletion of natural resources?

_____

_____

_____

AS-17 (③)

How is per unit amortization calculated?

_____

_____

_____

AS-18 (⑥)

List three examples of intangible assets.

_____

_____

_____

AS-19 (⑥)

What alternative is available for companies that do not want to own fixed tangible assets?

_____

_____

_____

AS-20 (❾)

What are some of control procedures for protecting capital assets?

_____

_____

_____

_____

AS-21 (❾)

What are the areas of ethical concerns when it comes to long-term assets?

_____

_____

_____

_____

AS-22 (❾)

Company XYZ has decided to change the residual value of its truck from $50,000 to $60,000 without any supporting evidence. What would be the impact of this change on net income of the current period?

_____

_____

_____

_____

Application Questions

AP-1 (❷)

Prepare the journal entry for the purchase of machinery worth $200,000 (on credit).

Date	Account Title and Explanation	Debit	Credit

AP-2 (❷)

Land, building and equipment were purchased for a total amount of $1.5 million. The assessed values of these purchases were, Land - $900,000; Building - $500,000; Equipment – $200,000. Write the journal entry that records the purchase. Round your percentages to two decimal points.

Item	Assessment	Percent	Applied to Cost

Date	Account Title and Explanation	Debit	Credit

AP-3 (❸)

Prepare the journal entry to record depreciation of $2,000 for a capital asset.

Date	Account Title and Explanation	Debit	Credit

AP-4 (❸)

Equipment was purchased at the beginning of the year for $50,000. The asset is expected to last for four years, at which time the estimated residual value will be $10,000. Prepare a table showing the year, the cost of the asset, the amount of depreciation expense each year, accumulated depreciation to date and net book value. The company uses straight-line depreciation.

Year	Cost of Capital Asset	Depreciation Expense	Accumulated Depreciation To Date	Net Book Value

AP-5 (❸)

Refer to the data supplied in AP-4. The asset was sold for $12,000 cash on the first day of year 5. Prepare the journal entry to record the sale.

Date	Account Title and Explanation	Debit	Credit

AP-6 (❸)

Use the data supplied in AP-4. Prepare the table assuming that the company used double-declining-balance depreciation and the asset had no residual value.

Year	Net Book Value at the Beginning of the Year	Depreciation Expense	Accumulated Depreciation To Date	Net Book Value at the End of the Year

AP-7 (❸)

Use the data supplied in AP-4. Assume that the company uses the units-of production method. The asset can produce 1 million units. Record of production: year 1 – 300,000 units; year 2 – 250,000; year 3 – 300,000 units; year 4 – 100,000 units. Prepare a table showing the year, the cost of the asset, the amount of depreciation expense each year, accumulated depreciation to date, and net book value. Hint: depreciate the cost of the asset minus its residual value.

Year	Cost of Capital Asset	Depreciation Expense	Accumulated Depreciation To Date	Net Book Value

AP-8 (❸,❹)

On July 1, 2004, Bob's Juice Factory purchased a new bottle-sealing machine for $102,000. The machine had an estimated useful life of 10 years and is expected to have no residual value. Assume that the company has adopted a partial-year depreciation policy, where depreciation is taken on a monthly basis. Prepare the table using these facts. The company uses straight-line depreciation. The asset is sold on November 1, 2012 for $20,500. The fiscal year-end for Bob's Juice Factory is December 31. Record the entry for the sale, assuming the depreciation expense for the year has already been recorded.

Year	Cost of Capital Asset	Depreciation Expense	Accumulated Depreciation To Date	Net Book Value

Date	Account Title and Explanation	Debit	Credit

AP-9 (❸)

At the beginning of Year 1, an entrepreneur purchased a group of assets as a "bulk purchase" at an auction sale. The entrepreneur paid $250,000 "as is" for two automobiles, a widget machine, a forklift truck and a trailer. The items were valued by a professional appraiser as follows:

Item	Estimated Value	Percentage	Estimated Remaining Life
Auto 1	$10,000	3.22%	3 Years
Auto 2	15,000	4.84%	5 Years
Widget Machine	258,000	83.23%	15 Years
Fork-lift	15,000	4.84%	5 Years
Trailer	12,000	3.87%	10 Years
Total	$310,000	100%	

After the auction, the entrepreneur had the machine moved to the factory. Moving the widget machine cost $2,000. After the machine was placed in the factory, an electrician was contracted to install additional power lines and hook up the machine at a cost of $1,000. A plumber was also needed to connect the machine to the water mains. This cost $500. A gas fitter was required to connect the widget machine to the gas line at a cost of $200.

Before placing Auto 1 and 2 into use, the entrepreneur took both autos to the local repair shop. The mechanic said that Auto 1 needed a new engine that would cost $2,000 and Auto 2 needed a major tune-up at a cost of $500 (the tune-up is required to get the car going). The entrepreneur paid cash for the repairs. Early on in Year 2, the entrepreneur advertised and sold Auto 1 for $8,000 and replaced the front brakes on Auto 2 for $300.

The entrepreneur's company uses a half-year method for depreciation (i.e. ½ year's depreciation in the year of purchase, and ½ year's depreciation in the year of sale). No depreciation is recorded if an item is bought and sold in the same year. The company uses straight-line depreciation, with an estimated residual value of 10% of cost for all assets.

Required:

Write the journal entries to record the following:

a) Using straight-line depreciation method, record all journal entries related to the above transactions. When allocating a bulk purchase, round up to the nearest dollar. If the numbers don't quite balance because of rounding, adjust the largest number up or down so that the journal entry balances. Note: the exact journal entry dates can be omitted for the purpose of this exercise. Simply indicate if each transaction belongs to year 1 or year 2.

b) Using the double-declining-balance depreciation method, redo the journal entries for the depreciation of the Trailer for years 1 and 2. Keep in mind that the company uses a half-year method for depreciation. Note: the exact journal entry dates can be omitted for the purpose of this exercise. Simply indicate if each transaction belongs to year 1 or year 2.

a)

Date	Account Title and Explanation	Debit	Credit

Date	Account Title and Explanation	Debit	Credit

b)

Date	Account Title and Explanation	Debit	Credit

Calculations

_____

_____

_____

_____

_____

_____

_____

_____

_____

AP-10 (❸)

Two years ago, a capital asset was purchased for $50,000. The asset was expected to last for four years (with an estimated residual value of $10,000). For the first two years, the company used the double declining balance. Suppose the company decides to switch to the straight–line method after recording the depreciation expense for year 2. Calculate the depreciation expense for year 3.

_____

_____

_____

_____

_____

_____

AP-11 (❸, ❹)

A company purchased equipment for $50,000. It is expected to last for four years and have a residual value of $10,000. Assume that the company has adopted a partial-year depreciation policy, wherein half a year's depreciation is taken in the year of purchase, and half a year's depreciation is recorded in the year of disposal and that the asset is sold during the first month of Year 3 for $20,000. Prepare the depreciation table and journal entry required to record the sale using these facts, assuming the depreciation expense in the third year has already been recorded. The company uses straight-line depreciation.

Year	Cost of Capital Asset	Depreciation Expense	Accumulated Depreciation To Date	Net Book Value

Date	Account Title and Explanation	Debit	Credit

AP-12 (❼)

John Partington purchased assets ($500,000) and liabilities ($400,000) of a company for which he paid $150,000. The company owns the rights to a unique product. Record the purchase transaction.

Date	Account Title and Explanation	Debit	Credit

AP-13 (❼)

Refer to AP-12. Subsequent to the purchase of the company, a competitor appeared. John assessed that the value of the goodwill which his company owned was now worth $20,000. Record the appropriate journal entry to reflect the reduction in the value of goodwill.

Date	Account Title and Explanation	Debit	Credit

AP-14 (❼)

Turpen Corporation purchased timber rights from the government. The license lasts for 10 years, during which time Turpen estimates that 10 million board feet (BF) of lumber can be harvested. The company paid $10,000,000 for the license. The license has zero value on expiry. Record the journal entry for the purchase of the timber rights.

Date	Account Title and Explanation	Debit	Credit

AP-15 (❺)

Refer to AP-14 above. Calculate the Unit Price for each BF to be extracted.

_____

_____

AP-16 (❺)

Refer to AP-14 and AP-15. During the current year, the company harvested 500,000 board feet. Record the journal entry to record the harvesting.

Date	Account Title and Explanation	Debit	Credit

AP-17 (❼)

Feggins Company purchased a patent from Marquette Limited for $200,000 on January 1, 2014. The patent has a remaining life of six years. Prepare the journal entry to record the purchase.

Date	Account Title and Explanation	Debit	Credit

AP-18 (❼)

Refer to AP-17. Prepare the journal entry to record amortization for one year on December 31, 2014. The company does not use the half-year rule. Assume the straight-line method of depreciation is used.

Date	Account Title and Explanation	Debit	Credit

AP-19 (❼)

Mirabella Manufacturing spent several years developing a process for producing widgets. Their lawyer suggested that they patent the process. Accordingly, the company proceeded to obtain the patent. In order to patent the process, the company paid $100,000 to the lawyer, plus $25,000 to the government for the patent. In addition, other fees incurred relating to the patent of $10,000. Prepare the journal entries to record the cost of the patent. Note: the journal entry date can be omitted for the purpose of this exercise.

Date	Account Title and Explanation	Debit	Credit

AP-20 (❼)

Refer to AP-19. The patent has a life of 17 years. Prepare the journal entry to amortize the patent for one year. Note: the journal entry date can be omitted for the purpose of this exercise.

Date	Account Title and Explanation	Debit	Credit

AP-21 (❸)

On January 1, 2014, South Company purchased a machine for $40,000. The salvage value was estimated to be $5,000. The machine will be depreciated over five years using the straight-line method. The company's year end is December 31.

Required: Prepare a depreciation schedule for machine's useful life using the following table.

Year	Cost of Capital Asset	Depreciation Expense	Accumulated Depreciation To Date	Net Book Value

AP-22 (❸, ❹)

Refer to AP-21. The machine was sold for $6,000 at the end of year 5. Prepare a journal entry to record the sale.

Date	Account Title and Explanation	Debit	Credit

AP-23 (❸)

Refer to AP-21. Assume that South Company uses the double-declining-balance depreciation method and the machine has no residual value.

Required: Prepare a depreciation schedule for machine's useful life using the following table.

Year	Net Book Value at the beginning of the year	Depreciation Expense	Accumulated Depreciation To Date	Net Book Value at the end of the year

AP-24 (❸)

Refer to AP-21. Assume that the company uses the units-of-production method, and the machine can produce 350,000 units. Record of production: Year 1 - 20,000 units; Year 2 - 60,000 units; Year 3 - 70,000 units; Year 4 - 100,000 units; Year 5 - 100,000 units

Required: Prepare a depreciation schedule for machine's useful life using the following table.

Year	Cost of Capital Asset	Depreciation Expense	Accumulated Depreciation To Date	Net Book Value

AP-25 (❸, ❹)

On September 30, 2013, ABC company purchased equipment worth $150,000. The equipment has a useful life of six years and no salvage value. Depreciation was not recorded in the year of acquisition. A yearly depreciation is recorded thereafter, including the year of the asset's disposition. The company uses the straight-line method of depreciation.

Required:

a) Given that the company's year end is December 31, complete the following table.

Year	Cost of Capital Asset	Depreciation Expense	Accumulated Depreciation To Date	Net Book Value

b) On June 30, 2019, ABC Company sold the equipment for $3,000. Prepare a journal entry to record the sale, assuming depreciation expense for 2019 has not yet been recorded.

Date	Account Title and Explanation	Debit	Credit

AP-26 (❸)

MNO Company purchased equipment worth $35,000 on January 1, 2014. The equipment has an estimated five-year service life with no salvage value. The company's policy for five-year assets is to use the double-declining-balance method for the first two years of the asset's life and then switch to the straight-line depreciation method. The company's year end is December 31.

Required: Calculate the depreciation expense on December 31, 2016.

_____

_____

_____

_____

_____

_____

AP-27 (❸, ❹)

Refer to AP-26. Assume that MNO Company's depreciation policy recognizes only half a year's depreciation in the year of purchase and half a year's depreciation in the year of disposal. The company uses the straight-line method. The asset was sold for $15,000 on May 15, 2016.

Required:

a) Prepare a depreciation schedule using the following table.

Year	Cost of Capital Asset	Depreciation Expense	Accumulated Depreciation To Date	Net Book Value

b) Prepare the required journal entry to record the depreciation on the disposal and the sale.

Date	Account Title and Explanation	Debit	Credit

AP-28 (❸)

On July 1, 2013, Earth Corporation purchased factory equipment for $150,000. The equipment is to be depreciated over 8 years using the double-declining-balance method. Earth Corporation's year-end is on September 30. Calculate the depreciation expense to be recorded for the year 2014. Earth Corporation depreciates their assets based on the number of months they owned the asset during the year.

AP-29 (❼)

On February 1, 2014, Eastern Company has acquired the assets ($800,000) and liabilities ($500,000) of XYZ Corporation. The agreed purchase price is $500,000 in cash. Prepare a journal entry to record the purchase.

Date	Account Title and Explanation	Debit	Credit

AP-30 (❼)

On January 1, 2014, Lava Company purchased a $90,000 patent for a new consumer product. However, the patent's useful life is estimated to be only 10 years due to the competitive nature of the product.

Required: Prepare a journal entry to record the purchase.

Date	Account Title and Explanation	Debit	Credit

AP-31 (❼)

Refer to AP-30. Prepare journal entry to record the amortization on December 31, 2014.

Date	Account Title and Explanation	Debit	Credit

AP-32 (❸)

Leonard Corporation acquired a machine in the first week of October 2013 and paid the following bills:

Invoice price	$40,000
Freight In	5,000
Installation Cost	7,000

The estimated useful life of the machine is eight years with no salvage value. The company has December 31 as their year-end and uses a straight-line depreciation method to depreciate long-term assets. Leonard Corporation depreciates their assets based on the number of months they owned the asset during the year.

Required: Calculate the book value of the machine on December 31, 2014.

_____

_____

_____

AP-33 (❽)

The following data pertains to ABC Company, for the year ended December 31, 2013:

Net Sales	$60,000
Net Income	15,000
Total Assets, 1/1/2013	200,000
Total Assets, 12/31/2013	300,000

Required: Calculate the ABC Company's return on assets for 2013. Explain what the ratio means.

_____

_____

_____

_____

_____

_____

AP-34 (⑧)

Joe Corporation's selected financial data is given below:

Net Sales for 2013	$180,000
Cost of Sales for 2013	99,000
Average total Assets for 2013	120,000

Required: Calculate the company's asset turnover. Explain what the ratio means.

_____

_____

_____

_____

_____

_____

AP-35 (③)

On January 1, 2013, Cutie Company purchased a piece of equipment for $90,000 and depreciated it by using the straight-line method. The company estimated that the equipment had a useful life of eight years with no residual value. On January 1, 2016, Cutie determined that the equipment only had a useful life of six years from the date of acquisition with no residual value.

Required: Calculate the accumulated depreciation as of December 31, 2016. Explain why the yearly amortization for 2016 is different from the three preceding years.

_____

_____

_____

_____

_____

_____

AP-36 (④)

Hawthorne Inc. has an old piece of equipment which has reached the end of its useful life. The original cost of the old equipment was $40,000 and accumulated depreciation is $38,000. While looking for a replacement, they found a supplier that was willing to take their old equipment as a trade-in and give them $800 for it. The new equipment will cost $50,000. On September 16, 2013, Hawthorne agrees to the deal and pays cash for the new equipment. Record the transaction for the trade-in and purchase of the equipment.

Date	Account Title and Explanation	Debit	Credit

Case Study

CS-1 (❻,❼,❽)

Apple Inc. reported the following information on their annual financial statements (all numbers in millions).

	Year End September 29, 2012	Year End September 24, 2011
Net Sales	$156,508	$108,249
Net Income	41,733	25,922

An excerpt from their balance sheet and notes to the financial statements is presented below.

CONSOLIDATED BALANCE SHEETS

(In millions, except number of shares which are reflected in thousands)

	September 29, 2012	September 24, 2011
ASSETS:		
Current assets:		
Cash and cash equivalents	$ 10,746	$ 9,815
Short-term marketable securities	18,383	16,137
Accounts receivable, less allowances of $98 and $53, respectively	10,930	5,369
Inventories	791	776
Deferred tax assets	2,583	2,014
Vendor non-trade receivables	7,762	6,348
Other current assets	6,458	4,529
Total current assets	57,653	44,988
Long-term marketable securities	92,122	55,618
Property, plant and equipment, net	15,452	7,777
Goodwill	1,135	896
Acquired intangible assets, net	4,224	3,536
Other assets	5,478	3,556
Total assets	$176,064	$116,371

Property, Plant and Equipment

Property, plant and equipment are stated at cost. Depreciation is computed by use of the straight-line method over the estimated useful lives of the assets, which for buildings is the lesser of 30 years or the remaining life of the underlying building; between two to five years for machinery and equipment, including product tooling and manufacturing process equipment; and the shorter of lease terms or ten years for leasehold improvements. The Company capitalizes eligible costs to acquire or develop internal-use software that are incurred subsequent to the preliminary project stage. Capitalized costs related to internal-use software are amortized using the straight-line method over the estimated useful lives of the assets, which range from three to five years. Depreciation and amortization expense on property and equipment was $2.6 billion, $1.6 billion and $815 million during 2012, 2011 and 2010, respectively.

Long-Lived Assets Including Goodwill and Other Acquired Intangible Assets

The Company does not amortize goodwill and intangible assets with indefinite useful lives, rather such assets are required to be tested for impairment at least annually or sooner whenever events or changes in circumstances indicate that the assets may be impaired. The Company performs its goodwill and intangible asset impairment tests in the fourth quarter of each fiscal year. The Company did not recognize any impairment charges related to goodwill or indefinite lived intangible assets during 2012, 2011 and 2010. The Company established reporting units based on its current reporting structure. For purposes of testing goodwill for impairment, goodwill has been allocated to these reporting units to the extent it relates to each reporting unit. In 2012 and 2011, the Company's goodwill was allocated to the Americas and Europe reportable operating segments.

The Company amortizes its intangible assets with definite lives over their estimated useful lives and reviews these assets for impairment. The Company is currently amortizing its acquired intangible assets with definite lives over periods typically from three to seven years.

Note 3 – Consolidated Financial Statement Details

The following tables show the Company's consolidated financial statement details as of September 29, 2012 and September 24, 2011 (in millions):

Property, Plant and Equipment

	2012	2011
Land and buildings	$ 2,439	$ 2,059
Machinery, equipment and internal-use software	15,743	6,926
Office furniture and equipment	241	184
Leasehold improvements	3,464	2,599
Gross property, plant and equipment	21,887	11,768
Accumulated depreciation and amortization	(6,435)	(3,991)
Net property, plant and equipment	$15,452	$ 7,777

1. Long-term assets make up what percentage of total assets in 2012?

_____

_____

_____

2. What method of depreciation does Apple use? How many years does Apple depreciate machinery and equipment?

_____

_____

_____

3. What is the value of goodwill in Apple at the end of 2012? Did Apple write off any impairment on goodwill in 2012?

_____

_____

_____

4. Calculate the return on assets for 2012. What does it mean?

_____

_____

_____

5. Calculate the asset turnover for 2012. What does it mean?

_____

_____

_____

Critical Thinking

CT-1 (❶, ❸)

a) Capital assets can constitute a significant portion of total assets. What specific criteria do you suggest for classifying an amount as a capital asset (i.e. cost, life, use)? Support your answer.

b) The calculation of depreciation may be performed using different methods. All methods are allowed under GAAP. Do you think that this is reasonable? Support your answer.

c) Which one method do you think is best for calculating depreciation? Support your answer.

d) Which one method is best for recording partial-year depreciation? Support your answer.

_____

_____

_____

_____

_____

_____

_____

_____

_____

_____

_____

_____

_____

_____

_____

_____

_____

CT-2 (⬤)

Since intangible assets have no physical existence, they cannot be seen. Stockholders may question showing an amount on the balance sheet for an "invisible" asset. Companies have staff with many years of experience who would be difficult to replace, and are therefore deemed valuable. However, the value of such staff is not reflected in the financial statements. Discuss.

_____

_____

_____

_____

_____

_____

_____

_____

_____

_____

_____

_____

_____

_____

_____

_____

_____

Notes

Chapter 13

CURRENT LIABILITIES

———————— **Assessment Questions** ————————

AS-1 (❶)

What are liabilities?

_____

_____

_____

AS-2 (❶)

Name the two classes of liabilities.

_____

_____

_____

AS-3 (❶)

How are current liabilities presented on the balance sheet?

_____

_____

_____

AS-4 (❶)

Define known (determinable) liabilities.

AS-5 (❶)

Provide four examples of determinable (known) liabilities.

AS-6 (❻)

Provide three examples of estimated or contingent (unknown) liabilities.

AS-7 (❶)

Define accrued expenses.

AS-8 (❼)

What is the normal source of funds used to pay current liabilities?

AS-9 (❼)

How should the purchase of capital assets be financed?

AS-10 (❷)

List the items you expect to find on a note payable.

AS-11 (❺)

Define gross pay.

AS-12 (❺)

What is net pay?

_____

_____

_____

_____

AS-13 (❺)

Identify two differences between employees who are paid a salary and employees who are paid hourly.

_____

_____

_____

_____

_____

AS-14 (❺)

Define statutory deductions, and identify the statutory deductions in the United States.

_____

_____

_____

_____

AS-15 (❺)

Define voluntary deductions, and provide three examples of voluntary deductions.

_____

_____

_____

_____

AS-16 (❺)

True or False: The total cost of paying an employee is equal to the amount of gross pay the employee earns.

_____

_____

_____

_____

AS-17 (❼)

What is the current ratio? What is the quick ratio?

_____

_____

_____

AS-18 (❼)

What is the main drawback of the current ratio? And how is it solved?

_____

_____

_____

_____

AS-19 (❽)

What are some of the control procedures that can possibly prevent abuse in the payroll system?

_____

_____

_____

_____

_____

_____

_____

AS-20 (❽)

What are two basic controls related to current liabilities?

_____

_____

_____

_____

AS-21 (❽)

What is the purpose of setting up an imprest bank account for payroll?

_____

_____

_____

_____

Application Questions

AP-1 (❶)

A company has repairs completed on the heating system. The service man hands the accountant an invoice for $1,000 dated May 25, due in one month. Write the journal entry the company must prepare to record this transaction.

Date	Account Title and Explanation	Debit	Credit

AP-2 (❶)

A company uses substantial amounts of utilities (electricity and water) with an average cost of $6,000 per month. They receive and pay the actual bill on the 15th of each month. In January 2014, the company received their bill in the amount of $6,207 for the period December 15 to January 15. The bill was paid right away. Assume the company prepares monthly financial statements.

Required:

    a) Give the journal entry to record the estimate of utilities expense for the period Dec. 16 – 31, 2013.

    b) Record the journal entry required for payment of the bill on January 15, 2014.

Date	Account Title and Explanation	Debit	Credit

AP-3 (❸)

Cervera Company borrowed $100,000 from the local branch on January 1, 2014. The loan is payable in equal installments over five years.

Required:

Write the journal entry to record the loan. How much of the loan would be considered current?

Date	Account Title and Explanation	Debit	Credit

AP-4 (❷)

NOTE PAYABLE

For the Value Received, the undersigned promises to pay to the order of

_____ U. Paymee _____ the sum of

_____ ***** $5,000 and 00/100 Dollars ********************** ($5,000.00) _____

with annual interest of 5% on any unpaid balance. This note shall mature and be payable,

along with accrued interest on:

_____ July 31, 2013 _____

_____ February 1, 2013 _____   _____ A. Notemaker _____

Issue Date   Maker Signature

Answer the following questions regarding the note shown above.

a) Who is the lender?

b) Who is the borrower?

c) When is payment due?

d) When was the note issued?

e) When is interest payable?

f) What amount must the borrower pay to the lender?

Lender	
Borrower	
Payment Due	
Issue Date	
Date Interest Payable	
Payable by Borrower to Lender	

AP-5 (❷)

On May 1, 2013, ACME Bank agreed to lend Mirza Enterprises $100,000. To that effect, Mirza signed a $100,000, 10-month, 12% note. Mirza Enterprises has a year-end of December 31.

Required:
Prepare the journal entry for Mirza Enterprises:

a) On the date the note was signed

b) At year-end

c) On March 1, 2014 when the note is repaid

Date	Account Title and Explanation	Debit	Credit

AP-6 (❷)

On June 15, 2013, Actor Surplus agreed to lend Wei Hong Enterprises $250,000. To that effect, Wei signed a $250,000, 8-month, 10% note. Wei Hong Enterprises has a year-end of November 30.

Required:

Prepare the journal entry for Wei Hong Enterprises:

a) On the date the note was signed

b) At year-end

c) On February 16, 2014 when the note is repaid

Date	Account Title and Explanation	Debit	Credit

AP-7 (❷)

Darren Spoon from Company ABC signed a 7% half-year note payable for $100,000 on November 1, 2013. The note is due with interest on May 1, 2014. Company ABC has a year-end of Dec 31.

Required:

a) journal entry recording receipt of cash

b) journal entry accruing interest at the year-end

c) ultimate payment of the note in the new year

Chapter 13

Date	Account Title and Explanation	Debit	Credit

AP-8 (❶)

The local transit company, in co-operation with local colleges and universities sells transit passes for the semester for $200 each. The passes are only sold prior to the start of the semester, and for the fall semester are good from September 1 to December 31. The transit company sold 1,000 passes on August 1.

Required:
Write the entry for:

a) The sale of the passes

b) The entry to be recorded on September 30.

Date	Account Title and Explanation	Debit	Credit

AP-9 (❻)

Lee-Yau Enterprises sells heavy-duty lawnmower equipment. On May 4, they sold a lawnmower (on account) for $45,000 which included a 4-year unlimited warranty. The corporation's accountant estimates that an amount of $3,000 will be paid out in warranty obligations. The cost of goods sold is $17,000. Assume Lee-Yau uses a perpetual inventory system. Prepare the journal entries relating to these transactions.

Date	Account Title and Explanation	Debit	Credit

AP-10 (❻)

Refer to AP-9 above. Suppose Lee-Yau is required to repair the lawnmower sold (there is a faulty wire) and Lee-Yau spends $500 in cash on October 15 remedying the problem. Record the journal entry for this transaction.

Date	Account Title and Explanation	Debit	Credit

AP-11 (❻)

Los Amigos Manufacturing Ltd. builds and sells cars. They recently sold 150 cars for $30,000 each. The cost to build each car is $7,000. Los Amigos does not sell warranties with the purchase of the car; however, the customer has the option to purchase the warranty separately. Los Amigos sold a 4-year warranty for each car sold. Each warranty sells for $2,000. Prepare the journal entries for the sale of the cars and warranties. Assume the cars were purchased on account and that the warranties were sold for cash. Los Amigos uses a perpetual inventory system.

Date	Account Title and Explanation	Debit	Credit

AP-12 (6)

Refer to AP-11 above. Record the journal entry related to unearned warranty revenue at the end of 1 year from date of sale of the cars.

Date	Account Title and Explanation	Debit	Credit

AP-13 (❼)

Shown below is a partial balance sheet for a manufacturer.

| | As at | |
	March 1, 2013	March 3, 2012
Assets		
Current		
Cash and cash equivalents (note 4)	1,184,398	677,144
Short-term investments (note 4)	420,709	310,082
Accounts receivables	1,249,381	612,811
Inventory (note 5)	396,267	255,907
Other current assets (note 18)	226,599	63,321
	3,477,354	1,919,265
Long-term investments (note 4)	738,889	425,652
Capital assets (note 6)	705,955	487,579
Intangible assets (note 7)	469,988	138,182
Goodwill (note 8)	119,001	118,271
	5,511,187	3,088,949
Liabilities		
Current		
Accounts Payable	271,076	130,270
Accrued Liabilities (notes 13 and 17(c))	690,442	287,629
Income taxes payable (note 9)	475,328	99,958
Deferred revenue	37,236	28,447
Current portion of long-term debt (note 10)	349	271
	1,474,431	546,575

Required:

a) Calculate the current ratio for 2013

b) Calculate the quick ratio for 2013

c) Comment on the current ratio and quick ratio

AP-14 (❷)

On September 1, 2013, Express Inc. purchased a delivery truck from MJ Trucks, costing $80,000. However, due to cash flow problems, Express Inc. is currently unable to make the payment. Therefore, in order to ensure MJ Trucks for the payment, Express Inc. signed a one-year note with 3% interest per annum, to be payable at maturity. Express Inc's year-end is on December 31. Prepare all the necessary journal entries related to the notes payable from the time it is signed to the maturity date.

Date	Account Title and Explanation	Debit	Credit

AP-15 (❷)

On February 1, 2013, Red Ball Inc. received a bank loan for $30,000. The loan bears an interest rate of 2.5% per annum, and will mature in two years. Red Ball Inc. has a December 31 year-end. The partial principal of $15,000 plus interest is payable every January 31. Prepare the necessary journal entries from February 1, 2013 to January 31, 2015.

Date	Account Title and Explanation	Debit	Credit

Date	Account Title and Explanation	Debit	Credit

AP-16 (❻)

Shining Star Corporation produces and sells washing machines, and provides the customers with a one-year warranty on all its products. It is estimated that the company incurs approximately $50 of warranty expense on each machine sold. During the year 2013, the company sold 400 washing machines.

Required:

a) Prepare a journal entry to record the estimated warranty liability.

Date	Account Title and Explanation	Debit	Credit

b) During the year 2014, the company used $5,000 worth of inventory parts and paid $10,000 for maintenance staff salaries. Prepare a journal entry to record this transaction.

Date	Account Title and Explanation	Debit	Credit

c) At the end of year 2014, the company decided to decrease its estimated liability by the remaining balance. Prepare a journal entry to record this transaction.

Date	Account Title and Explanation	Debit	Credit

AP-17 (❻)

Refer to AP-16. Shining Star Corporation also provides its customers with an option to purchase a three-year warranty on machines. On March 1, 2013, Shining Star received $30,000 cash from customers who purchased extended warranty life for their washing machines.

Required:

a) Prepare a journal entry to record the transaction.

Date	Account Title and Explanation	Debit	Credit

b) Prepare the journal entry required on March 1, 2014.

Date	Account Title and Explanation	Debit	Credit

AP-18 (❼)

The Balance Sheet of Pinewood Electronics Inc. for 2012 and 2013 is shown below:

Pinewood Electronics Inc. Balance Sheet As at December 31, 2013		
	2013	**2012**
Current Assets		
Cash	$90,000	$63,000
Accounts Receivable	120,000	107,000
Inventory	212,000	140,000
Short-term Investments	100,000	15,000
Total Current Assets	522,000	325,000
Other Assets	210,000	210,000
Total Assets	$732,000	$535,000
Current Liabilities	90,000	70,000
Long term debt	110,000	40,000
Total Liabilities	200,000	110,000
Shareholders' Equity	532,000	425,000
Total Liabilities and Equity	$732,000	$535,000

Required:

a) Calculate the current ratio for both years.

b) Calculate the quick ratio for both years.

_____

_____

_____

_____

_____

c) In which year does Pinewood Electronics Inc. have a better performance?

_____

_____

AP-19 (❼)

EPZA Enterprises had the following account information for the year 2014:

Accounts Receivable	$200,000
Accounts Payable	80,000
Bonds Payable, due in 10 years	300,000
Cash	100,000
Interest Payable, due in 3 months	10,000
Inventory	400,000
Land	250,000
Notes Payable, due in 6 months	50,000
Prepaid Expenses	40,000

Required:

a) Calculate the current ratio.

_____

_____

_____

_____

b) Calculate the quick ratio.

_____

_____

_____

_____

AP-20 (❶, ❻)

Good Job Ltd. buys and sells home appliances and uses the perpetual inventory system. During the year 2014, the company had the following transactions:

Jan 15	Purchased vacuum cleaners worth $60,000 from V Wholesalers, on account.
Feb 4	Sold vacuum cleaners for $45,000 cash, which includes a 3-year warranty. GoodJob bought these vacuum cleaners for $30,000.
Feb 4	Recorded $15,000 of estimated warranty liability for the year.
Feb 15	Paid the full amount owing to V Wholesalers.
May 8	Received utilities bill for $3,000, to be paid exactly after 15 days.
May 23	Paid the bill from May 8.
Jul 11	Received $42,000 cash for the sale of vacuum cleaners which cost the company $30,000. The delivery is to be made on August 31.
Aug 31	Delivered the vacuum cleaners from July 11.

Required: Prepare journal entries to record the above transactions.

Date	Account Title and Explanation	Debit	Credit

Date	Account Title and Explanation	Debit	Credit

AP-21 (❶, ❷)

Shawn Clarity owns a consulting firm called Clarity Solutions. The firm had the following transactions during the year 2013:

Jan 1	Received $10,000 cash for consulting fees from a client. $5,000 worth of services have been provided, and the rest will be provided on February 16.
Feb 16	Provided the service that was prepaid on January 1.
Mar 11	Purchased office equipment worth $500, on account.
Apr 1	Purchased new office furniture for $7,000 from JJ Store by issuing a 6-month note with 4% interest. Interest and principal payment is due at maturity.
May 11	Paid $500 cash for the purchase of equipment on Mar 11.
Jun 12	Received a $600 invoice for repair services, to be paid after 45 days.
Jul 27	Paid for the repairs from June 12.
Sep 30	Paid the note and interest due from the April 1 purchase.
Oct 19	Received $2,000 cash from a client for consulting services provided.

Required: Prepare journal entries to record the above transactions.

Date	Account Title and Explanation	Debit	Credit

AP-22 (❶, ❸)

During the year 2013, FitnessFirst Ltd. had the following transactions:

Feb 1	Borrowed a five-year loan for $150,000 with an interest rate of 5% per annum. Annual principal payment of $30,000 and interest is payable at the end of January.
Mar 1	Sold 100 three-month club membership to customers for a total $6,000 cash. Regardless of the number of times a customer visits the club, the monthly memberships are not refundable. Record an adjustment at the end of each of the next three months to account for what has been earned.
Apr 14	Purchased treadmills worth $20,000 from RunRun Company, on account.
May 25	Received utilities bill for $1,000, to be paid after 30 days.
Jun 14	Paid $10,000 cash to RunRun Company to reduce the balance owing.
Jun 24	Paid the amount owing from May 25.
Sep 1	Received $10,000 cash from a group of customers for the sale of one-day passes for September 1.

Required: Prepare journal entries to record the above transactions.

Date	Account Title and Explanation	Debit	Credit

Date	Account Title and Explanation	Debit	Credit

AP-23 (❶, ❹)

Porch Living sells outdoor furniture and accessories. They operate in a state which has a 7% sales tax. Porch Living uses the perpetual inventory system. The following transactions occurred during May 2013.

May 5	Sold inventory to a customer for $2,000 plus sales tax on account. The inventory had a cost of $1,200.
May 25	Sold inventory to a customer for $6,000 plus sales tax for cash. The inventory had a cost of $3,200.
May 27	Received the total amount owing from the customer from May 5.
May 31	Prepared the sales tax remittance to the government.

Required: Record the transactions for May 2013.

Date	Account Title and Explanation	Debit	Credit

AP-24 (❶, ❹)

Signet Sales operates in a state where sales tax is applied to all sales at 6%. During July 2013, they had the following sales. Signet Sales uses the perpetual inventory system.

Jul 10   Sold inventory to a customer for $1,000 plus sales tax on account. The inventory had a cost of $700.

Jul 12   Sold inventory to a customer for $4,000 plus sales tax for cash. The inventory had a cost of $2,900.

Required: Record the transactions for July 2013.

Date	Account Title and Explanation	Debit	Credit

AP-25 (❶, ❹)

Toy Retailer operates in a state where sales tax is applied at 5%. During August 2013, they had the following transactions. Toy Retailer uses the perpetual inventory system.

Aug 12   Sold inventory to a customer for $2,000 plus sales tax for cash. The inventory had a cost of $1,100.

Aug 31   Prepared the sale tax remittance to the government.

Required: Record the transactions for August 2013.

Date	Account Title and Explanation	Debit	Credit

AP-26 (❺)

Identify the following items as statutory or voluntary deductions.

Description	Statutory	Voluntary
Federal income taxes		
Dental benefits		
Union dues		
Pensions		
Uniform allowance		
Loan payments		
State unemployment taxes		
Prescription coverage		
Retirement deduction		
Federal insurance contribution		
Purchase of company stock		
Professional dues		
Charitable donations		
Tools and safety apparel		

AP-27 (❺)

The records of Magic Delivery Inc. show the following figures:

Employee Earnings	
Salaries for the month	?
Overtime Pay	2,200
Total	?
Deductions and Net Pay	
Withheld Statutory Deductions	990
Charitable Contributions	?
Medical Insurance	780
Total Deductions	2,270
Net Pay	6,630

Required:
Calculate the missing amounts.

_____

_____

_____

AP-28 (❺)

Answer the following questions related to Saleem Enreprises.

a) On May 31, Saleem Enterprises had gross pay for employees of $42,500. Total employee contribution to the retirement savings plan is $1,700. The appropriate deduction rates are provided. Record the entry for salaries expense on May 31.

- Federal income tax rate is 9%
- State income tax rate is 6%
- FICA is 7.65%
- FUTA is 0.6%
- SUTA is 5.4%

b) Using the data from above and assuming Saleem Enterprises contributes the same amount towards the employee retirement savings plan, prepare the journal entry for the employer's payroll contributions.

c) What is the total amount of cash that Saleem Enterprises will pay? How much will Saleem Enterprises pay for every $1.00 earned by employees?

a)

Date	Account Title and Explanation	Debit	Credit

b)

Date	Account Title and Explanation	Debit	Credit

c) _____

_____

AP-29 (❺)

Rippling Waters rents canoes and other water crafts to campers and hikers. On May 15, 2013, Rippling Waters prepared their semi-monthly payroll for their employees. Payroll information for May 15, 2013 is listed below:

Employee	Total Hours	Hourly Rate	Health Care (employee portion)
M. Swift	87.5	$14.50	$18.00
S. Current	85.5	15.00	20.00
B. Wavey	73.5	13.50	14.00

The employer pays half of the health care premium, and the employees pay the other half. The appropriate deduction rates are provided below:

- Federal income tax rate is 9%
- State income tax rate is 6%
- FICA is 7.65%
- FUTA is 0.6%
- SUTA is 5.4%

a) Prepare the payroll journal entries for May 15, 2013 to record the salaries payable to the employees and accrue the employer contributions:

Date	Account Title and Explanation	Debit	Credit

b) Prepare the entry to pay the employees on May 17, 2013.

Date	Account Title and Explanation	Debit	Credit

c) Prepare the entry to pay the liability to the health insurance company on May 31, 2013.

Date	Account Title and Explanation	Debit	Credit

d) Prepare the entry to pay the liabilities to the government on June 15, 2013:

Date	Account Title and Explanation	Debit	Credit

AP- 30 (❺)

Answer the following questions related to Morales Inc.

a) On September 30, Morales Inc. had gross pay for employees of $37,000.00. Withholdings for employees are $1,367.00 for state income taxes, $2,960.00 for federal income taxes,$2,830.50 for FICA, $1,300.00 for the retirement savings plan and $400.00 for charitable donations. Record the entry for wage expense on September 30.

b) Using the data from Part (a) and assuming Morales Inc. does not contribute towards the employee retirement savings plan, prepare the journal entry for the employer's taxes and benefit costs. Assume FUTA is $222.00 and SUTA is $1,998.00.

c) What is the total amount of cash that Morales Inc. will pay? How much will Morales Inc. pay for every $1.00 earned by employees?

a)

Date	Account Title and Explanation	Debit	Credit

b)

Date	Account Title and Explanation	Debit	Credit

c) _____

_____

AP- 31 (❺)

Tristan Industries has the following numbers for their payroll for November 15.

- Gross pay is $42,000
- Federal income tax is $3,780
- State income tax is $2,100
- FICA is $3,213
- FUTA is $252
- SUTA is $2,268

Prepare the journal entry to accrue the employee's payroll and the employer benefits expense on November 15.

Date	Account Title and Explanation	Debit	Credit

AP- 32 (5)

Ledger Services has prepared their weekly payroll for the week ending October 19. Gross pay is $25,000. Employees have a health plan that costs $200 per week. This cost is shared equally between the employees and the employer. Using the deduction rates provided below, prepare the journal entries to record the salaries payable to the employees and to accrue the employer contributions.

- Federal income tax rate is 9%
- State income tax rate is 5%
- FICA is 7.65%
- FUTA is 0.6%
- SUTA is 5.4%

Date	Account Title and Explanation	Debit	Credit

Case Study

CS-1 (❾)

- Locate the financial statements of a company with total assets greater than $1 billion.
- State the name of the company
- Note the date of the financial statements
- Locate the liabilities section
    - What is the amount of current liabilities?
    - What is the amount of long-term liabilities?
    - What is the amount of current assets?
    - What is the amount of owner's equity?
    - Calculate the ratio of total liabilities to owners' equity
    - Does the company have any shareholder loans?
- Calculate the current ratio
- Calculate the quick ratio
- Comment on the current and quick ratios
- Does the company have any contingencies?
- Review the notes to the financial statements. Summarize any notes related to liabilities.

_____

_____

_____

_____

_____

_____

_____

_____

_____

_____

_____

_____

_____

_____

Critical Thinking

CT-1 (❽)

Contingent liabilities arise when the payment of a liability depends on uncertain future events, such as the result of a lawsuit.

Current accounting practice requires that when a contingent liability is likely, and the amount can be reasonably estimated, the amount must be accrued on the balance sheet.

Is this practice reasonable, (in light of the fact that the liability is not definite), and only estimates are used? Does this practice mislead owners regarding the actual state of affairs surrounding liabilities? Discuss.

_____

_____

_____

_____

_____

_____

_____

_____

_____

_____

Notes

Chapter 14

LONG-TERM LIABILITIES

———————————— **Assessment Questions** ————————————

AS-1 (❶)

Name the typical forms of long-term debt.

_____

_____

_____

AS-2 (❶)

What is a bond?

_____

_____

_____

AS-3 (❹)

An investor pays $83,333 for a bond, but will receive $100,000 when the bond matures. Has the investor bought the bond at a discount or at a premium?

_____

_____

_____

AS-4 (❸, ❹)

Bonds can be issued at different prices relative to their face value. Name the three types of bonds relative to face value.

_____

_____

_____

AS-5 (❹)

When would a bond be issued at a discount? At a premium?

_____

_____

_____

_____

AS-6 (❹)

A $100,000 bond is issued for $110,000. Is the current market interest rate for bonds above or below the rate stated in the bond contract?

_____

_____

_____

AS-7 (❹, ❺)

What amount remains in the discount on bond amortized account or premium on bonds account related to a bond on the maturity date of the bond?

_____

_____

_____

AS-8 (❻)

What is generally considered the maximum acceptable debt-to-total assets ratio? Why?

_____

_____

_____

_____

_____

AS-9 (❶)

Funds raised from long-term debt are usually used for what kind of investments?

_____

_____

_____

_____

_____

_____

AS-10 (❶)

What is the difference between bonds and stock?

_____

_____

_____

_____

_____

_____

AS-11 (❼)

What are some the controls related to balance sheet?

_____

_____

_____

_____

_____

_____

AS-12 (❼)

What is off-balance sheet financing? Provide two or three examples.

_____

_____

_____

_____

_____

_____

_____

Application Questions

AP-1 (❸)

A company issued $500,000 of bonds at par on July 1, 2013. Write the journal entry to record the transaction.

Date	Account Title and Explanation	Debit	Credit

AP-2 (❹)

A company issued $500,000 of bonds at a discount of 5% on February 1, 2013. Write the journal entry to record the transaction.

Date	Account Title and Explanation	Debit	Credit

AP-3 (❹)

A company issued $500,000 of bonds at a premium of 1% on August 1, 2013. Write the journal entry to record the transaction.

Date	Account Title and Explanation	Debit	Credit

AP-4 (❹, ❺)

A company is issuing $300,000 worth of 5-year bonds on January 1, 2013, bearing an interest rate of 4%, payable annually. Assume that the current market rate of interest is 5%.

a) Will the bond be issued at a discount or at a premium?

b) Calculate the value of the resulting discount or premium.

c) Record the journal entry to reflect the sale of bonds and the appropriate discount or premium.

Note that the present value factor for the principal is 0.7835 (5%, 5-years) and that the present value factor for the recurring interest payments is 4.3295 (5%, 5-years).

a)

_____

_____

_____

b)

_____

_____

_____

_____

_____

c)

Date	Account Title and Explanation	Debit	Credit

AP-5 (❹, ❺)

Refer to AP-4. Assuming interest is paid annually on December 31, write the journal entry to record payment of interest.

Date	Account Title and Explanation	Debit	Credit

_____

_____

AP-6 (❹, ❺)

On January 1, 2013, Metro Inc. issued a 5-year bond with a par value of $700,000. The bond bears an interest rate of 6% per annum, with the interest paid semi-annually. On January 1, 2013, the market interest rate was 8%.

Required:

a) Calculate the amount of a bond discount or a bond premium.

_____

_____

_____

_____

_____

b) Prepare the journal entry to record the sale of bond.

Date	Account Title and Explanation	Debit	Credit

AP-7 (❷)

On April 1, 2013, Dixon Company issued $300,000 worth of bonds, with the interest rate of 12% per annum. The bonds will mature on March 31, 2020. Interest will be paid semi-annually on September 30 and March 31. The company has a December 31 year-end.

Required: Calculate the accrued interest payable on December 31, 2014.

_____

_____

AP-8 (❷, ❹)

On July 1, 2013, Marky Corporation issued $1,500,000 worth of bonds with 9% interest rate. Interest is payable semi-annually on June 30 and December 31. The bonds mature on June 30, 2020. At the time of the bond issuance, the market interest rate was 8%. The company has a March 31 year-end. Any discount or premium resulting from the sale of the bonds will be amortized using the straight-line amortization method.

Required:

a) Calculate the total price of the bonds on the issue date and determine the amount of a bond discount or a bond premium.

_____

_____

_____

_____

b) Prepare a journal entry to record the issuance of the bond and the first interest payment.

Date	Account Title and Explanation	Debit	Credit

c) Prepare the journal entry required on March 31, 2014.

Date	Account Title and Explanation	Debit	Credit

d) Prepare the journal entry required on June 30, 2014.

Date	Account Title and Explanation	Debit	Credit

AP-9 (❹)

Refer to AP-8. Calculate the book value (carrying amount) of bonds payable at December 31, 2015. Note: round your answer to the nearest whole number in every step.

_____

_____

_____

_____

AP-10 (❹)

On July 1, 2013, Dilly Company received $516,440 cash for the sale of a 10-year bond with the face value of $500,000. The bond bears an interest rate of 12%, to be paid semi-annually. At the time of the sale, the market interest rate was 10%.

Required: Prepare a journal entry to record the issuance of bond.

Date	Account Title and Explanation	Debit	Credit

AP-11 (❹, ❺)

On May 1, 2013, Ezzy Company issued a 6-year bond worth $400,000 with an interest rate of 8% per annum. Interest is to be paid semi-annually on October 31 and April 30. At the time of the issuance, the market interest rate was 6%. Ezzy Company amortizes any premium or discount using the straight-line method.

Required: Calculate the bond issue price and the resulting premium or discount.

_____

_____

_____

_____

AP-12 (❹)

Refer to AP-11. Prepare journal entries to record the following bonds payable transactions:

Note: round your answer to the nearest whole number in every step.

a. Issuance of bonds on May 1, 2013.
b. Payment of interest and amortization of premium on October 31, 2013.
c. Accrual of interest and amortization of premium on December 31, 2013, which is the company's year-end.
d. Payment of interest and amortization of premium on April 30, 2014.
e. Redemption of the bond at fair value on May 1, 2018 (1 year before maturity).

Date	Account Title and Explanation	Debit	Credit

Date	Account Title and Explanation	Debit	Credit

AP-13 (❷, ❹)

A company issued $1,200,000 worth of 15-year bonds with a 3% interest rate. Interest is to be paid annually.

Required: Calculate the bond issue price under each market interest rate:

Market Interest Rate	Bond Price
2%	
3%	
4%	

_____

_____

_____

_____

_____

_____

_____

_____

_____

_____

_____

_____

_____

AP-14 (❹)

Refer to AP-13. For each market condition, prepare a journal entry to record the bond issuance.

Market Interest Rate - 2%

Date	Account Title and Explanation	Debit	Credit

Market Interest Rate - 3%

Date	Account Title and Explanation	Debit	Credit

Market Interest Rate - 4%

Date	Account Title and Explanation	Debit	Credit

AP-15 (❹, ❺)

On April 30, year 1, a company issued $600,000 worth of 4% bonds. The term of the bonds is 10 years, with interest payable semi-annually on October 31st and April 30th. The year-end of the company is November 30. Record the journal entries related to interest for year 1, and year 2. Note that interest must be accrued at the end of each year.

Date	Account Title and Explanation	Debit	Credit

Date	Account Title and Explanation	Debit	Credit

AP-16 (❹, ❺)

Sam's Construction is a construction company (with a December 31 year-end) that is planning to expand its facilities by constructing a new building, and acquiring new equipment. In order to complete this project, the company has decided to issue $100,000 worth of 10-year bonds at 5% on March 1, 2013. The interest payment is made semi-annually on September 1 and March 1. Just as the company completes all the necessary contracts, and is ready to issue the bonds, the market rate increases to 6%, resulting in a price of $92,640 for these bonds.

Note: The premium/discount is amortized using the straight-line method.

a) Are these bonds issued at a discount or at a premium? Prepare the journal entry for the issuance of bonds on March 1, 2013.

b) Prepare the journal entry for the first payment of interest on September 1, 2013.

c) Prepare the adjusting entry on December 31, 2013.

a)

Date	Account Title and Explanation	Debit	Credit

b)

Date	Account Title and Explanation	Debit	Credit

c)

Date	Account Title and Explanation	Debit	Credit

AP-17 (❹, ❺)

Burroughs Corporation (with a December 31 year-end) issued $450,000, 9.5% bonds due in 8 years on May 1, 2013. Interest is paid semi-annually on November 1 and May 1 of each year. On the issuance date, the market rate of interest was 8.5%, resulting in a price of $475,000 for these bonds.

Note: The premium/discount is amortized using the straight-line method.

a) Is this bond issued at a discount or at a premium? Prepare the journal entry on May 1, 2013, to issue the bonds.

b) Prepare the journal entry on November 1, 2013, to record the first interest payment and the amortization of the premium/discount.

c) Prepare the adjusting entry on December 31, 2013.

d) Show the balance sheet presentation of Bonds Payable and related accounts as at December 31, 2013.

a)

Date	Account Title and Explanation	Debit	Credit

b)

Date	Account Title and Explanation	Debit	Credit

c)

Date	Account Title and Explanation	Debit	Credit

d)

_____

_____

_____

_____

_____

AP-18 (❷, ❹)

Mustafa has recently graduated from an Aerospace Engineering program and is training to become an astronaut. Part of the training program includes a basic course in accounting and finance (it is important for astronauts to be well-rounded). Mustafa is posed with the following question on his exam:

MT Biotech has issued $3,500,000, 5% callable bonds due in 12 years. At the time of issue the market interest rate is 6% (interest is due annually). Calculate the discount at which the bonds were issued.

The following present value factors may be of use to you:

> **Single:**
>
> 0.5568 (5%, 12 years)
>
> 0.4970 (6%, 12 years)
>
> **Annuity:**
>
> 8.8633 (5%, 12 years)
>
> 8.3838 (6%, 12 years)

Unfortunately, Mustafa spent the previous day in the centrifuge (G-force training) and, as a result, he is finding it difficult to concentrate. Please help Mustafa solve this problem.

_____

_____

_____

_____

_____

_____

_____

_____

_____

_____

AP-19 (❻)

The balance sheet of Benevolent Company is presented below:

Benevolent Company Balance Sheet December 31, 2013		
	2013	**2012**
Cash	$106,000	$82,000
Accounts Receivable	566,000	444,000
Inventories	320,000	300,000
Total Current Assets	992,000	826,000
Property and equipment,Net of Depreciation	740,000	550,000
Patents	26,000	26,000
Other Intangible Assets	14,000	14,000
Total Assets	**$1,772,000**	**$1,416,000**
Accounts Payable	$170,000	$100,000
Income Tax Payable	32,000	20,000
Miscellaneous Accrued Payables	38,000	44,000
Total Current Liabilities	240,000	164,000
Bonds Payable	300,000	300,000
Total Liabilities	540,000	464,000
Stockholders' Equity		
Common Stock	512,000	512,000
Retained Earnings	720,000	440,000
Total Stockholders' Equity	1,232,000	952,000
Total Liabilities and Stockholders' Equity	**$1,772,000**	**$1,416,000**

Required:

a) Calculate the debt-to-total assets ratio.

_____

_____

_____

_____

_____

b) In which year does the company have a better debt-to-total assets ratio?

_____

_____

_____

c) Calculate the debt-to-equity ratio.

_____

_____

_____

_____

d) In which year does the company have a better debt-to-total equity ratio?

_____

_____

_____

_____

_____

_____

AP-20 (❻)

Invention4U Inc. is a medium-sized company which is planning to grow internationally; therefore, it requires some financing from the bank. The bank asked for the current period's audited financial statements of the company and is interested in the company's debt-to-total assets and debt-to-equity ratios. Here is the summary of what the bank needs in order to calculate the ratios.

Total Current Assets	$584,000
Total Non-Current Assets	300,000
Total Current Liabilities	404,000
Total Non-Current Liabilities	100,000

Required: Calculate the required ratios by the bank and conclude if the bank should provide Invention4U with the financing.

_____

_____

_____

_____

_____

_____

_____

_____

_____

_____

_____

_____

_____

Case Study

CS-1 (❶, ❼)

Research and describe the role of credit rating agencies in the bond market.

Name three major credit rating agencies.

Describe and list the major categories of credit ratings for these agencies.

_____

_____

_____

_____

_____

_____

_____

_____

_____

_____

_____

_____

_____

_____

_____

_____

_____

_____

_____

Critical Thinking

CT-1 (❷, ❹)

Companies can choose to record interest expense on bonds using the straight-line method, or by using a method that incorporates the time value of money. Which method do you recommend that a company use? Support your answer.

_____

_____

_____

_____

_____

_____

_____

_____

_____

_____

_____

_____

_____

_____

_____

_____

_____

_____

_____

Notes

Chapter 15

PARTNERSHIPS

Assessment Questions

AS-1 (❶)

Define a partnership.

_____

_____

_____

AS-2 (❷)

Compare and contrast characteristics of proprietorships and partnerships.

Characteristic	Proprietorship	Partnership

AS-3 (❹)

List the different ways in which partnership earnings may be divided.

_____

_____

_____

_____

_____

_____

AS-4 (❷)

What are the advantages of organizing a business as a partnership over a proprietorship?

_____

_____

_____

_____

AS-5 (❹)

How is the division of partnership earnings decided?

_____

_____

_____

_____

_____

AS-6 (❹)

What methods may partners choose to pay themselves, other than straight division of profits?

_____

_____

_____

_____

AS-7 (❹)

Explain the closing of the income summary account for partnerships.

_____

_____

_____

_____

AS-8 (❹)

During the year, partners may withdraw cash or other assets. What account is used to accumulate these withdrawals?

_____

_____

_____

_____

AS-9 (❹)

What happens to partners' drawings at year end?

_____

_____

_____

AS-10 (❺)

What happens in a partnership when a partner leaves, or another is added?

_____

_____

_____

AS-11 (❺)

True or False. If a partner is added, a new set of books need to be opened.

_____

_____

_____

_____

AS-12 (❻)

In liquidating a partnership, what happens if assets are sold for amounts other than their book values?

_____

_____

_____

_____

Application Questions

AP-1 (❸)

Chandra Heesch and Allie Owenby have decided to form a partnership on January 1, 2013. Each partner has agreed to contribute $10,000. Write the journal entry to record the formation of the partnership.

Date	Account Title and Explanation	Debit	Credit

AP-2 (❸)

Ted Coverdale and Julio Kadlec are setting up a new partnership on March 10, 2013. Ted will contribute a warehouse and land worth a combined $1,000,000. Market value of the warehouse is $300,000. Julio will contribute $1,000,000 in cash. Write the journal entry to record the contributions to the partnership.

Date	Account Title and Explanation	Debit	Credit

AP-3 (❹)

Selena Hegarty, Cody Debruyn and Lenore Raap operate their business as a partnership. According to their partnership agreement, Selena and Lenore split 51% of the profits equally. The remainder of the profits goes to Cody. Record the entry for the division of profits of $100,000 on December 31, 2013. Assume that revenues and expenses have already been closed to the income summary account.

Date	Account Title and Explanation	Debit	Credit

AP-4 (4)

Mallory Longshore, Lakisha Laffey and Avis Hemsley set up a partnership at the beginning of 2013. Mallory contributed $10,000 in cash. Lakisha contributed a van worth $20,000. Avis contributed equipment worth $15,000. The partnership made $9,000 net income for the year. According to the partnership agreement, profits are divided in the ratio of their initial contributions. Record the entry for the division of the profits on December 31, 2013. Assume that revenues and expenses have already been closed to the income summary account.

Date	Account Title and Explanation	Debit	Credit

AP-5 (4)

Refer to AP-4. Assume that the partnership recorded a loss of $4,500. Record the entry for the division of the loss. Assume that revenues and expenses have already been closed to the income summary account.

Date	Account Title and Explanation	Debit	Credit

AP-6 (4)

Tanisha Vanscyoc and Kurt Vicini operate a partnership that produces custom-made furniture. On April 12, Tanisha withdrew $50,000 in cash. On April 15, Kurt removed a sofa and chairs worth $30,000 for use in his own home. Write the journal entry to record these transactions.

Date	Account Title and Explanation	Debit	Credit

AP-7 (❹)

Refer to AP-6. Write the journal entry to close the Drawings accounts on December 31.

Date	Account Title and Explanation	Debit	Credit

AP-8 (❹)

Noemi Loop, Lilia Hopkin and Guy Scoggin perform in a band operating as a partnership. According to the partnership agreement, Noemi receives a salary of $22,000, Lilia receives a salary of $30,000, and Guy a salary of $28,000. They are also to receive nominal interest of 5% on the capital at the end of the preceding year (Noemi's capital - $1,000, Lilia's capital - $10,000, Guy's capital - $20,000). The remainder is divided equally. During the year partners withdrew $22,000 each as an advance to their share of partnership earnings. The band made $100,000 after paying all other expenses.

Required: Prepare a schedule showing changes in the partners' capital during the year.

_____

_____

_____

_____

_____

_____

_____

_____

AP-9 (❹)

Refer to AP-8. Assume that the net income remaining is distributed on the ratio of the opening balance of capital. Prepare the schedule showing the changes in capital.

_____

_____

_____

_____

_____

_____

_____

_____

AP-10 (❹)

Refer to AP-9. Prepare the journal entry to recording the distribution of net income and close the drawings accounts on December 31. Assume that revenues and expenses have already been closed to the income summary account.

Date	Account Title and Explanation	Debit	Credit

AP-11 (❸)

Nataliya, Sam and Seechi have decided to form a partnership and open a small convenience store. All the partners are investing $10,000 cash, while Nataliya has invested additional equipment worth $5,000.

Required:

a) Calculate the total contribution of each partner.

	Nataliya	Sam	Seechi

b) Prepare a journal entry to set up the partnership, and to record the additional investment.

Date	Account Title and Explanation	Debit	Credit

AP-12 (❸)

Consider the following table:

Biyanka Lee	
Cash	$14,000
Accounts Receivable	5,000
Allowance for Doubtful Accounts	600
Note Payable	2,500

Bob Fire	
Cash	$55,000
Equipment	11,000
Accumulated Depreciation	1,000
Bank Loan	8,000

Larry Ding	
Cash	$28,000
Building	240,000

Freeda Red	
Cash	$60,000

Note: An independent appraiser determined that the allowance for doubtful accounts should be $600. All other assets are recorded at their fair market values.

Required: When a partnership is formed, show the accounts and balances that will be listed in the company's books.

ACCOUNTS	DR	CR
Cash		
Accounts Receivable		
Allowance for Doubtful Accounts		
Equipment		
Accumulated Depreciation		
Building		
Bank Loan		
Note Payable		
Biyanka Lee, Capital		
Bob Fire, Capital		
Larry Ding, Capital		
Freeda Red, Capital		
Total		

AP-13 (❹)

Refer to AP-12. Earnings are equally divided among the partners. During the year 2013, the company earned a net income of $360,000. Prepare a journal entry to close the income summary account at year-end.

Date	Account Title and Explanation	Debit	Credit

AP-14 (❹)

Refer to AP-12. Assume that at the beginning of the year, it was decided that Biyanka Lee will receive 10%, Bob Fire will receive 25%, Larry Ding will receive 40%, and Freeda Red will receive 25% of the earnings. During the year 2014, the company had a net loss of $15,000. Prepare a journal entry to close the income summary account at year-end.

Date	Account Title and Explanation	Debit	Credit

AP-15 (❹)

Refer to AP-12. Assume that at the beginning of the year, it was decided that the earnings will be divided based on each partner's capital contribution. During the year 2015, the company earned a net income of $86,000. Prepare a journal entry to close the income summary account at year-end.

Date	Account Title and Explanation	Debit	Credit

AP-16 (❹)

A. Anna, P. Peter and J. Jackson formed a partnership in the year 2013. In 2015, the beginning capital balance of each partner was $25,000, $35,000 and $30,000 respectively. During the year 2015, the company earned a net income of $63,000, and A. Anna withdrew $25,000 while P. Peter and J. Jackson withdrew $40,000 and $35,000 respectively.

Required:

a) Calculate the amount of net income each partner will receive if:

(i)   the earnings are divided equally.
(ii) A. Anna receives 30%, P. Peter receives 40%, and J. Jackson receives 30% of the earnings.
(iii) the earnings are divided based on the partner's capital balance at the beginning of the year.

	(i)	(ii)	(iii)
A. Anna			
P. Peter			
J. Jackson			

b) Calculate the ending capital balance of each partner, assuming that method (ii) is used to divide earnings.

	A. Anna	P. Peter	J. Jackson
Beginning Capital Balance			
Add: Additional contribution			
Share of net income			
Subtotal			
Less: Drawings			
Ending Capital Balance			

AP-17 (❹)

Refer to AP-16. During the year 2016, it is decided that A. Anna, P. Peter and J. Jackson will receive a salary of $40,000, $55,000 and $45,000 respectively. The remaining earnings will be divided among each partner equally.

Required:

a) During the year 2016, the company earned a net income of $149,000. Calculate the amount of net income that each partner will receive.

	Total	A. Anna	P. Peter	J. Jackson
Net Income				
Salary				
Remainder				
Total share				

b) During the year 2016, A. Anna, P. Peter and J. Jackson withdrew $10,000, $15,000 and $12,000 respectively. Prepare the journal entries to record the drawings.

Date	Account Title and Explanation	Debit	Credit

c) Calculate the ending capital balance of each partner.

_____

_____

_____

_____

_____

AP-18 (❹)

Brian, Miley and Adriana operate a business under partnership. It was decided that Brian, Miley and Adriana will receive a salary of $65,000, $70,000 and $55,000 respectively. The remaining earnings will be equally divided among the partners. During the year 2013, the company made a net income of $160,000. Calculate the amount of net income each partner will receive.

	Total	Brian	Miley	Adriana

AP-19 (❺)

Sylvia, Sonia and Sana are all partners who operate a beauty salon called S3 Beauty. On January 1, 2013, Sylvia, Sonia and Sana had a capital balance of $320,000, $215,000 and $360,000 respectively. Due to the successful growth of the business, S3 Beauty have agreed to add an additional partner, Sharon. Sharon will be investing $300,000 cash in the business.

Required:

a) Calculate the new capital balance for each partner after Sharon has been added to the partnership.

	Sylvia	Sonia	Sana	Sharon	Total

b) Prepare the journal entry to record the admission of Sharon.

Date	Account Title and Explanation	Debit	Credit

AP-20 (❺)

Refer to AP-19. S3 Beauty has made a good reputation for itself in the market and has a large base of loyal customers. Since the company has a higher market value, Sharon has agreed to invest $390,000 into the business and receive a $300,000 share of the business' book value. Any difference is split equally among the original partners.

Required:

a) Calculate the new capital balance for each partner after Sharon has been added to the partnership.

	Sylvia	Sonia	Sana	Sharon	Total

b) Prepare the journal entry to record the admission of Sharon.

Date	Account Title and Explanation	Debit	Credit

AP-21 (❺)

Refer to AP-19. S3 Beauty has made a good reputation for itself in the market and has a large base of loyal customers. Since a partnership with Sharon will be very beneficial for S3 Beauty, S3 Beauty will provide Sharon $300,000 share of the business' book value for $285,000 investment. Any difference is split equally among the original partners.

Required:

a) Calculate the new capital balance for each partner after Sharon has been added to the partnership.

	Sylvia	Sonia	Sana	Sharon	Total

b) Prepare the journal entry to record the admission of Sharon.

Date	Account Title and Explanation	Debit	Credit

AP-22 (❺)

Jack, John, and Joe have been operating a business as a partnership for several years. On January 1, 2013, Jack, John and Joe had a capital balance of $255,000, $180,000 and $132,000 respectively. However, due to a business conflict, Joe decided to withdraw from the partnership.

Required:

a) Calculate the new capital balance for each partner after the withdrawal of Joe.

	Jack	John	Joe	Total

b) Prepare the journal entry to record the withdrawal of Joe

Date	Account Title and Explanation	Debit	Credit

AP-23 (❺)

Refer to AP-22. After Joe has left, Jack and John added Jim to the partnership. A partnership with Jim would considerably increase the value of the business. Therefore, Jim will receive $100,000 share of the business' book value for $80,000 investment.

Required:

a) Calculate the new capital balance for each partner after Joe has been withdrawn and Jim has been added to the partnership.

	Jack	John	Jim	Total

b) Prepare the journal entry to record the admission of Jim.

Date	Account Title and Explanation	Debit	Credit

c) Assume, instead, that Jim will receive a $100,000 share of the business' book value for $130,000 investment. Calculate the new capital balance for each partner after Joe has been withdrawn and Jim has been added to the partnership.

	Jack	John	Jim	Total

d) Prepare the journal entry to record the admission of Jim.

Date	Account Title and Explanation	Debit	Credit

e) Assume, instead, that Jim will purchase the full investment (equity) held by Joe, and 20% of the investment (equity) held by Jack. Calculate the new capital balance for each partner.

	Jack	John	Joe	Jim	Total

f) Prepare the journal entry to record the admission of Jim and the withdrawal of Joe.

Date	Account Title and Explanation	Debit	Credit

AP-24 (❻)

Patricia, Karla, and Nathan operated a small law firm under a partnership. However, due to some internal conflicts, all the partners have agreed to end the partnership. The following items remained in the balance sheet after all the assets have been liquidated.

Cash	$450,000
Capital - Patricia	188,000
Capital - Karla	82,000
Capital - Nathan	210,000

Required: Prepare the journal entries to allocate any profit or loss on sale of assets, and to record cash distribution.

Date	Account Title and Explanation	Debit	Credit

AP-25 (❸, ❹, ❺)

On January 1, 2014, Bob, Mike and Amy decided to form a partnership to start a small public accounting firm. Bob, Mike and Amy have invested $64,000, $55,000 and $80,000 respectively. Mike has also invested a piece of equipment that is worth $2,000. During the first year of operations in 2014, the firm earned a net income of $280,000. All earnings are to be divided according to the initial capital contribution of each partner. In addition, Bob and Amy withdrew $5,000 and $7,000 cash from the business. During the second year of operations in 2015, a new partner (Mia) was added to the firm. Mia purchased 80% of Amy's investment and 10% of Mike's investment (equity) in the business.

Required:

a) Assume year-end is on December 31, prepare the journal entries to set up the partnership, record the drawings, and distribute the income. Also, prepare any additional closing or adjusting entries.

Date	Account Title and Explanation	Debit	Credit

b) Prepare the journal entry to record the admission of Mia.

Date	Account Title and Explanation	Debit	Credit

c) Calculate the ending capital balance of each partner. Assume no income for the second year.

	Bob	Mike	Amy	Mia

AP-26 (❻)

LIN partnership has to be terminated due to the death of one of the partners. After the liquidation, the following items remained in the balance sheet.

LIN Partnership Balance Sheet As at March 31, 2014	
Cash	**$150,000**
Partners' Equity	
Partner A	30,000
Partner B	55,000
Partner C	20,000
Partner D	45,000
Total	**$150,000**

Required: Prepare the journal entries to record cash distribution. Assume that the assets were sold at their book value.

Date	Account Title and Explanation	Debit	Credit

AP-27 (❻)

20 years ago, three brothers formed a partnership which now has to end due to their increasing conflicts. Before the liquidation, the partnership had assets valued at $500,000 and liabilities valued at $300,000; also partners' equity balances were $50,000 for Brother A, $70,000 for Brother B and $80,000 for Brother C. The brothers sold the net assets for $230,000. Note that any profit or loss would be distributed equally among the partners according to the terms of their partnership agreement. Prepare the journal entries for:

a) The sale of net assets.
b) The allocation of the gain or loss on the sale of net assets.
c) The cash distribution to the three brothers.

Date	Account Title and Explanation	Debit	Credit

Case Study

CS-1 (❹)

For the year ended December 31, 2014, a partnership had sales of $500,000 and expenses of $400,000 before payment of partners' salaries, interest on capital, and charges for equipment.

There are two partners who own the business. Each partner will receive earnings based on four factors. Each partner will receive a salary of $40,000. Each partner will receive interest on capital contributions which amounts to $2,000 for Partner A, and $1,000 for Partner B. Partner B puts equipment into the business and receives $2,000 "rent" on the equipment each year. Remaining profits are divided equally. The opening balances of capital were $200,000 for Partner A and $100,000 for Partner B.

During the year, the partners withdrew $30,000 as advances on their yearly salary.

Required:

a) Calculate the net income of the partnership.

b) Show the calculation of the share of income to be distributed to each partner.

c) Prepare journal entries to record the distribution of income, drawings, and closing entries.

d) Explain why salaries, interest and rental of equipment are not included in the closing entries.

e) Prepare the equity section of the statement of financial position.

a)

_____

_____

_____

b)

_____

_____

_____

_____

_____

_____

c)

Date	Account Title and Explanation	Debit	Credit

d)

_____

_____

_____

_____

e)

_____

_____

_____

_____

Critical Thinking

CT-1 (❶, ❸)

Sometimes a person simply wants to invest in a business as an owner, rather than actively participate in the business. This is simple when the business is organized as a corporation. By definition, a proprietorship has only one owner. If the investor participates in a partnership, the investor assumes unlimited liability for the partnership.

Is it wise to invest in a partnership if one does not want to actively participate in the partnership?

Are there any steps an investor could take to limit their liability? Discuss.

_____

_____

_____

_____

_____

_____

_____

_____

_____

_____

_____

_____

_____

_____

_____

_____

_____

_____

Chapter 16

CORPORATIONS: CONTRIBUTED CAPITAL AND DIVIDENDS
Assessment Questions

AS-1 (❶, ❷)

List four advantages and two disadvantages of the corporate form of ownership.

Advantages:

_____

_____

_____

_____

_____

_____

_____

_____

_____

_____

_____

_____

_____

_____

_____

_____

Disadvantages

_____

_____

_____

_____

_____

_____

_____

_____

_____

_____

AS-2 (❸)

Which portion of the equity section of a set of corporate financial statements relates to money invested by the owners? Which relates to accumulated earnings?

_____

_____

_____

AS-3 (❸)

You are preparing the financial statements for a corporation. You must disclose the number of shares authorized. Where would you find the number of shares authorized?

_____

_____

_____

AS-4 (❸)

What is meant by "outstanding shares"?

_____

_____

_____

AS-5 (❸)

Define "retained earnings".

_____

_____

_____

AS-6 (❹)

What may stock be issued for?

_____

_____

_____

AS-7 (❺)

What is the main difference between common and preferred stock?

_____

_____

_____

_____

_____

_____

AS-8 (❺)

List the usual characteristics of common stock.

_____

_____

_____

_____

_____

_____

_____

AS-9 (❺)

List the usual characteristics of preferred stock.

_____

_____

_____

_____

AS-10 (❻)

List and describe the three important dates associated with accounting for dividends.

_____

_____

_____

_____

_____

_____

AS-11 (⑥)

Who decides the amount of a dividend to be paid to stockholders? Discuss.

_____

_____

_____

_____

Application Questions

AP-1 (❹)

Earnestine, Kepplinger & Co. issued 10,000 common shares for $100,000 on May 1, 2013. Write the journal entry to record the transaction.

Date	Account Title and Explanation	Debit	Credit

AP-2 (❹)

Refer to AP-1. In addition to stock issued for cash on May 1, 2013, Earnestine, Kepplinger & Co. issued an additional 10,000 common shares in exchange for land and a building. The land was valued at $60,000 and the building valued at $50,000. Record the transaction.

Date	Account Title and Explanation	Debit	Credit

AP-3 (❹)

The lawyer that handled the stock issue discussed in AP-1 and AP-2 above has sent a bill for $5,000. The lawyer has agreed to accept 500 common shares instead of cash. Record the transaction on May 10, 2013.

Date	Account Title and Explanation	Debit	Credit

AP-4 (❺)

Liang Inc. is authorized to issue an unlimited number of $8 par value common shares. Suppose 3,000 of these shares are sold for $14 each. Record the entry to record the issuance.

Date	Account Title and Explanation	Debit	Credit

AP-5 (⑥)

On July 1st, Jonus Enterprises declares a dividend of $5,000 to stockholders on record on July 4th. Record the journal entry associated with this transaction.

Date	Account Title and Explanation	Debit	Credit

AP-6 (⑥)

Using the facts from AP-5, record the journal entry when Jonus Enterprises pays out the dividend on August 15th.

Date	Account Title and Explanation	Debit	Credit

AP-7 (⑥)

On November 1st, 2013, Mistry Inc. declared $850,000 of dividends payable to stockholders on January 15, 2014. Outstanding are 220,000 common shares and 30,000, $4 cumulative preferred shares. Dividends were last paid in 2009. Calculate how much Mistry Inc. owes the preferred stockholders. Write the journal entry to record the declaration and subsequent payout of the dividends.

Date	Account Title and Explanation	Debit	Credit

AP-8 (❻)

On December 1st, 2013, Fickle Feline Inc. (a distributor of cat products) declared $200,000 of dividends payable to stockholders on January 3, 2014. There are 20,000 common shares and 10,000, $0.50 cumulative preferred shares. Dividends were last paid in 2010. Calculate how much Fickle Feline Inc. owes the preferred stockholders. Write the journal entry to record the declaration and subsequent payout of the dividends.

_____

_____

_____

_____

Date	Account Title and Explanation	Debit	Credit

AP-9 (❼)

Bishop Lutz Hockey Paraphernalia Ltd has 50,000 common shares issued. On January 1st, 2013, the organization declared a 25% stock dividend. Prepare the journal entry to record the declaration and distribution (on February 1st, 2013) of the dividend. The current market price per share is $15.

Date	Account Title and Explanation	Debit	Credit

AP-10 (❼)

Silang Vayman Ltd is a travel agency that specializes in tours to the Philippines and Russia. It has 75,000 common shares issued. On March 15th, 2013, the organization declared a 45% stock dividend. Prepare the journal entry to record the declaration and distribution (on April 1st, 2013) of the dividend. The current market price per share is $25.

Date	Account Title and Explanation	Debit	Credit

AP-11 (❼)

Naidu Inc. (a record company) decided to buy back 2,000 shares of its own common stock at a price of $10 per share. Give the journal entry to record the purchase.

Date	Account Title and Explanation	Debit	Credit

AP-12 (❼)

Given the following data for Khan Enterprises, determine total stockholders' equity.

Treasury stock, common (2,000 shares at cost)	20,000
Contributed capital	
Common stock, $10 par value 1, 000,000 shares authorized,	
40,000 shares issued, 38,000 shares outstanding	2,000,000
Retained earnings	375,000
Additional paid–in capital	105,000

AP-13 (❸, ❹, ❺, ❻)

Ping Pong Inc. began operations on January 1, 2013. The following transactions relating to stockholders' equity occurred in the first two years of the company's operations:

2013

Jan 1   The corporate charter authorized the issuance of unlimited common shares up to a maximum of $10,000,000 and 200,000, $3 non-cumulative preferred shares worth $100 each.

Jan 2   Issued 400,000 common shares for $11 per share.

Jan 3   Issued 200,000 common shares in exchange for a building valued at $750,000 and inventory valued at $320,000.

Jan 4   Instead of paying a $40,000 fee in cash, the company offered the accountant 400, $3 preferred shares.

Jan 5   Issued 15,000, $3 preferred shares for $100 cash per share.

For the year ended December 31, 2013, the newly incorporated company had a net income of $950,000. At the directors' meeting on January 15, 2014, the company decided to pay out a total of 20% of the net income to preferred and common stockholders. The date of record of the dividends is January 30, 2014.

The dividend payment date is February 28, 2014. During the period January 1 – February 28, 2014, the company had a net income of $160,000.

2014

The following transactions were incurred by Ping Pong Inc. during the year ended December 31, 2014:

Jun 4   Issued 100,000 common shares for $15 per share.

For the year ended December 31, 2014, the company had a net income of $1,540,000. At the board of directors' meeting held on January 15, 2015, the company decided to pay out a total of 25% of the net income to preferred and common stockholders. The date of record of dividend is January 31, 2015.

The dividend is to be paid on February 28, 2015.

During the period January 1 – February 28, 2015, the company had a net income of $250,000.

Required:

a) Prepare journal entries to record the above transactions.

Date	Account Title and Explanation	Debit	Credit

Date	Account Title and Explanation	Debit	Credit

b) Prepare the statement of retained earnings for the year 2013 and for the period January 1 to February 28, 2014.

Ping Pong Inc.
Statement of Retained Earnings
For the Year Ended December 31, 2013

Ping Pong Inc.
Statement of Retained Earnings
For the Two Months Ended February 28, 2014

c) Prepare the statement of retained earnings for the year 2014 and for the period January 1 to February 28, 2015.

Ping Pong Inc.
Statement of Retained Earnings
For the Year Ended December 31, 2014

Ping Pong Inc.
Statement of Retained Earnings
For the Two Months Ended February 28, 2015

d) Prepare the stockholders' equity section of the balance sheet as at December 31, 2013 and December 31, 2014.

Ping Pong Inc.
Stockholders' Equity
December 31, 2013

```
                        Ping Pong Inc.
                     Stockholders' Equity
                      December 31, 2014
```

AP-14 (❸, ❻, ❼)

At the beginning of the year 2013, Mystery Corporation had the following balances:

Contributed Capital:	
Common stock up to a maximum 1,000,000 shares authorized; 200,000 shares issued and outstanding	$2,000,000
Retained Earnings	$925,000

The following transactions occurred during 2013:

Jan 10	The Board decided to declare $40,000 dividends to common stockholders.
Feb 15	Paid the cash dividend declared on January 10.
Nov 30	Declared a 20% stock dividend. The market value was $12 per share.
Dec 15	Distributed the stock dividend declared on November 30.

Mystery Corporation generated a $250,000 net income during the year.

Required:

a) Prepare journal entries to record the above transactions.

Date	Account Title and Explanation	Debit	Credit

b) Prepare the statement of retained earnings for the year ended December 31, 2013.

Mystery Corporation Statement of Retained Earnings For the Year Ended December 31, 2013

c) Prepare the stockholders' equity section of the balance sheet as at December 31, 2013.

Mystery Corporation Stockholders' Equity December 31, 2013

AP-15 (❸, ❼)

On May 31, 2013, XYZ Corporation's stockholders' equity section shows the following balances:

Contributed Capital:	
Common stock, unlimited authorized 30,000 shares issued and outstanding	$450,000
Retained Earnings	370,000
Total Stockholders' Equity	$820,000

Scenario 1

May 31   After preparing the equity section shown, the company declared and immediately distributed a 100% stock dividend. Current market price was $10. The company recorded the stock dividends by debiting Retained Earnings.

Required:

a) Prepare the statement of retained earnings after the stock dividend.

_____

_____

_____

_____

b) Prepare the new stockholders' equity section of balance sheet as at May 31, 2013 (after the stock dividend has been distributed).

_____

_____

_____

_____

Scenario 2

May 31   After preparing the equity section shown, the company implemented a 2-for-1 stock split.

Required:

a) Calculate the number of outstanding shares.

_____

b) Prepare the stockholders' equity section of the balance sheet as at May 31, 2013.

XYZ Corporation **Stockholders' Equity** **May 31, 2013**

AP-16 (❸, ❺, ❻, ❼)

The stockholders' equity of East West Corporation at January 1, 2013 was as follows:

Contributed Capital:	
Authorized: common stock - unlimited; preferred stock - 200,000	
Issued:	
30,000 Common Shares	$1,500,000
1,000, $5 non-cumulative Preferred Shares	100,000
Total Contributed Capital	1,600,000
Retained Earnings	1,970,000
Total Stockholders' Equity	$3,570,000

The following transactions incurred in 2013:

Jan 15	The Board decided to declare a total cash dividend of $120,000 to common and preferred stockholders.
Jan 28	Date of record of dividend.
Feb 10	Paid the cash dividend declared on January 15.
Nov 30	Declared a 20% stock dividend to common stockholders. Current market price was $55.
Dec 12	Distributed the stock dividends.

East West Corporation generated a $980,000 net income during the year.

Required:

a) Prepare the journal entries to record the above transactions.

Date	Account Title and Explanation	Debit	Credit

Date	Account Title and Explanation	Debit	Credit

b) Prepare the statement of retained earnings for the year ended December 31, 2013.

East West Corporation
Statement of Retained Earnings
For the Year Ended December 31, 2013

c) Prepare the stockholders' equity section of the balance sheet as at December 31, 2013.

East West Corporation
Stockholders' Equity
December 31, 2013

AP-17 (❸, ❺, ❻)

The stockholders' equity of Khan Corporation at January 1, 2013 was as follows:

Contributed Capital:	
Authorized: common stock - unlimited; preferred stock - 200,000	
Issued:	
32,000 Common Shares	$1,200,000
2,000, $3 non-cumulative Preferred Shares	200,000
Total Contributed Capital	1,400,000
Retained Earnings	320,000
Total Stockholders' Equity	$1,720,000

No dividend was declared for common stockholders. However on December 15, 2013 the directors decided to pay dividends to preferred stockholders. The dividend payment date was December 28, 2013. Net income for the year was $180,000.

Required:

a) Calculate the amount of dividend to be paid to preferred stockholders.

b) Prepare journal entry for declaration and payment of preferred dividend.

Date	Account Title and Explanation	Debit	Credit

c) Prepare statement of retained earnings for the year ended December 31, 2013.

Khan Corporation **Statement of Retained Earnings** **For the Year Ended December 31, 2013**

AP-18 (❸, ❺, ❻)

On November 1, 2013, the financial records of Sam Inc. showed the following balances:

Contributed Capital:	
Authorized: common stock - unlimited; preferred stock - 200,000	
Issued:	
25,000 Common Shares	$1,300,000
2,000, $5 Cumulative Preferred Shares	200,000
Total Contributed Capital	1,500,000
Retained Earnings	620,000
Total Stockholders' Equity	$2,120,000

On November 15, 2013, Sam Inc. declared $320,000 of dividends payable to stockholders. Dividends were last paid in 2010. The declared dividend was paid on December 5, 2013.

During the period November 1 – December 31, 2013 the company earned net income of $50,000.

Required:

a) Calculate how much Sam Inc. owes the preferred stockholders.

_____

_____

_____

b) Prepare the journal entries to record the declaration and payment of dividends.

Date	Account Title and Explanation	Debit	Credit

c) Prepare the statement of retained earnings for the 2 month period of November 1 –
   December 31, 2013.

Sam Inc. Statement of Retained Earnings For the Two Months Ended December 31, 2013

AP-19 (❻, ❼)

At the end of ABC Inc.'s 3rd fiscal quarter, the balance of stockholders' equity was:

Contributed Capital Issued:	
Common Shares, 60,000	$960,000
Total Contributed Capital	960,000
Retained Earnings	580,000
Total Stockholders' Equity	$1,540,000

In the fourth quarter, the following entries related to its equity accounts were recorded:

Date	Account Title and Explanation	Debit	Credit
Oct 2	Retained Earnings	110,000	
	Common Dividends Payable		110,000
Oct 25	Common Dividends Payable	110,000	
	Cash		110,000
Oct 31	Retained Earnings	140,000	
	Common Stock Dividend Distributable		140,000
Nov 5	Common Stock Dividends Distributable	140,000	
	Common Stock		140,000

Required:

a) Explain each journal entry.

_____

_____

_____

_____

_____

_____

b) Complete the following table showing the equity balances at each indicated date.

	October 2	October 25	October 31	November 5
Common Stock				
Common Stock Dividends Distributable				
Retained Earnings				
Total Equity				

AP-20 (❹, ❺, ❻)

Given below is the equity section of Lizzy Dizzy Corporation at December 31, 2013. Preferred shares were sold at $100 each.

```
Contributed Capital:
Authorized: common stock - 5,000,000; preferred stock - 200,000
Issued:
        4,000,000 Common Shares                        $59,000,000
        $7, Cumulative Preferred Shares                 20,000,000
Total Contributed Capital                               79,000,000
Retained Earnings                                       64,450,000
Total Stockholders' Equity                            $143,450,000
```

Required:

From the information provided above, calculate the following:

a) Calculate the number of preferred shares issued.

_____

b) Calculate total amount of annual dividend payable to preferred stockholders.

_____

c) Calculate the average issuance price per common share.

_____

d) Calculate the amount due to preferred stockholders if the company last paid dividends in 2009.

_____

e) Suppose that the company declared to pay $25,000,000 as dividend on December 31, 2013 and paid dividends on January 10, 2014. Prepare journal entries to record the declaration and payment of dividends.

Date	Account Title and Explanation	Debit	Credit

AP-21 (❹, ❺, ❻)

Given below is the equity section of Hudson Corporation at December 31, 2013:

Contributed Capital	
Issued:	
40,000 common shares	$2,000,000
$9 cumulative preferred shares, 20,000 shares	2,000,000
$12 non-cumulative preferred shares, 8,000 shares	800,000
Total Contributed Capital	$4,800,000

Assume that no dividends were paid in 2011 or 2012. On December 31, 2013, Hudson Corporation declared a total cash dividend of $736,000.

Required:

a) Calculate the amount of cash dividend paid to each of the three classes of contributed capital.

_____

_____

_____

b) Calculate the dividend paid per share for each of the three classes of contributed capital.

_____

_____

_____

c) Calculate the average issue price of each type of stock.

_____

_____

_____

d) Prepare the journal entry required in 2011 and 2012 for recording dividends in arrears.

_____

_____

AP-22 (❶, ❹, ❺, ❻)

In 2013, Elizabeth and some of her friends invested money to start a company named "FRIENDZ" Corporation. The following transactions occurred during 2013:

Jan 1	The corporate charter authorized to issue 70,000, $5 cumulative preferred stock and unlimited common stock up to a maximum amount of $20,000,000.
Jan 6	Issued 200,000 common shares at $16 per share. Stock was issued to Elizabeth and other investors.
Jan 7	Issued another 500 common shares to Elizabeth in exchange for her services in organizing the corporation. The stockholders agreed that the services were worth $60,000.
Jan 12	Issued 3,500 preferred stock for $350,000.
Jan 14	Issued 10,000 common stock in exchange for a building acquired. For this purpose stock was valued at $16 per share.
Nov 15	The first annual dividend on preferred stock was declared.
Dec 20	Paid the dividends declared on preferred stock.

FRIENDZ Corporation generated a $125,000 net income during the year.

Required:

a) Prepare the journal entries to record the above transactions.

Date	Account Title and Explanation	Debit	Credit

b) Prepare the statement of retained earnings for the year ended December 31, 2013.

FRIENDZ Corporation Statement of Retained Earnings For the Year Ended December 31, 2013

c) Prepare the stockholders' equity section of the balance sheet as at December 31, 2013.

FRIENDZ Corporation Stockholders' Equity December 31, 2013

d) Suppose one of Elizabeth's friends (who is also a board member of Doda Dola, a public corporation) informs her that the company will be releasing its financial statements for the quarter next week and that the earnings are excellent! Elizabeth's friend encourages her to buy stock in Doda Dola now so that she can benefit from the increase in stock price after the earnings are released next week. Comment on this scenario if Elizabeth decides to purchase shares in Doda Dola using this information.

_____

_____

_____

_____

Case Study

CS-1 (❶, ❸)

McIntosh Pharmaceutical develops and manufactures cancer related drugs. For the last 10 years, they have been developing a unique chemical that has been shown to reduce the risk of breast cancer in middle-aged women. Unfortunately, just before going into mass production, scientists within McIntosh uncovered harmful side-effects of the drug and strongly recommended to management that mass production be delayed for another five years so as to better study the drug. McIntosh management contemplated their response and after three days, they announced this news to the public. Following the announcement, McIntosh stock price dropped 40%. During the three days of meetings, however, many managers decided to sell their stock in McIntosh.

Was their decision to sell stock ethically sound? Why is insider trading not tolerated?

_____

_____

_____

_____

_____

_____

_____

_____

_____

_____

_____

_____

_____

_____

_____

Critical Thinking

CT-1 (❻)

John Maynard Nash, a budding economist, noticed that the stock market price seemed to decline after the date of record of a cash dividend. Can you suggest why this might be the case?

_____

_____

_____

_____

_____

_____

_____

_____

_____

_____

_____

_____

_____

_____

_____

_____

_____

_____

Notes

Chapter 17

CORPORATIONS: THE FINANCIAL STATEMENTS

─────────── **Assessment Questions** ───────────

AS-1 (❶)

How are income taxes recorded for accounting purposes (cash basis vs accrual basis)?

_____

_____

_____

_____

AS-2 (❶)

Define accounting income and taxable income.

_____

_____

_____

_____

AS-3 (❶)

What does "deferred income taxes" refer to?

_____

_____

_____

AS-4 (❷)

Describe the steps in preparing closing entries for corporations (assuming the income summary account is used).

_____

_____

_____

AS-5 (❸)

Define discontinued operations.

_____

_____

_____

_____

AS-6 (❸)

Define an extraordinary item.

_____

_____

_____

_____

_____

_____

_____

AS-7 (❸)

Define other comprehensive income.

_____

_____

_____

_____

AS-8 (❹)

What information must a corporation disclose relative to income and retained earnings?

_____

_____

_____

_____

_____

AS-9 (❼)

Define and discuss book value per share.

_____

_____

_____

_____

_____

_____

_____

_____

_____

AS-10 (❼)

What ratio is used to assess debt relative to the amount of equity? Discuss.

_____

_____

_____

_____

_____

_____

_____

_____

_____

_____

AS-11 (❼)

What ratio is used to determine what amount of a company's earnings is paid out in dividends?

_____

_____

_____

_____

AS-12 (❼)

How do you calculate earnings per share?

_____

_____

_____

_____

Application Questions

AP-1 (❶)

At year end, Shuster Home Decor Inc. (a small home furnishings retail store run by Terri) has accounting income (before income tax expense calculation) of $102,000. Write the journal entry to record the income tax expense. Assume the tax rate is 30%.

Date	Account Title and Explanation	Debit	Credit

AP-2 (❶)

At year end, F'Brae Cheerleading Inc. (a medium sized distributor of cheerleading outfits) has accounting income of $210,000. Write the journal entry to record the income tax expense. Assume the tax rate is 30%.

Date	Account Title and Explanation	Debit	Credit

AP-3 (❶)

CoreeMonTeeth Dental Inc. is a manufacturer of high quality dental equipment. In the current year it had accounting income of $300,000 which included $40,000 of warranty expenses. Per income taxation law, however, the warranty expenses are not deductible until they are actually paid. Write the journal entry to record income tax payable. Assume the tax rate is 30%.

Date	Account Title and Explanation	Debit	Credit

AP-4 (❸)

Green Light Emissions Everyday (otherwise known as GLEE Inc.) has sales of $400,000 and expenses of $280,000 (before calculation of income tax expense). Prepare a basic income statement for GLEE taking into account income tax expense. Assume a tax rate of 30%.

GLEE Inc. Income Statement For the Year Ended December 31, 2014		

AP-5 (❶)

Nacho Libray Inc. has income from continuing operations of $200,000. Their total expenses amounted to $100,000 and, of that, $50,000 pertained to income tax expense. Calculate the income tax rate used.

AP-6 (❺)

The bookkeeper for GIFT Inc. noticed that she made an error when recording a $44,000 purchase in the prior fiscal year. She recorded the amount to the Repairs and Maintenance expense account instead of posting to the Equipment account. Write the journal entry that should be recorded to correct the Equipment account. Ignore the impact of depreciation. Assume the tax rate is 30%.

Date	Account Title and Explanation	Debit	Credit

AP-7 (❺)

An auditor noticed that TFK Inc. accidently recorded an insurance expenditure of $50,000 as an expense instead of properly recording it as a prepaid. The purchase was made on the last day of the fiscal period. Write the journal entry that should be recorded to correct the Prepaid Insurance account. Assume the tax rate is 30%.

Date	Account Title and Explanation	Debit	Credit

AP-8 (❼)

Shown below are sections of the financial statements of Tech World. Calculate the book value per share for 2013.

Stockholders' Equity	
Contributed Capital	
Authorized – unlimited number of non-voting, cumulative, redeemable, retractable preferred stock; unlimited number of non-voting, redeemable, retractable Class A common stock and an unlimited number of voting common shares issued – 562,652 voting common shares (March 3, 2012 – 557,613)	$2,169,856
Retained Earnings	1,653,094
Paid-in Capital	80,333
Accumulated other comprehensive income (loss)	30,283
Total Stockholders' Equity	3,933,566
Total Liabilities and Stockholders' Equity	$5,511,187

Information regarding number of shares:

Balance as at March 3, 2012	557,613
Exercise of stock option	5,039
Balance at March 1, 2013	562,652

AP-9 (❼)

Refer to AP-8 above. The Tech World income statement shows the following:

Net income		$1,293,897
Earnings per share		
Basic		$2.31
Diluted		$2.26

Calculate the earnings per share. Your calculation of EPS may not agree with the numbers shown above. See the Critical Thinking Exercise at the end of this chapter for further discussion.

AP-10 (❼)

Tech World's balance sheet shows total liabilities of $1,577,621. Refer to the equity section of the statements shown in AP-8 above, and calculate the debt-to-equity ratio. Note your comments on the ratio.

AP-11 (❼)

Part of the financial statements of Toromont Industries is shown below:

Consolidated Statements of Retained Earnings For the Year Ended December 31, 2013 ($ thousands)	
Retained Earnings, beginning of year	$477,820
Net Earnings	122,280
Dividends	(31,061)
Retained Earnings, end of year	$539,039

Calculate the dividend payout ratio and discuss.

_____

_____

_____

_____

_____

AP-12 (❸, ❹, ❻)

The following information was taken from the accounting records of Cutler Inc. at December 31, 2013.

Line Item	Amount
Prior-year error – debit to Retained Earnings	$15,000
Income tax expense on operating income from discontinued operations	19,600
Total dividends	67,000
Common stock, 75,000 shares issued	201,000
Sales revenue	605,000
Interest expense	17,000
Operating income, discontinued operations	56,000
Loss due to lawsuit	16,000
Sales discounts	30,000
Income tax savings on sale of discontinued operations (sold at a loss)	(8,750)
General expenses	23,000
Income tax expense on continuing operations	73,150
Preferred stock, $7.00, 1,000 shares issued	60,000
Retained earnings, January 1, 2013 (prior to adjustment)	135,000
Loss due to an unusual earthquake	20,000
Loss on sale of discontinued operations	25,000
Income tax savings on loss caused by the earthquake	7,000
Cost of goods sold	310,000

Required:

a) Prepare an income statement for the year ended December 31, 2013.

b) Prepare a statement of retained earnings for Cutler Inc. for the year ended December 31, 2013.

c) Prepare the stockholders' equity section of the balance sheet for December 31, 2013.

d) Calculated the EPS ratio.

Assume a tax rate of 35%. During the year, no new shares were issued or redeemed.

a)

Cutler Inc. Income Statement For the Year Ended December 31, 2013		

b)

Cutler Inc. Statement of Retained Earnings For the Year Ended, December 31, 2013	

c)

Culter Inc. Stockholders' Equity Section of Balance Sheet As at December 31, 2013	

d)

_____

_____

_____

AP-13 (❷)

For the year that just passed, a company experienced a net loss of $140,000. The revenues and expenses have already been closed to the income summary account. Prepare the final entry to complete the closing process.

Date	Account Title and Explanation	Debit	Credit

AP-14 (❷)

An extract from MC Consulting's pre-closing trial balance for the year ended December 31, 2013 is shown below. The company's net income for the year was $82,000.

MC Consulting Trial Balance (Extract) December 31, 2013		
Account	Debit	Credit
Sales Revenue		$240,000
Cost of Goods Sold	$85,000	
Salaries Expense	50,000	
Rent Expense	10,000	
Income Tax Expense	13,000	

Prepare the closing entries for MC Consulting assuming the company uses the income summary account.

Date	Account Title and Explanation	Debit	Credit

AP-15 (❼)

Marry Inc. provided you following information from its accounting records for year ending December 31, 2014 and 2013.

	2014	2013
Income from continuing operations (net of tax)	$840,000	$740,000
Income from discontinued operations (net of tax)	150,000	70,000
Net income	990,000	810,000
Each year, 100,000 common shares were outstanding. No new shares were issued in either year.	1,000,000	1,000,000
Beginning Retained Earnings	1,990,000	1,580,000
Current liabilities	560,000	420,000
Long-term debt	980,000	760,000
Market price per share	15	13
Total dividends paid	500,000	400,000

No shares were issued during the two years.

Required:

Calculate the following ratios for both years:

    (a) EPS Ratio

    (b) EPS for each type of income reported on the income statement

    (c) Dividend Payout Ratio

    (d) Price- Earnings Ratio.

    (e) Debt-To-Equity Ratio

    (f) Book Value per Share

(a) EPS Ratio

(b) EPS for each area reported on the income statement:

(c) Dividend Payout Ratio

(d) Price - Earnings Ratio

(e) Debt-to-Equity Ratio

(f) Book Value per Share

_____

_____

_____

AP-16 (❼)

The following data is available for two companies, Sam Corporation and Tally Corporation for the year ended December 31, 2013.

	Sam Corporation	Tally Corporation
Income from continuing operations (net of tax)	$710,000	$510,000
Income from discontinued operations (net of tax)	120,000	60,000
Net income	830,000	570,000
Average number of shares outstanding during the year: 100,000 issued by Sam and 50,000 by Tally	800,000	450,000
Beginning Retained Earnings	2,070,000	1,580,000
Current liabilities	560,000	420,000
Long-term debt	980,000	760,000
Market price per share	14	11
Total dividends paid	200,000	120,000

Required:

a) Calculate the following ratios for both companies:

   1. EPS Ratio
   2. EPS for each area reported on the income statement
   3. Dividend Payout Ratio
   4. Price - Earnings Ratio
   5. Debt-to-Equity Ratio

1. EPS Ratio

_____

_____

_____

2. EPS for each area reported on the income statement:

_____

_____

_____

_____

3. Dividend Payout Ratio

_____

_____

_____

_____

4. Price - Earnings Ratio

_____

_____

_____

_____

5. Debt-to-Equity Ratio

_____

_____

_____

_____

b) Compare the performance and position of the two companies by interpreting the ratios calculated in Part a.

_____

_____

_____

_____

_____

_____

_____

_____

_____

_____

_____

Case Study

CS-1 (❼)

Obtain the current financial statements of a large capitalization company (i.e. > $5 Billion), and answer the following questions.

a) Name of company	
b) Capitalization of the company	
c) Industry in which the company is engaged	
d) Contributed capital amount	
e) Retained earnings amount	
f) Total Liabilities	
g) Total stockholders' equity	
h) Debt-to-Equity Ratio	
i) Earnings per share (basic)	
j) Dividend per share	
k) Dividend payout ratio	
l) Book value per share (show calculation)	
m) Current market price per share (note the date)	

Critical Thinking

CT-1 (❼)

In this chapter, you have learned how to calculate earnings per share. Often, a corporation's annual report will report earnings per share as calculated by the corporation. Rarely do the corporation's reported earnings per share agrees with a financial analyst's calculation of this number. Discuss why these two calculations may differ.

_____

_____

_____

_____

_____

_____

_____

_____

_____

_____

_____

CT-2 (❸, ❹, ❻)

The following information was taken from the accounting records of Splinter Inc. at December 31, 2013.

Line Item	Amount
Common stock, 50,000 shares outstanding on January 1, 2013	$120,000
Common stock, 70,000 shares outstanding on December 31, 2013	350,000
Cost of Goods Sold	468,000
Dividends paid	50,000
Gain on Sale of Assets	6,200
General operating expenses	210,000
Income tax expense on continuing operations	29,850
Income tax expense on operating income from discontinued operations	18,600
Interest Expense	8,700
Operating income from discontinued operations	62,000
Loss due to an unusual and infrequent natural disaster	50,000
Prior year error – debit to Retained Earnings	6,000
Income tax savings caused by the natural disaster loss	15,000
Retained Earnings, January 1, 2013 (prior to adjustment)	410,000
Sales revenue	780,000

Required:

a) Prepare the income statement for the year ended December 31, 2013.

b) Prepare the statement of retained earnings for the year ended December 31, 2013.

c) Prepare the stockholders' equity section of the balance sheet for December 31, 2013.

Assume the tax rate is 30%.

a) Income statement

Splinter Inc. **Income statement** **For the Year Ended December 31, 2013**		

b) Statement of Retained Earnings

Splinter Inc. **Statement of Retained Earnings** **For the Year Ended December 31, 2013**	

c)

Splinter Inc. Stockholders' Equity Section of Balance Sheet As at December 31, 2013	

Chapter 18

INVESTMENTS

────────── **Assessment Questions** ──────────

AS-1 (❷)

What are the characteristics of debt investments?

_____

_____

_____

AS-2 (❸)

What are the characteristics of equity investments?

_____

_____

_____

AS-3 (❶)

Define short-term investments.

_____

_____

_____

AS-4 (❹)

Define long-term investments.

_____

_____

_____

AS-5 (❶,❹)

Why do businesses make investments in debt or equity?

_____

_____

_____

AS-6 (❶,❹)

What are the three investment categories according to GAAP?

_____

_____

_____

AS-7 (❶)

Define trading investments.

_____

_____

_____

AS-8 (❶,❹)

Define held to maturity investments.

_____

_____

_____

AS-9 (❶,❹)

Define available for sale investments.

_____

_____

_____

_____

AS-10 (❶,❹)

Differentiate interest revenue from dividend revenue.

_____

_____

_____

_____

AS-11 (❷,❸)

What are brokerage fees? What do brokers do?

_____

_____

_____

AS-12 (❹)

Where does a long-term investment show up on the balance sheet?

_____

_____

_____

AS-13 (❹)

What does the significant influence mean in terms of the percentage of ownership?

_____

_____

_____

AS-14 (❹)

What accounting method should be used by a company who has significant influence over its investment?

_____

_____

_____

AS-15 (❺)

When it comes to managing and controlling investments, what are some of the common procedures?

_____

_____

_____

_____

_____

_____

_____

Application Questions

AP-1 (❷)

Julio Ivors operates a proprietorship. Sales have been very good in recent months, resulting in a substantial amount of cash on hand. However, Julio knows that in six months, he will have to purchase more inventory for the next season. He realizes that if he leaves the cash in the bank, he will receive an insignificant amount of interest. He therefore decides to loan his excess cash of $20,000 to his brother-in-law, charging interest at an annual rate of 12%. Assume Julio Ivors' proprietorship has a year-end of December 31. Also assume that Julio's brother repays the loan and interest in six months.

Required:

1. Record the entry when issuing the loan on August 15.

2. Record any required entries related to the loan as of December 31.

3. Record the deposit of the re-payment of the loan with interest on February 15.

Date	Account Title and Explanation	Debit	Credit

AP-2 (❸)

Hoops & Co. generated $500,000 extra cash from the sale of a subsidiary operation. The company treasurer thinks it would be prudent to invest in some bonds as a short-term investment. The company's investment advisor, suggested they use the proceeds to purchase bonds that yield interest of 5% paid annually.

The bonds were purchased for $500,000 on October 1 and sold the following year on June 30 for principal value plus interest. The bond last paid interest on September 30, the day before the purchase. The company has a July 31 year-end.

Required:

Record the journal entries required on October 1 and June 30.

Date	Account Title and Explanation	Debit	Credit

AP-3 (❸)

Mailhot Company receives a $1 million government research grant to develop a new product. At the present time, Mailhot is finishing up its previous project, and will not be able to start on its new project for eight months. The controller discovers that some corporate bonds were offering a good interest rate over the short term. The bonds pay 6% interest and were bought on September 1 for $1,020,000 (including $20,000 of accrued interest). Interest is payable semi-annually on October 31 and April 30 each year. Assume Mailhot Company has a June 30th year-end.

Required:
a) Record the purchase of the bonds on September 1.
b) Record the receipts of interest on October 31 and April 30.

Date	Account Title and Explanation	Debit	Credit

AP-4 (❹)

XYZ Tools made a large cash sale of power saws and find themselves with unexpected surplus cash of $50,000. With this surplus cash, XYZ purchases stock and pays a brokerage fee of $250 on September 1.

Required: Record the purchase of stock on September 1.

Date	Account Title and Explanation	Debit	Credit

AP-5 (❹)

Tannenbaum Company decides to use its excess cash to take advantage of the recent drop in stock prices. The company has $100,000 of cash and uses part of the cash to purchase 2,000 shares of Goodlett Ltd. These shares represent less than 20% of the shares of Goodlett Ltd. On October 7, Tannenbaum paid $47 per share, plus a 1% brokerage fee. Tannenbaum plans to sell the stock within the next 12 months.

Required:

Record the purchase of the stock.

Date	Account Title and Explanation	Debit	Credit

AP-6 (❹)

Refer to AP-5. Goodlett Ltd. declares a dividend of $1 per share on September 15, payable to stockholders of record on October 1. The dividend will be paid out on October 31.

Required:

Prepare the required journal entry for Tannenbaum Company as of October 31.

_____

_____

_____

AP-7 (❹)

Refer to AP-5. Assume that on November 30, Tannenbaum sold the stock for $45 per share and no brokerage fee was paid when selling the shares.

Required:

Prepare the journal entry required as of November 30.

Date	Account Title and Explanation	Debit	Credit

AP-8 (❹)

Refer to AP-5. Assume that on March 31, Tannenbaum Company sold the stock for $50 per share. No brokerage fee was paid when selling the shares.

Required:

Prepare the journal entry required as of March 31.

Date	Account Title and Explanation	Debit	Credit

AP-9 (❹)

Snelgrove Company purchases 1,000 shares of Kelch Limited on November 7, at a total cost of $40,000. Prior to the purchase date, on October 15, the directors of Kelch Limited declared a dividend of 5 cents per share, payable to stockholders of record on November 9. The dividend will be paid on November 15.

Required:

Prepare the journal entry required on November 15 for Snelgrove Company.

Date	Account Title and Explanation	Debit	Credit

AP-10 (❹)

Sam's Gardening Tools purchased 100 shares of Green Company for $25 per share on February 1, 2011 for short-term investment purpose. These shares represent less than 20% of the total shares of Green Company. On May 30, Sam's Gardening Tools received dividends of $2 per share.

Required:

    a) Record the journal entry for February 1, 2011

    b) Record the journal entry for May 30, 2011

    c) If Sam's Gardening Tools has a year-end of May 31 and reports income of $45,000 from operations (before any investing income or expense) for the year, what amount of net income will it report after considering the investing activity?

a)

Date	Account Title and Explanation	Debit	Credit

b)

Date	Account Title and Explanation	Debit	Credit

c) _____

_____

_____

AP-11 (❸)

Assume Star Furniture made a big cash sale and would like to invest the extra cash in bonds, but plans to sell the bonds in less than one year. On July 1, 2011 (the day the bonds were issued) the company purchases 10, $1,000 short-term bonds. The bonds mature in 18 months on December 31, 2012. The interest rate on the bond is 10%, payable quarterly. A fee of $200 is paid to the broker. Assume Star Furniture has an October 31 year-end.

Required:

a) Record the journal entry on July 1, 2011

b) Record the first interest payment Star Furniture received

c) Record appropriate journal entries on October 31, 2011

a)

Date	Account Title and Explanation	Debit	Credit

b)

Date	Account Title and Explanation	Debit	Credit

c)

Date	Account Title and Explanation	Debit	Credit

AP-12 (❸)

Refer to the exercise above and assume Star Furniture sold the bonds for $10,500 on December 31, 2011 after receiving the second interest payment. Record all appropriate transactions for December 31, 2011. No brokerage fee was paid on the sale of the bonds.

Date	Account Title and Explanation	Debit	Credit

Date	Account Title and Explanation	Debit	Credit

AP-13 (❷, ❸, ❹)

Beta Inc. is a medium size company with a September 30 year-end. From time to time, the company has extra cash on hand which it uses to make short-term investments. During the past year, the company completed the following transactions:

Jan. 1 – Lent $30,000 to another company at an annual rate of 4% and due in 6 months.

Mar. 30– Purchased 10 Star Company bonds priced at $1,000 each with interest payable semi-annually on September 1 and March 1 at an annual rate of 6%. The company also paid for the amount of accrued interest owing. Beta Inc. plans to sell the bonds in less than one year.

Apr.1 – Purchased 500 shares of ABC Company at $60 per share. These shares represent less than 20% of the total shares of ABC Company.

July 1 – Received full proceeds from the loan of Jan. 1, including interest.

Sep. 1 – Received 6 months interest payment on the Star Company bonds.

Sep. 1 – Received dividend of $1 per share on the ABC Company shares.

Sep. 30– Year-end adjustment: record the interest accrued on the Star Company bonds.

Oct. 5 – Sold 200 ABC Company shares for $65 per share.

Dec. 1 – Sold 300 ABC Company shares for $57 per share.

Note: Brokerage fees are ignored for simplicity.

Required:

Record journal entries for each of the above transactions.

Date	Account Title and Explanation	Debit	Credit

AP-14 (❹)

Mister Motors has some excess cash and decides to invest that extra cash. They purchased $200,000 worth of bonds at par value on October 1, 2013, and no brokerage fee was charged. The bonds pay 4% interest every March 31 and September 30. The bonds will mature on September 30, 2016, and Mister Motors plans to keep the bonds until they mature. Mister Motors has a year end of December 31.

a) Prepare the journal entry on October 1, 2013.

Date	Account Title and Explanation	Debit	Credit

b) Prepare the journal entry at the year end December 31, 2013.

Date	Account Title and Explanation	Debit	Credit

c) Prepare the journal entries fro the receipt of each of the two interest payments on March 31, 2014 and September 30, 2014.

Date	Account Title and Explanation	Debit	Credit

d) Prepare the journal entries on the maturity date of September 30, 2016.

Date	Account Title and Explanation	Debit	Credit

AP-15 (❹)

On May 25, 2013, Akbar Fishery purchases 800 shares of Company A for $23 per share. No brokerage fee was charged. Akbar Fishery does not intend to sell the shares In the near future. The 800 shares represent 12% of the total shares of Company A. On October 20, 2013, Company A pays dividends of $0.90 per share. Company A has a year end of November 30 and reported a net income of $30,000. The next day, on December 1, 2013, Akbar Fishery sells all their shares when the market price is $28 per share.

a) Prepare the journal entry on May 25, 2013.

Date	Account Title and Explanation	Debit	Credit

b) Prepare the journal entry on October 20, 2013.

Date	Account Title and Explanation	Debit	Credit

c) Prepare the journal entry on November 30, 2013.

Date	Account Title and Explanation	Debit	Credit

d) Prepare the journal entry on December 1, 2013.

Date	Account Title and Explanation	Debit	Credit

AP-16 (❹)

On May 25, 2013, Akbar Fishery purchases 800 shares of Company A for $23 per share. No brokerage fee was charged. Akbar Fishery does not intend to sell the shares in the near future. The 800 shares represent 30% of the total shares of Company A. On October 20, 2013, Company A pays dividends of $0.90 per share. Company A has a year end of November 30 and reported a net income of $30,000. The next day, on December 1, 2013, Akbar Fishery sells all their shares when the market price is $28 per share.

a) Prepare the journal entry on May 25, 2013.

Date	Account Title and Explanation	Debit	Credit

b) Prepare the journal entry on October 20, 2013.

Date	Account Title and Explanation	Debit	Credit

c) Prepare the journal entry on November 30, 2013.

Date	Account Title and Explanation	Debit	Credit

d) Prepare the journal entry on December 1, 2013.

Date	Account Title and Explanation	Debit	Credit

AP-17 (❹)

Greasy Spoon purchased $50,000 worth of bonds at par value on January 1, 2013. No brokerage fee was charged. The bonds pay 5% on June 30 and December 31. The bonds will mature on December 31, 2016 and Greasy Spoon plans to keep the bonds until they mature.

a) Prepare the journal entry on January 1, 2013.

Date	Account Title and Explanation	Debit	Credit

b) Prepare the journal entry on June 30, 2013.

Date	Account Title and Explanation	Debit	Credit

AP-18 (❹)

LoremIpsum purchased 1,000 shares of Company B for $34 per share on February 16, 2013. No brokerage fee was charged. LoremIpsum does not plan to sell these shares in the near future. These shares represent 8% of the total shares of Company B. On June 16, 2013, Company B paid dividends of $1.20 per share.

a) Prepare the journal entry on February 16, 2013.

Date	Account Title and Explanation	Debit	Credit

b) Prepare the journal entry on June 16, 2013.

Date	Account Title and Explanation	Debit	Credit

AP-19 (❹)

LoremIpsum purchased 1,000 shares of Company B for $34 per share on February 16, 2013. No brokerage fee was charged. LoremIpsum does not plan to sell these shares in the near future. These shares represent 40% of the total shares of Company B. On June 16, 2013, Company B paid dividends of $1.20 per share.

a) Prepare the journal entry on February 16, 2013.

Date	Account Title and Explanation	Debit	Credit

b) Prepare the journal entry on June 16, 2013.

Date	Account Title and Explanation	Debit	Credit

Case Study

CS-1 (❷, ❸, ❹, ❻)

Your friend, Jami Ringdahl, recently started a new job at Kelly A. Wait Ltd. Jami is responsible for the preparation of the monthly financial statements. Jami commented to you, "The company sure has a lot of cash in the bank!" Since Jami is new to the position and wants to impress her boss, she asks your opinion on the situation. Here are the questions that Jami wants answered:

1. What should the company do with the extra cash?

2. What happens if the company needs the cash for operating activities?

3. How does the above affect the financial statements?

4. Using any values on a journal entry, demonstrate the manner in which cash can be invested (include brokerage fees, interest, returns and other costs or gains where applicable).

5. What internal controls are necessary to ensure that the investments are safeguarded?

6. List some potential ethical issues that may arise when investing.

1. What should the company do with the extra cash?

_____

_____

_____

_____

_____

_____

_____

_____

_____

_____

_____

2. What happens if the company needs the cash for operating activities?

_____

_____

_____

_____

_____

_____

3. How does the above affect the financial statements?

_____

_____

_____

_____

_____

_____

_____

_____

4. Using any values on journal entries, demonstrate the manner in which cash can be invested. (Include brokerage fees, interest, returns and other costs or gains where applicable).

   a) Loaning money to another company. The loan will be paid back in six months.

Date	Account Title and Explanation	Debit	Credit

   b) Collecting interest on a short-term loan

Date	Account Title and Explanation	Debit	Credit

c) Collected the loan on its due date

Date	Account Title and Explanation	Debit	Credit

d) Purchasing bonds

Date	Account Title and Explanation	Debit	Credit

e) Receiving interest on the bonds

Date	Account Title and Explanation	Debit	Credit

f) Recording an accrual for interest at year-end

Date	Account Title and Explanation	Debit	Credit

g) Receiving interest that, previously, was accrued for

Date	Account Title and Explanation	Debit	Credit

h) Purchasing stock of another company for selling in less than 2 months

Date	Account Title and Explanation	Debit	Credit

i)   Receiving dividends

Date	Account Title and Explanation	Debit	Credit

j)   Selling stock held as short term-investment

Date	Account Title and Explanation	Debit	Credit

5.   What internal controls do you think are necessary to ensure that investments are well
     safeguarded?

_____

_____

_____

_____

_____

_____

_____

_____

_____

_____

_____

_____

_____

_____

_____

_____

_____

_____

_____

_____

_____

_____

6. List some potential ethical issues that may arise when investing.

_____

_____

_____

_____

_____

_____

_____

_____

_____

_____

_____

_____

_____

_____

_____

_____

_____

_____

_____

_____

_____

_____

_____

Critical Thinking

CT-1 (❶, ❷, ❸, ❹, ❻)

1. Discuss the importance to companies of investments, and their effect on the balance sheet and income statement.

_____

_____

_____

_____

2. Investing involves deciding which investments to make, investigating possible components, and identifying risks associated with each possible investment. Discuss how you would decide:

    – When to invest in investments

_____

_____

_____

    – What you would invest in

_____

_____

_____

_____

    – How much risk your company should assume

_____

_____

_____

_____

_____

3. One of the objectives of using investments is to increase income. Are there other ways in which this objective can be accomplished without using investments?

_____

_____

_____

_____

_____

_____

_____

4. Are investments necessary?

_____

_____

_____

_____

5. Are investments wise?

_____

_____

_____

_____

6. What assumptions are made by a company when it uses short-term investments?

_____

_____

_____

_____

7. Do investments expose a company to excess risk?

_____

_____

_____

_____

8. Are there alternative uses of cash that can be used to increase income?

_____

_____

_____

_____

Chapter 19

THE STATEMENT OF CASH FLOW

────────── **Assessment Questions** ──────────

AS-1 (❶)

Is the cash flow statement an optional statement? Explain.

_____

_____

_____

AS-2 (❷)

Identify the three ways a business can generate and use cash.

_____

_____

_____

AS-3 (❷)

What does cash flow from operations represent?

_____

_____

_____

AS-4 (❷)

What does cash flow from investments represent?

_____

_____

_____

AS-5 (❷)

What does cash flow from financing represent?

_____

_____

_____

AS-6 (❸)

What financial statements are required to prepare a cash flow statement?

_____

_____

_____

AS-7 (❸)

Which items appear in the cash flow from operations section of the cash flow statement that is prepared using the indirect method?

_____

_____

_____

AS-8 (❸)

Which items appear in the cash flow from investing section of the cash flow statement?

_____

_____

_____

AS-9 (❸)

Which items appear in the cash flow from financing section of the cash flow statement?

_____

_____

_____

AS-10 (❸)

What does a gain on the sale of equipment indicate?

_____

_____

AS-11 (❸)

How is a gain on the sale of equipment shown on the cash flow statement that is prepared using the indirect method?

_____

_____

_____

AS-12 (❶)

True or False: Net income does translate into cash in the bank; thus the cash flow statement is used to show how net income is converted to cash.

AS-13 (❹)

What are the three ways of generating and using cash under the direct method?

AS-14 (❹)

Why do most companies prefer to use the indirect method over the direct method?

AS-15 (❺)

Provide two examples of non-cash transactions under either the financing or investing sections of the cash flow statement.

AS-16 (⑤)

How do you calculate the proceeds from the sale of a property, plant and equipment?

_____

_____

_____

AS-17 (⑤)

How should the cash related to discontinued operations and extraordinary items be presented on the cash flow statement?

_____

_____

_____

Application Questions

AP-1 (❶)

For each item listed, indicate how the item will impact cash flow (increase, decrease or no change) using the indirect method.

Item	Effect on Cash
Net Income	
Increase in Accounts Payable	
Decrease in Accounts Receivable	
Purchase of Property, Plant and Equipment	
Payment of Bank Loan	
Increase in Inventory	
Pay Dividends	
Increase in Notes Payable	
Increase in Prepaid Insurance	

AP-2 (❷)

Indicate the section of the cash flow statement where each item would be located (operations, investing or financing).

Item	Section
Change in Accounts Payable	
Change in Inventory	
Change in Property, Plant and Equipment	
Change in Long-Term portion of Bank Loan	
Change in Current portion of Bank Loan	
Change in Prepaid Rent	
Change in Accounts Receivable	
Change in Common Stock	
Gain on Sale of Property, Plant and Equipment	

AP-3 (❷)

The net income for the year ended on December 31, 2013 for RC Corporation was $120,000.
Additional data for the year is provided below:

Purchase of property, plant and equipment	$280,000
Depreciation of property, plant and equipment	14,000
Dividends declared	50,000
Net decrease in accounts receivable	29,000
Loss on sale of equipment	13,000

Required:

Calculate the increase (decrease) in cash from operating activities.

_____

_____

_____

_____

AP-4 (❷)

Bonus Company had the following amounts in its cash flow statement for the year ended
December 31, 2013:

Net decrease in cash from operations	$100,000
Net decrease in cash from investment	400,000
Net increase in cash from financing	350,000
Cash balance, January 1, 2013	600,000

Required:

Calculate the cash balance at December 31, 2013.

_____

_____

_____

_____

AP-5 (❷)

The following information is taken from Bush Company for the fiscal year 2013:

Purchase of plant and equipment	$33,000
Sale of long-term investment	12,000
Increase in accounts payable	6,000
Repayment of bonds payable	15,000
Depreciation on plant assets	7,000

Required:

Calculate the increase (decrease) in cash from investing activities.

_____

_____

_____

AP-6 (❷)

The net income for the year ended December 31, 2013 for the Kersley Company was $73,000. Additional information is as follows:

Interest expense on borrowing	$8,000
Increase in accounts receivable	10,000
Decrease in prepaid expense	3,000
Decrease in accounts payable	4,000
Dividends paid to common stockholders	14,000

Required:

Calculate the increase (decrease) in cash from operating activities.

_____

_____

_____

AP-7 (❷)

The Grading Company's cash account decreased by $14,000 and its long-term investment account increased by $18,000. Cash increase from operations was $21,000. Net cash decrease from investments was $22,000.

Required:

Based on the information given, calculate the cash increase (or decrease) from financing.

_____

_____

_____

_____

AP-8 (❸)

Balance sheet accounts for Planet Inc. contain the following amounts at the end of 2013 and 2014:

Planet Inc. Balance Sheet As at December 31		
	2014	**2013**
Assets		
Current Assets		
Cash	$7,500	$5,000
Accounts Receivable	21,000	15,000
Prepaid Expenses	2,500	2,000
Inventory	37,000	28,000
Total Current Assets	68,000	50,000
Long-Term Assets		
Property Plant and Equipment	196,000	175,000
Less: Accumulated Depreciation	(41,000)	(32,000)
Total Long-Term Assets	155,000	143,000
Total Assets	**$223,000**	**$193,000**
Liabilities		
Current Liabilities	$33,000	$33,000
Long-Term Liabilities	30,000	35,000
Total Liabilities	**63,000**	**68,000**
Stockholders' Equity		
Common Stock	75,000	60,000
Retained Earnings	85,000	65,000
Total Stockholders' Equity	**160,000**	**125,000**
Total Liabilities and Equity	**$223,000**	**$193,000**

Assume current liabilities include only items from operations (e.g., accounts payable, tax payable). Long-term liabilities include items from financing (e.g. bonds and other long-term liabilities).

Note that there was no sale of property, plant & equipment throughout the year.

Required:

Prepare the cash flow statement for 2014 using the indirect method. Assume the net income for 2014 was $20,000.

Planet, Inc. Cash Flow Statement For the Year Ended December 31, 2014		

AP-9 (❸)

Flax Corporation's balance sheet accounts as of December 31, 2014 and 2013 are presented below:

Flax Corp. Balance Sheet As at December 31		
	2014	**2013**
Assets		
Current Assets		
Cash	$460,000	$300,000
Short-term Investments	600,000	-
Accounts Receivable	1,020,000	1,020,000
Inventory	1,360,000	1,200,000
Total Current Assets	3,440,000	2,520,000
Long-Term Assets		
Long-term Investments	400,000	800,000
Property, Plant and Equipment	3,100,000	2,500,000
Less: Accumulated Depreciation	(900,000)	(600,000)
Total Long-Term Assets	2,600,000	2,700,000
Total Assets	**$6,040,000**	**$5,220,000**
Liabilities		
Current Liabilities	$2,300,000	$2,000,000
Long-Term Liabilities	800,000	700,000
Total Liabilities	**3,100,000**	**2,700,000**
Stockholders' Equity		
Common Stock	1,800,000	1,680,000
Retained Earnings	1,140,000	840,000
Total Stockholders' Equity	**2,940,000**	**2,520,000**
Total Liabilities and Equity	**$6,040,000**	**$5,220,000**

Assume current liabilities include only items from operations (e.g., accounts payable, tax payable). Long-term liabilities include items from financing (e.g. bonds and other long-term liabilities).

Note that there was no sale of property, plant & equipment throughout the year.

Required:

Prepare the cash flow statement for 2014 using the indirect method. Assume the net income for 2014 was $300,000.

Flax Corp. Cash Flow Statement For the Year Ended December 31, 2014		

AP-10 (❶)

Ashe Inc. reported the following data for 2013:

Income Statement	
Net Income	$30,000
Depreciation	4,000
Balance Sheet	
Increase in Accounts Receivable	9,000
Decrease in Accounts Payable	7,000

Required:

Calculate the increase (decrease) in cash from operations.

_____

_____

_____

_____

_____

AP-11 (❸)

Use the following information to prepare the operations section of a cash flow statement for MNO Co. for 2013 using the indirect method.

Net income	$140,000
Increase in inventory	30,000
Increase in accounts payable	20,000
Depreciation expense	55,000
Increase in accounts receivable	18,000
Gain on sale of land	25,000

_____

_____

_____

_____

_____

_____

_____

AP-12 (❸)

Breakwater Boats sells boating accessories. At the end of 2014, the income statement and comparative balance sheet were prepared as shown below. Based on the information given, prepare a cash flow statement for Breakwater Boats using the indirect method.

Breakwater Boats
Balance Sheet
As at December 31

	2014	2013
ASSETS		
Current Assets		
Cash	$73,870	$62,500
Accounts receivable	94,800	87,500
Inventory	327,000	245,700
Prepaid expenses	14,500	14,500
Total Current Assets	510,170	410,200
Long-Term Assets		
Property, plant & equipment[1]	340,000	384,000
Less: Accumulated depreciation	(26,200)	(24,500)
Total Long-Term Assets	313,800	359,500
TOTAL ASSETS	$823,970	$769,700
LIABILITIES AND EQUITY		
Liabilities		
Current Liabilities		
Accounts payable	$52,600	$45,700
Current portion of bank loan	8,500	8,500
Total Current Liabilities	61,100	54,200
Long-term portion of bank loan	50,100	58,600
TOTAL LIABILITIES	111,200	112,800
Stockholders' Equity		
Common stock	150,000	150,000
Retained earnings[2]	562,770	506,900
TOTAL STOCKHOLDERS' EQUITY	712,770	656,900
TOTAL LIABILITIES AND EQUITY	$823,970	$769,700

Additional Information:

1. Property, Plant & Equipment
   During 2014, land was sold for a gain of $6,000. The cash proceeds from the sale totaled $50,000. There was no purchase of property, plant & equipment throughout the year.

2. Retained Earnings
   Breakwater Boats declared and paid $35,000 in dividends in 2014.

Breakwater Boats
Income Statement
For the Year Ended December 31, 2014

Sales	$562,000
COGS	365,300
Gross Profit	196,700
Operating Expenses	
Depreciation Expense	1,700
Other Operating Expenses	61,200
Total Operating Expenses	62,900
Operating Income	133,800
Other Income	
Gain on Sale of Land	6,000
Net Income Before Tax	139,800
Income Tax	48,930
Net Income	$90,870

Required:

Create the cash flow statement.

Breakwater Boats Cash Flow Statement For the Year Ended December 31, 2014		

AP-13 (❸)

Vortex Manufacturing makes and sells integrated circuit boards. At the end of 2014, the income statement and comparative balance sheet were prepared as shown below. Based on the information given, prepare a cash flow statement for Vortex Manufacturing using the indirect method.

Vortex Manufacturing Balance Sheet As at December 31		
	2014	2013
ASSETS		
Current Assets		
Cash	$239,820	$135,640
Accounts receivable	242,100	265,300
Inventory	503,200	465,300
Prepaid expenses	26,500	26,500
Total Current Assets	1,011,620	892,740
Long-Term Assets		
Property, plant & equipment[1]	840,400	856,400
Less: Accumulated depreciation	(102,300)	(95,600)
Total Long-Term Assets	738,100	760,800
TOTAL ASSETS	$1,749,720	$1,653,540
LIABILITIES AND EQUITY		
Liabilities		
Current Liabilities		
Accounts payable	$305,600	$324,500
Current portion of bank loan	32,000	23,000
Total Current Liabilities	337,600	347,500
Long-term portion of bank loan	205,000	185,000
TOTAL LIABILITIES	542,600	532,500
Stockholders' Equity		
Common stock	290,000	260,000
Retained earnings[2]	917,120	861,040
TOTAL STOCKHOLDERS' EQUITY	1,207,120	1,121,040
TOTAL LIABILITIES AND EQUITY	$1,749,720	$1,653,540

Additional Information:

1. Property, Plant & Equipment
   During 2014, land was sold for a loss of $5,000. The cash proceeds from the sale totaled $11,000. There was no purchase of property, plant & equipment throughout the year.

2. Retained Earnings
   Vortex Manufacturing declared and paid $50,000 in dividends in 2014.

Vortex Manufacturing Income Statement For the Year Ended December 31, 2014	
Sales	$2,650,000
COGS	1,722,500
Gross Profit	927,500
Operating Expenses	
Depreciation Expense	6,700
Other operating expenses	752,600
Total Operating Expenses	759,300
Operating Income	168,200
Other Income	
Loss on Sale of Land	(5,000)
Net Income Before Tax	163,200
Income Tax	57,120
Net Income	$106,080

Required:

Create the cash flow statement.

Vortex Manufacturing Cash Flow Statement For the Year Ended December 31, 2014		

AP-14 (❹)

Using the following information from their accounting records, prepare the cash flow statement for Alvirina Corporation (year-end December 31, 2013) using the direct method.

Amortization Expense	$12,000
Cash Sales	314,000
Credit Sales	500,000
Dividends received from investments in stock	2,000
Warranty Expense	5,000
Cash received issuing common stock	10,000
Sale of capital assets for cash	20,000
Payments to suppliers	15,000
Cost of Goods Sold	212,000
Dividends paid	23,000
Cash purchase of capital assets	150,000
Cash balance on January 1, 2013	165,000
Cash balance on December 31, 2013	323,000

Alvirina Corporation Cash Flow Statement For the Year Ended December 31, 2013		

AP-15 (④)

Using the following information from their accounting records, prepare the cash flow statement for E-Game Corporation (year-end July 31, 2014) using the direct method.

Cash sales	$278,000
Cash received from sale of investments,	34,000
Payments to employees (in cash)	240,000
Cash received issuing common stock	20,000
Sale of capital assets for cash	65,000
Interest received (in cash) on notes receivable	19,000
Payments to suppliers	7,000
Cost of Goods Sold	112,000
Dividends paid	100,000
Cash purchase of capital assets	50,000
Dividends received from investments in stock	4,000
Cash balance on August 1, 2013	34,000
Cash balance on July 31, 2014	57,000

E-Game Corporation Cash Flow Statement For the Year Ended July 31, 2014		

AP-16 (❺)

Allen Woods has just started working as an accountant for Stickla Supplies. Unfortunately, the company had no proper accounting system in place and Allen had to start everything from the scratch. He has been provided with some items from the company's balance sheet and income statement for the end of 2013.

Going through the company's purchase receipts and some other financial documents, Allen realized that Stickla purchased $2,500 of equipment in 2013 and the balance of property, plant and equipment and accumulated depreciation at the end of 2012 was $11,000 and $2,900 respectively.

Accounts	2013
Property, Plant & Equipment	$10,000
Accumulated Depreciation	$3,600
Accounts Payable	$4,000
Current Portion of Bank Loan	$15,000
Retained Earnings	$5,400
Depreciation Expense	$1,200
Loss on Sale of Equipment	$300

Based on the information provided, help Allen calculate the missing items in the table below.

Which section of the Cash Flow Statement is affected?	
How much PPE was sold in 2013?	
What was the accumulated depreciation for the PPE sold?	
What is the book value of the PPE sold?	
How much cash was received from the sale?	
How much cash is paid out for the purchase?	
What is the net change in cash resulting from PPE?	

AP-17 (❺)

Factsy Inc. is planning to make the best use out of its cash on hand by purchasing some additional long-term investments. Factsy's long-term investments are held at cost. In January 2013, Factsy bought additional investments. The company also sold part of its investments in November 2013 due to a sudden growth in the value of its holdings. December 31 is their year end.

a) Factsy's bookkeeper believes that the net change in cash from the investing activities above must be a positive number (a cash inflow) as a result of a big gain on the sale of investment. Do you agree with this comment? Explain.

_____

_____

_____

_____

_____

_____

_____

b) Calculate the net change in cash resulting from the long-term investment?

Below are the data of Factsy Company.

Accounts	2013	2012
Long-Term Investment	$120,000	$110,000
Purchase of Investment	$40,000	
Gain on Sale of Investment	$5,000	

_____

_____

_____

_____

_____

_____

AP-18 (❺)

2013 has been a great year for Exany Company which managed to earn $56,000 of net income. Therefore, the board decided to declare and pay dividends by year end.

Based on the following information, answer the following questions.

Accounts	2013	2012
Retained Earnings	$91,000	$67,000
Common Stock	$120,000	$110,000

a) How much dividends were paid in 2013?	
b) Which section of the Cash Flow Statement is affected?	
c) Assuming only the information given impacted the section of the Cash Flow Statement indicated in b), what is the net change in cash for this section?	

AP-19 (❺)

The balance sheet and income statement for Zooyo Appliance are presented below:

Zooyo Appliance Balance Sheet As at December 31		
	2013	2012
Assets		
Cash	$37,580	$15,000
Accounts Receivable	17,000	16,000
Inventory	21,000	27,000
Total Current Assets	75,580	58,000
Land	110,000	80,000
Property, Plant & Equipment	130,000	160,000
Less Accumulated Depreciation	-26,500	-30,000
Total Assets	$289,080	$268,000
Liabilities		
Accounts Payable	$29,000	$35,000
Current Portion of Bank Loan	18,000	18,000
Current Liabilities	47,000	53,000
Long-term portion of Bank Loan	80,000	65,000
Total Liabilities	127,000	118,000
Stockholders' Equity		
Common Stock	75,000	70,000
Retained Earnings	87,080	80,000
Stockholders' Equity	162,080	150,000
Liabilities + Stockholders' Equity	$289,080	$268,000

Zooyo Appliance Income Statement For the year ended December 31, 2013	
Sales	$142,000
COGS	92,000
Gross Profit	50,000
Expenses	
Insurance Expense	1,500
Rent Expense	6,800
Salaries Expense	7,100
Telephone Expense	800
Interest Expense	1,700
Depreciation Expense	4,500
Loss on Sale of Equipment	3,200
Total Expenses	25,600
Operating Profit Before Tax	24,400
Income Tax Expense	7,320
Net Income (Loss)	$17,080

Notes: There was no sale of land or purchase of property, plant & equipment during the year. The company declared and paid dividends during the year.

Prepare the cash flow statement for December 31, 2013 using the indirect method.

Zooyo Appliance Cash Flow Statement For the year ending December 31, 2013		

AP-20 (❺)

The balance sheet and income statement for Vispara Company are presented below:

Vispara Company Balance Sheet As at December 31	2013	2012
Assets		
Cash	$191,410	$94,000
Accounts Receivable	30,000	34,000
Inventory	42,000	50,000
Total Current Assets	263,410	178,000
Land	90,000	100,000
Property, Plant & Equipment	125,000	130,000
Less Accumulated Depreciation	-62,000	-60,000
Total Assets	$416,410	$348,000
Liabilities		
Accounts Payable	$76,000	$65,000
Current Portion of Bank Loan	45,000	40,000
Current Liabilities	121,000	105,000
Long-term portion of Bank Loan	120,000	95,000
Total Liabilities	241,000	200,000
Stockholders' Equity		
Common Stock	85,000	75,000
Retained Earnings	90,410	73,000
Stockholders' Equity	175,410	148,000
Liabilities + Stockholders' Equity	$416,410	$348,000

Vispara Company Income Statement For the year ended December 31, 2013	
Sales	$380,000
COGS	255,000
Gross Profit	125,000
Expenses	
Insurance Expense	8,200
Salaries Expense	15,000
Telephone Expense	2,100
Interest Expense	3,200
Depreciation Expense	42,000
Loss on Sale of Equipment	5,400
Total Expenses	75,900
Operating Income	49,100
Other Income	
Gain on Sale of Land	3,200
Net Income Before Tax	52,300
Income Tax Expense	15,690
Net Income (Loss)	$36,610

Notes: Property, plant & equipment and land were purchased for amounts of $115,000, and $200,000 respectively.

The company declared and paid dividends during the year.

The company did not pay off any amount of the bank loan.

Prepare the cash flow statement for December 31, 2013 using the indirect method.

Vispara Company Cash Flow Statement For the year ending December 31, 2013		

AP-21 (⑤)

The balance sheet and income statement for Demgo Inc. are presented below:

Demgo Inc. Balance Sheet As at December 31		
	2013	**2012**
Assets		
Cash	$20,140	$21,000
Accounts Receivable	17,000	19,000
Inventory	21,000	15,000
Total Current Assets	**58,140**	**55,000**
Land	110,000	60,000
Property, Plant &Equipment	100,000	140,000
Less Accumulated Depreciation	-40,500	-60,000
Total Assets	**$227,640**	**$195,000**
Liabilities		
Accounts Payable	$29,000	$25,000
Current Portion of Bank Loan	22,000	22,000
Current Liabilities	**51,000**	**47,000**
Long-term portion of Bank Loan	70,000	65,000
Total Liabilities	**121,000**	**112,000**
Stockholders' Equity		
Common Stock	85,000	70,000
Retained Earnings	21,640	13,000
Stockholders' Equity	**106,640**	**83,000**
Liabilities + Stockholders' Equity	**$227,640**	**$195,000**

Demgo Inc. Income Statement For the year ended December 31, 2013	
Sales	$130,000
COGS	72,000
Gross Profit	58,000
Expenses	
Insurance Expense	2,200
Salaries Expense	9,700
Telephone Expense	1,000
Interest Expense	1,100
Depreciation Expense	20,500
Total Expenses	34,500
Operating Income	23,500
Other Income	
Gain on Sale of Equipment	1,700
Net Income Before Tax	**25,200**
Income Tax Expense	7,560
Net Income (Loss)	**$17,640**

Notes: There was no sale of land.

Property, plant and equipment was purchased for an amount of $80,000.

The company declared and paid dividends during the year.

Prepare the cash flow statement for December 31, 2013 using the indirect method.

Demgo Inc. Cash Flow Statement For the year ending December 31, 2013		

AP-22 (⑤)

The balance sheet and income statement for Twely Inc. are presented below:

Twely Inc. Balance Sheet As at December 31		
	2013	**2012**
Assets		
Cash	$62,927	$56,000
Accounts Receivable	27,000	23,000
Inventory	24,500	18,000
Total Current Assets	**114,427**	**97,000**
Long-Term Investment	42,000	45,000
Land	119,000	100,000
Property, Plant &Equipment	89,000	76,000
Less Accumulated Depreciation	-28,200	-24,000
Total Assets	**$336,227**	**$294,000**
Liabilities		
Accounts Payable	$29,000	$25,000
Current Portion of Bank Loan	22,000	22,000
Total Current Liabilities	**51,000**	**47,000**
Long-term portion of Bank Loan	79,000	65,000
Total Liabilities	**130,000**	**112,000**
Stockholders' Equity		
Common Stock	85,000	85,000
Retained Earnings	121,227	97,000
Stockholders' Equity	**206,227**	**182,000**
Liabilities + Stockholders' Equity	**$336,227**	**$294,000**

Twely Inc. Income Statement For the year ended December 31, 2013	
Sales	$140,000
COGS	76,000
Gross Profit	64,000
Expenses	
Insurance Expense	2,700
Salaries Expense	10,350
Telephone Expense	540
Interest Expense	1,200
Depreciation Expense	8,200
Total Expenses	22,990
Operating Income	41,010
Other Income	
Gain on Sale of Investment	1,100
Gain on Sale of Equipment	2,500
Net Income Before Tax	44,610
Income Tax Expense	13,383
Net Income (Loss)	$31,227

Notes: There was no sale of land.

Property, plant and equipment and long-term investment were purchased for amounts of $30,000 and $10,500 respectively.

The long-term investment is held at cost.

The company declared and paid dividends during the year.

Prepare the cash flow statement for December 31, 2013 using the indirect method.

Twely Inc. Cash Flow Statement For the year ending December 31, 2013		

Case Study

CS-1 (❸)

Granite Surfaces specializes in making granite countertops. A new accounting clerk has compiled the following information to prepare the cash flow statement for the year ended December 31, 2013.

- Net income for the year was $114,140.
- Depreciation expense was $15,300.
- Equipment was sold for a gain of $16,000. Cash proceeds from the sale were $36,000.
- Equipment was purchased for $250,000.
- Dividends of $50,000 were paid.
- Accounts receivable increased by $31,400.
- Inventory decreased by $38,700.
- Accounts payable increased by $41,100.
- Bank loans increased by $55,000.
- Stock was sold for $50,000 (also their book value).
- Cash balance on January 1, 2013 was $114,800.
- Cash balance on December 31, 2013 was $117,640.

The cash flow statement the accounting clerk prepared is shown below.

Granite Surfaces Cash Flow Statement For the Year Ended December 31, 2013		
Cash Flow from Operations		
Net income	$114,140	
Add: Depreciation	15,300	
Changes in Current Assets & Current Liabilities:		
Increase in accounts receivable	31,400	
Decrease in inventory	(38,700)	
Increase in accounts payable	41,100	
Sale of equipment	36,000	
Purchase of equipment	(250,000)	
Change in Cash due to Operations		($50,760)
Cash Flow from Investments		
Receipt of bank loan	55,000	
Change in Cash due to Investments		55,000

Cash Flow from Financing		
Payment of cash dividend	(50,000)	
Sale of common stock	50,000	
Change in Cash due to Financing		0
Net increase (decrease) in cash		4,240
Cash at the beginning of the year		114,800
Cash at the end of the year		$119,040

Required:

1) Identify the problems with the cash flow statement that the accounting clerk prepared.

2) Prepare a corrected cash flow statement.

Granite Surfaces Cash Flow Statement For the Year Ended December 31, 2013		

Critical Thinking

CT-1 (❶)

The requirement that a statement of cash flow be included with other financial statements of a company is a recent requirement. Discuss the advantages and disadvantages of including the cash flow statement. Why do you think that various accounting bodies decided to include the statement of cash flows?

Notes

Chapter 20

FINANCIAL STATEMENT ANALYSIS

───────── **Assessment Questions** ─────────

AS-1 (❶)

What is financial analysis?

_____

_____

_____

AS-2 (❷)

What is the formula for gross profit margin?

_____

_____

_____

AS-3 (❷)

What does gross profit margin tell us?

_____

_____

_____

_____

AS-4 (❷)

What does EBIT refer to?

_____

_____

_____

_____

AS-5 (❷)

What is the formula for the interest coverage ratio?

_____

_____

_____

AS-6 (❷)

Is it more preferable to have a higher or lower interest coverage ratio? Explain.

_____

_____

_____

AS-7 (❷)

How do you calculate net profit margin?

_____

_____

_____

AS-8 (❷)

What is the formula for return on equity?

_____

_____

_____

AS-9 (❷)

For a particular company, if net income increased significantly from one year to the next, does this guarantee that the return on equity will also increase? Explain.

_____

_____

_____

AS-10 (❷)

How do you calculate return on assets?

_____

_____

_____

AS-11 (❷)

What are some possible reasons why return on assets may have decreased from one period to the next?

_____

_____

_____

AS-12 (❷)

Suppose that company A and company B generate the same level of net income each period. However, company A is more capital-intensive than company B. Which company will likely have the higher return on assets?

_____

_____

_____

AS-13 (❸)

In the DuPont framework, return on equity is represented as a product of which three measurements?

_____

_____

_____

_____

_____

AS-14 (❸)

What is the purpose of using the DuPont framework in examining a company's ROE from period to period?

_____

_____

_____

_____

_____

_____

_____

AS-15 (❹)

What is the formula for the current ratio?

_____

_____

_____

AS-16 (❹)

What does the current ratio tell you?

_____

_____

_____

AS-17 (❹)

If current assets stays constant from one period to the next, but current liabilities increases, what will happen to the current ratio?

_____

_____

_____

AS-18 (❹)

What is the formula for the quick ratio?

_____

_____

_____

AS-19 (❹)

How do you calculate the debt-to-equity ratio?

_____

_____

_____

AS-20 (❺)

What is the formula for days-sales-outstanding?

_____

_____

_____

AS-21 (❺)

What does days-sales-outstanding tell you?

_____

_____

_____

AS-22 (❺)

How do you calculate accounts receivable turnover?

_____

_____

_____

AS-23 (❺)

How is inventory days on hand calculated?

_____

_____

_____

AS-24 (❺)

What is the formula for the inventory turnover ratio?

_____

_____

_____

AS-25 (❶)

Define debt covenant.

_____

_____

_____

AS-26 (❻)

Why is it necessary to compare a company's calculated ratios with industry benchmarks?

_____

_____

_____

_____

_____

_____

_____

—————————— **Application Questions** ——————————

AP-1 (❷)

A company reported the following:

- Sales: $1 million
- Cost of Goods Sold: $0.7 million
- Operating Expenses: $0.4 million
- Income Taxes: $0.2 million

Calculate the gross profit margin. Differentiate between gross profit margin and gross profit.

_____

_____

_____

_____

_____

_____

_____

_____

AP-2 (❷)

Gross profit increased from $0.3 million in 2012, to $0.4 million in 2013. Gross profit margin decreased from 30% in 2012, to 28% in 2013. Comment on whether or not the company's profitability improved or deteriorated.

_____

_____

_____

_____

AP-3 (❷)

A company reported the following:

Sales	$2.0 million
Cost of Goods Sold	0.7 million
Operating Expenses	0.4 million
Interest expense included in operating expenses	0.05 million
Income taxes	40% of income before tax
Owners' Equity (Average)	$20.0 million

Required: Calculate EBIT

_____

_____

_____

_____

_____

_____

_____

_____

_____

_____

_____

_____

AP-4 (❷)

Use the information supplied in AP-3. Calculate the net profit margin.

_____

_____

_____

AP-5 (❷)

Use the information supplied in AP-3. Calculate the interest coverage ratio.

_____

_____

_____

AP-6 (❷)

Use the information supplied in AP-3. Calculate the return on equity. Banks are currently paying interest on deposits of 4% for money invested for 2 or more years. Comment on the ratio.

_____

_____

_____

_____

_____

_____

_____

AP-7 (❸)

Using the DuPont framework, calculate the missing item for each independent scenario.

i)

Net Profit Margin	10.30%
Asset Turnover Ratio	2.5
Equity Multiplier	2.3
ROE	?

ii)

Net Profit Margin	6.70%
Asset Turnover Ratio	?
Equity Multiplier	1.8
Net Income	$500,000
Beginning Stockholders' Equity	$800,000
Ending Stockholders' Equity	$1,300,000

iii)

Net Income	$200,000
Revenue	$600,000
Beginning Total Assets	$150,000
Ending Total Assets	$420,000
Equity Multiplier	?
ROE	35%

AP-8 (❸)

Du Inc. and Pont Manufacturer have been rival competitors in the hardware manufacturing for several years. The following data was compiled for 2013:

	Du	Pont
Net Profit Margin	15.00%	5.00%
Asset Turnover	0.42	1.24
Equity Multiplier	2.45	2.48

Required:

a) Using the DuPont Framework, calculate the ROE for both companies.
b) Compare the ROEs determined in part a). By analysing the three components of ROE in the DuPont Framework, explain and compare how both companies achieved their respective ROEs.

_____

_____

_____

_____

_____

_____

_____

_____

_____

_____

AP-9 (❹)

A company reports current assets of $6,572, and current liabilities of $2,786. Calculate the current ratio.

_____

_____

_____

AP-10 (❹)

Total current liabilities for a company is $2,786. If cash is $2,000, short-term investments are $3,000, long-term investments are $1,000 and accounts receivable is $1,200, calculate the quick ratio.

_____

_____

_____

AP-11 (❹)

A company had a debt to equity ratio last year of 1.46. This year, the ratio is 2.0. Are things getting better or worse? Explain your answer.

_____

_____

_____

_____

_____

AP-12 (❺)

ABC Company sells on credit, with the balance due in 30 days. The company's DSO ratio has changed from 60 days last year to 42 days this year. Are things getting better or worse? Explain the relationship between the sales terms and DSO.

_____

_____

_____

_____

_____

AP-13 (❺)

At the end of 2013, accounts receivable amounts to $210,000. At the beginning of the year it was $200,000. Net credit sales for the year amounted to $900,000 and net income was calculated to be $205,000.

Determine the days sales outstanding ratio and the accounts receivable turnover ratio.

_____

_____

_____

AP-14 (❺)

At the beginning of 2013, Acatela Corp. had inventory of $350,000. During the year, they purchased $220,000 worth of raw materials and sold $500,000 worth of inventory. Determine the inventory turnover ratio and the inventory days on hand ratio.

_____

_____

_____

_____

_____

_____

_____

_____

AP-15 (❶)

The income statement of Ellen Corporation for the years 2012 and 2013 showed the following gross profit.

	2013	2012
Sales Revenue	$97,200	$80,000
Cost of Goods Sold	72,000	50,000
Gross Profit	$25,200	$30,000

Required:

a) Calculate the gross profit margins for both years.

_____

_____

_____

_____

b) In which year does Ellen Corporation have a better gross profit margin? Explain.

_____

_____

_____

_____

_____

AP-16 (❶)

Selected information for the Universal Company is as follows:

	December 31		
	2013	**2012**	**2011**
Common Stock	$840,000	$648,000	$550,000
Retained Earnings	370,000	248,000	150,000
Net income for the year	240,000	122,000	98,000

Required:

a) Calculate the return on equity ratio for 2013 and 2012.

_____

_____

_____

_____

b) Has The Universal Company's performance improved in 2013? Explain using the return on equity ratio.

_____

_____

_____

AP-17 (❶)

Presented below is the comparative income statement of Newton Company for 2013 and 2012.

Newton Company Income Statement For the Year Ended December 31, 2013		
	2013	**2012**
Sales	$194,890	$108,345
Cost of Goods Sold	116,934	65,007
Gross Profit	77,956	43,338
Operating Expenses:		
Advertising	4,000	2,000
Bank Charges	580	0
Communication	5,380	3,684
Legal and Professional	6,000	3,950
Utilities	3,330	1,503
Rent	3,500	3,500
Repairs and Maintenance	4,000	2,500
Salaries and Wages	3,000	1,800
Transportation	3,200	1,700
Interest	1,248	580
Depreciation	1,550	990
Total Operating Expenses	35,788	22,207
Operating Profit before tax	42,168	21,131
Income Tax	12,650	6,339
Net Profit	**$29,518**	**$14,792**

Required:

a) Calculate the following ratios for both years:

• EBIT Percentage to Sales
• Interest Coverage Ratio

b) In which year does the company have a better performance with respect to the ratios calculated in part a)? Explain.

_____

_____

_____

_____

_____

_____

AP-18 (❷)

Selected financial data from Crew Company is provided below:

	As at December 31, 2013
Cash	$75,000
Accounts Receivable	225,000
Merchandise Inventory	270,000
Short-Term Investments	40,000
Land and Building	500,000
Current Portion of Long-Term Debt	30,000
Accounts Payable	120,000

Required:

a) Calculate the quick ratio.

_____

_____

_____

_____

_____

b) What does Crew Company's quick ratio suggest about the company's performance?

_____

_____

_____

AP-19 (❷)

Information from Silky Company's year-end financial statements is as follows:

	2013	2012
Current Assets	$200,000	$210,000
Current Liabilities	100,000	90,000
Stockholders' Equity	250,000	270,000
Net Sales	830,000	880,000
Cost of Goods Sold	620,000	640,000
Operating Income	50,000	55,000

Required:

a) Calculate the current ratio for both years.

_____

_____

_____

_____

b) In which year does Silky Company have a better current ratio? Explain.

_____

_____

_____

AP-20 (❻)

Perform a horizontal analysis for Groff Inc. Use 2010 as the base year and comment on the results.

Groff Inc.			
In Millions of Dollars			
	2013	2012	2011	2010
---	---	---	---	---
Revenue	500	400	300	200
Net Income	166	158	144	120

Groff Inc.				
In Millions of Dollars				
	2013	2012	2011	2010
Revenue				
Revenue Ratio				
Net Income				
Net Income Ratio				

_____

_____

_____

AP-21 (⑥)

Perform a vertical analysis (use Sales as the base) for Hiltonia Inc. Comment on the results. Note that figures are in millions of dollars.

	Hiltonia Inc.	
	2013	2012
Sales	210	250
COGS	150	200
Gross Profit	60	50
Selling Expenses	5	4
Wages	2	2
Rent	5	5
Total Expenses	12	11
Income before tax	48	39
Taxes (35%)	16.8	13.65
Net Income	31.2	25.35

AP-22 (⑥)

The following financial statements are taken from the records of Abaya Inc.

Abaya Inc. Balance Sheet As at December 31, 2013			
	2013	**2012**	**2011**
Current Assets			
Cash	$315,000	$325,000	$210,000
Accounts Receivable	140,000	198,000	92,000
Inventory	411,000	397,000	428,000
Short-Term Investments	115,000	100,000	100,000
Total Current Assets	981,000	1,020,000	830,000
Other Assets	356,000	250,000	403,000
Total Assets	$1,337,000	$1,270,000	$1,233,000
Current Liabilities	214,000	265,000	90,000
Long-Term Debt	22,000	150,000	100,000
Total Liabilities	236,000	415,000	190,000
Stockholders' Equity	1,101,000	855,000	1,043,000
Total Liabilities and Equity	$1,337,000	$1,270,000	$1,233,000

Abaya Inc. Income Statement For the Year Ended December 31, 2013			
	2013	**2012**	**2011**
Sales	$701,000	$689,000	$514,000
Cost of Goods Sold	379,000	396,000	385,000
Gross Profit	322,000	293,000	129,000
Operating Expenses:			
Depreciation	2,500	2,500	2,500
Advertising	4,200	3,100	1,800
Bank Charges	2,400	1,600	1,500
Communication	5,600	3,700	4,300
Professional Fees	11,800	5,400	6,800
Utilities	8,600	7,580	5,250
Rent	5,000	5,000	5,000
Repairs and Maintenance	3,000	3,000	3,000
Salaries and Wages	41,000	11,500	9,800
Transportation	8,950	6,400	6,150
Total Operating Expenses	93,050	49,780	46,100
EBIT	228,950	243,220	82,900
Interest	18,600	12,600	8,500
Operating Profit before tax	210,350	230,620	74,400
Income Tax	63,105	69,186	22,320
Net Profit	$147,245	$161,434	$52,080

Required:

a) Use the horizontal analysis techniques to compare the changes between 2013 and 2012 balance sheet items.

Abaya Inc. Balance Sheet As at December 31, 2013				
	2013	2012	$ Change	% Change
Current Assets				
Cash	$315,000	$325,000		
Accounts Receivable	140,000	198,000		
Inventory	411,000	397,000		
Short-Term Investments	115,000	100,000		
Total Current Assets	981,000	1,020,000		
Non-Current Assets	356,000	250,000		
Total Assets	$1,337,000	$1,270,000		
Current Liabilities	214,000	265,000		
Non-Current Liabilities	22,000	150,000		
Total Liabilities	236,000	415,000		
Stockholders' Equity	1,101,000	855,000		
Total Liabilities and Equity	$1,337,000	$1,270,000		

_____

_____

b) Using 2011 as a base year, provide horizontal analysis of Sales, Gross Profit, Operating Expenses, and Net Income.

	2013	2012	2011
Sales			
Gross Profit			
Operating Expenses			
Net Income			

_____

_____

c) Prepare a common-size income statement for 2013, 2012 and 2011 and state all the income statement items as a percentage of net sales.

Abaya Inc. Income Statement For the Year Ended December 31, 2013			
	2013	**2012**	**2011**
Sales			
Cost of Goods Sold			
Gross Profit			
Operating Expenses:			
Depreciation			
Advertising			
Bank Charges			
Communication			
Professional Fees			
Utilities			
Rent			
Repairs and Maintenance			
Salaries and Wages			
Transportation			
Total Operating Expenses			
EBIT			
Interest			
Operating Profit before tax			
Income Tax			
Net Profit			

_____

_____

_____

_____

_____

AP-23 (❺)

Testa Inc. had a net income of $158,000 for the year ended December 31, 2013. The company does not have any preferred stock and has 45,000 common stock outstanding for the entire year. During the year, they paid out $20,000 in dividends.

Required:

a) Calculate earnings per share

_____

_____

_____

_____

b) Calculate the dividend payout ratio

_____

_____

_____

_____

c) Calculate the price earnings ratio assuming the market price is $24 per share.

_____

_____

_____

_____

AP-24 (❺)

Bluebird Inc. had a net income of $387,400 for the year ended August 31, 2013. The company does not have any preferred stock and has 125,000 common shares outstanding for the entire year. During the year, they paid out $60,000 in dividends.

Required:

a) Calculate earnings per share.

_____

_____

_____

_____

b) Calculate the dividend payout ratio.

_____

_____

_____

_____

c) Calculate the price earnings ratio assuming the market price is $12 per share.

_____

_____

_____

_____

Case Study

CS-1(❶, ❷, ❹, ❺)

Suppose that you have decided to invest some money in the stock market. After some research online, you come across the financial statements of Bore Marketing. Before you can make a decision to invest in the company, you will need to calculate some key financial ratios and then analyze them. The statements are presented below.

Bore Marketing Consolidated Balance Sheet (in thousands) As at February 28, 2013 and February 28, 2012		
	Feb 2013	**Feb 2012**
Assets		
Cash	1,550,861	835,546
Short-term Investments	360,614	682,666
Accounts Receivable	2,800,115	2,269,845
Inventory	621,611	682,400
Other Current Assets	479,455	371,129
Total Current Assets	**5,812,656**	**4,841,586**
Long-Term Investment	958,248	720,635
Property, plant & equipment net	1,956,581	1,334,648
Intangible Assets	1,476,924	1,204,503
Total Assets	**$10,204,409**	**$8,101,372**
Liabilities		
Accounts Payable	$615,620	$448,339
Accrued Liabilities	1,638,260	1,238,602
Income Taxes Payable	95,650	361,460
Other Current Liabilities	82,247	66,950
Total Current Liabilities	**2,431,777**	**2,115,351**
Long-term Liabilities	169,969	111,893
Total Liabilities	**2,601,746**	**2,227,244**
Stockholders' Equity		
Common Stock	2,113,146	2,208,235
Retained Earnings	5,489,517	3,665,893
Stockholders' Equity	**7,602,663**	**5,874,128**
Liabilities + Stockholders' Equity	**$10,204,409**	**$8,101,372**

Bore Marketing Consolidated Income Statement (in thousands) For the Year Ended February 28, 2013 and February 28, 2012		
	Feb 2013	**Feb 2012**
Revenue	$14,953,224	$11,065,186
Cost of Sales	8,368,958	5,967,888
Gross Profit	6,584,266	5,097,298
Operating expenses		
Research and Development	964,841	684,702
Selling, Marketing and Admin	1,907,398	1,495,697
Amortization	310,357	194,803
Litigation	163,800	0
Total Expenses	3,346,396	2,375,202
Operating Income Before Tax	3,237,870	2,722,096
Investment Income	28,640	78,267
Income Before Income Tax	3,266,510	2,800,363
Income Tax	809,366	907,747
Net Income	**$2,457,144**	**$1,892,616**

Bore Marketing Summary of the Cash Flow Statement (in thousands) For the Year Ended February 28, 2013 and February 28, 2012		
	Feb 2013	**Feb 2012**
Net Cash Provided by Operations	$3,034,874	$1,451,845
Net Cash Used by Investing	($1,470,127)	($1,823,523)
Net Cash Used by Financing	($849,432)	$22,826
Net Increase (Decrease) in Cash	**$715,315**	**($348,852)**

Required:

a) Calculate the following ratios for Bore Marketing for 2013 and 2012. For any ratios that require an average (i.e. ROE), use the closing balance for the year.

	2013	2012
Gross Profit Margin		
EBIT		
EBIT Percentage to Sales		
Net Profit Margin		
Return on Equity		
Return on Assets		
Asset Turnover		
Current Ratio		
Quick Ratio		
Debt-to-Equity Ratio		

b) Based on the figures you calculated, has the company shown improvement in 2013 over 2012? Would you invest in Bore Marketing? Explain.

_____

_____

_____

_____

_____

_____

_____

_____

_____

_____

_____

CS-2 (❶, ❷, ❹, ❺)

The following information has been taken from the financial statements of Ivory Inc.

Ivory Inc.	
Current Assets, December 31, 2014	175,000
Total Assets, January 1, 2014	500,000
Total Assets, December 31, 2014	575,000
Current Liabilities, December 31, 2014	75,000
Total Liabilities, December 31, 2014	175,000
Stockholders' Equity, January 1, 2014	300,000
Stockholders' Equity, December 31, 2014	400,000
Net Sales	900,000
Depreciation Expense	10,000
Interest Expense	20,000
Income Tax Expense	25,000
Net Income	40,000

a) Given the above data for Ivory Inc., calculate the following ratios for 2014 (round to two decimal places). The company's ratios for 2013 are given for comparison.

	Ratio	2013
i)	Current Ratio	3.5
ii)	Interest Coverage Ratio	5.40
iii)	Debt to Equity	25.00%
iv)	Return on Assets	12.50%
v)	Return on Equity	20.20%
vi)	Net Profit Margin	8.60%

b) Using 2013 as a comparison, discuss whether the company improved or deteriorated in its ability to (i) pay current liabilities as they come due, (ii) meet its long-term debt obligations and (iii) profitability. Be sure to make reference to specific ratios in your answers.

Your Answer:

a)

	Ratio	2014	2013
i)			
ii)			
iii)			
iv)			
v)			
vi)			

b)

Critical Thinking

CT-1 (❶)

Financial statement analysis is performed on historical information. Since the past cannot be changed, calculating financial ratios is of no use. What management and investors are really interested in is the future, specifically the future profitability of a company. Discuss.

_____

_____

_____

_____

_____

_____

_____

Notes